John A. Amstutz

READINGS IN ECOLOGY

PRENTICE-HALL BIOLOGICAL SCIENCE SERIES
William D. McElroy and Carl P. Swanson, *Editors*

BIOCHEMICAL SYSTEMATICS,* by Ralph E. Alston and B. L. Turner
CLASSIC PAPERS IN GENETICS, by James A. Peters
EXPERIMENTAL BIOLOGY, by Richard W. Van Norman
FOUNDATIONS OF EXPERIMENTAL EMBRYOLOGY, by Benjamin H. Willier and Jane M. Oppenheimer
GENERAL AND COMPARATIVE PHYSIOLOGY, by William S. Hoar
MECHANISMS OF BODY FUNCTIONS, by Dexter M. Easton
MILESTONES IN MICROBIOLOGY, by Thomas D. Brock
PAPERS ON HUMAN GENETICS, by Samuel H. Boyer, IV
POISONOUS PLANTS OF THE UNITED STATES AND CANADA, by John M. Kingsbury
PRINCIPLES OF BIOLOGY, by Neal D. Buffaloe
RADIOTRACER METHODOLOGY IN BIOLOGICAL SCIENCE, by C. H. Wang and David L. Willis
READINGS IN ECOLOGY, by Edward J. Kormondy
SELECTED BOTANICAL PAPERS, by Irving W. Knobloch
SELECTED PAPERS ON VIROLOGY, by Nicholas Hahon
A SYNTHESIS OF EVOLUTIONARY THEORY, Herbert H. Ross

Concepts of Modern Biology Series

BEHAVIORAL ASPECTS OF ECOLOGY,* by Peter H. Klopfer
MOLECULAR BIOLOGY: GENES AND CHEMICAL CONTROL OF LIVING CELLS, by J. M. Barry
POPULATION, ENVIRONMENT, AND EVOLUTION, by G. Ledyard Stebbins

Foundations of Modern Biology Series

ADAPTATION, 2nd ed., by Bruce Wallace and A. M. Srb
ANIMAL BEHAVIOR, 2nd ed., by Vincent Dethier and Eliot Stellar
ANIMAL DIVERSITY, 2nd ed., by Earl D. Hanson
ANIMAL PHYSIOLOGY, 2nd ed., by Knut Schmidt-Neilsen
THE CELL, 2nd ed., by Carl P. Swanson
CELL PHYSIOLOGY AND BIOCHEMISTRY, 2nd ed., by William D. McElroy
CHEMICAL BACKGROUND FOR THE BIOLOGICAL SCIENCES, by Emil H. White
GROWTH AND DEVELOPMENT, 2nd ed., by Maurice Sussman
HEREDITY, 2nd ed., by David M. Bonner and Stanley E. Mills
THE LIFE OF THE GREEN PLANT, 2nd ed., by Authur W. Galston
MAN IN NATURE, 2nd ed., by Marston Bates
THE PLANT KINGDOM, 2nd ed., by Harold C. Bold

*These titles are also in the Prentice-Hall International Series in Biological Science. Prentice-Hall, Inc.; Prentice-Hall International, United Kingdom and Eire; Prentice-Hall of Canada, Ltd., Canada.

READINGS IN
ECOLOGY

Edited by Edward J. Kormondy
ASSOCIATE PROFESSOR OF BIOLOGY, OBERLIN COLLEGE

Prentice-Hall, Inc., Englewood Cliffs, New Jersey

PRENTICE-HALL INTERNATIONAL, INC., *London*
PRENTICE-HALL OF AUSTRALIA, PTY., LTD., *Sydney*
PRENTICE-HALL OF CANADA, LTD., *Toronto*
PRENTICE-HALL OF INDIA (PRIVATE) LTD., *New Delhi*
PRENTICE-HALL OF JAPAN, INC., *Tokyo*

Current printing (last digit):
11 10 9 8 7 6 5 4 3 2

 Library of Congress Catalog Card Number: 65—26924. Printed in the United States of America. *75586—C*

PREFACE

This group of papers represents as wide a range of the ecological literature as could be encompassed within a reasonably sized volume. Although it is compiled as a textbook supplement for the beginning student in ecology, certain papers are suitable for college students in beginning biology or general science and for high school students in advanced biology. For the graduate student and research ecologist it provides an opportunity to become reacquainted with the sources of their endeavors.

With few exceptions, all of these papers have been used in my course in general ecology at Oberlin College because of the tremendous potential inherent in exposure to the original literature. Although I have used them largely in synchrony with textbook declamations, their real value lies in the excitement and flavor, and the relating of the adventure, hard work, and creativity which is science. There is ample testimony that these savors are experienced and that scientific literature is comprehensible.

The criteria which guided the filtering out of few papers from the myriad for my own students have operated in meeting the exigencies imposed by publication. The prime criterion is a paper which has made a highly significant contribution; this is fairly readily attested by the frequency of its citation in subsequent literature. In most instances, this standard also placed in the list most of the ecologists who have given direction to their field. Other papers were selected as exemplary of good scientific procedure (trenchant analysis, incisive logical argument, stimulating theoretical discourse) and others to achieve an indication of the range of ecological investigation.

Each paper has been abridged (indicated by an ellipse, . . .) and had literature citations omitted primarily to conserve space. There are recognized dangers here, not the least is that the reader may not be made fully aware of the dependence of a scientist on his predecessors and contemporaries.

Noble criteria notwithstanding, there is the hazard of autocracy in compiling a set of papers, perhaps more so for so diversified a field as ecology. No two ecologists would likely develop identical lists nor present them in the order used here. Most would concur in certain papers having classic status, but at that juncture divergence of considerable magnitude would begin. There is an historic and functional reasonableness to both the selections and order used but not such as to deny great flexibility in selecting papers to meet individual requirements.

Because one's perspectives are always circumscribed and his hindsight wanting, the utility of this volume can be increased in the future through criticism, charitable and otherwise, by its users. I will appreciate receiving that criticism.

Each of my teachers, students and colleagues (in person and through the literature) has contributed in some way to the development of this volume. None is singled out since each is completely absolved from the final errors of commission and omission, all of which are mine. I do, however, acknowledge the cooperation of the authors and publishers whose permission made the volume possible, the translations by Mrs. Ursula Stechow and Dr. Lawrence Wilson, and the invaluable and diversified help of the library staff and facilities at Oberlin College, the South Branch of the University of Georgia, and the Savannah River Laboratory. I am continually grateful to my wife, Peggy, for her editorial assistance but more for her encouragement and understanding. A sabbatical leave from Oberlin (1963–64) provided the time to complete this undertaking.

EDWARD J. KORMONDY

CONTENTS

THE STUDY OF POPULATIONS

Nature of Population Growth

Interaction of Populations

Regulation of Populations

INTRODUCTION

It has been said that ecology is as diversified in its scope and meaning as are the diverse Homo sapiens *that call themselves ecologists. While this belies the situation, it does intimate the great disparity in orientation and approach to the field. One of the beneficial results of this diversity has been the accumulation of a wealth of data and interpretation providing fertile ground for the development of theory. Among the less salutary consequences of this protean posture has been the judgment that ecology is but a point of view rather than a scientific discipline. An anthology provides an opportunity for different ecologists to react indirectly to that criticism and in so doing to indicate the particular province of nature which they have carved out as their special area of inquiry.*

Underlying the varied formulations describing ecology is the theme that it deals with the interactions of organisms and environment. Although Haeckle is usually credited with the event, Reiter appears to have been the first to combine the Greek words oikos *(= house) and* logos *(=study of) to form the term* ecology; *this was in 1865. It was Haeckle, however, who in 1866 first gave definition to the term as "the body of knowledge concerning the economy of nature—the investigation of the total relations of the animal to its inorganic and organic environment."*

A few years earlier, in 1859, Geoffroy St. Hilaire had constructed the term ethology *to describe "the relations of the organism with the family and society in the aggregate and in the community." During this same general period, Mivart proposed the term* hexicology *and ultimately defined it as being "devoted to a study of the relations which exist between organisms and their environment." Why Haeckle's (Reiter's) term superseded the others may be at least partially explained by the stature which Haeckle enjoyed. Neither Mivart nor St. Hilaire had the prestige of position or privilege of such influential colleagues as did Haeckle. In any event, Mivart's term has been completely eclipsed, but St. Hilaire's has subsequently become synonomous with the study of animal behavior.*

Although the majority of formal definitions of ecology approximate that of Haeckle, emended to include plants as well, some seem to represent more than just a modulation. For example, Charles Elton defined ecology as "scientific natural history" concerned with the "sociology and economics of animals." Victor Shelford defined ecology as the "science of the community" and Eugene Odum has stated it is "the study of the structure and function of nature."

Whether any one of these definitions is without ambiguity or adequately delineates ecology's area of inquiry and its paramount objectives is debatable. Ecology is a field of broad base and its fringes become progressively less capable of precise demarcation. This is at once one of the frustrating obstacles and heuristic dimensions that confronts the ecologist. The reality of this circumstance will become apparent in the following pages.

READINGS IN ECOLOGY

EARLY NATURAL HISTORY

In the present day, the term "natural history" has become opprobrious among ecologists in connoting anecdotal, unsystematic, and casual investigation. Indeed, much natural history observation and writing is of this sort, and is not likely to make any very fundamental contribution. There is, however, a different kind of natural history—that which provided the beginning of a tradition leading to modern ecology and which, in many respects, is a fundamental component of it. Among the salutary characteristics of this true naturalist tradition, as evidenced in the following selections, are careful attention to detail, precision of recording, recognition, and manipulation of variable influences, and awareness of the observations of others.

The period of the great naturalists, arbitrarily represented here from Theophrastus to Reáumur, is, in some respects, actually without termination. Excellent natural histories continue to appear in the twentieth century, but their audience and function would appear to have changed, at least in part. Serving always to inform, instruct, and often to persuade, these treatises were as much directed to students of science as to the literary public in a former day. Modern natural histories have too generalized and insufficiently critical an approach for scientific purposes, but do provide considerable motivation and enjoyable reading for scientist and nonscientist alike. There is a great tradition in such natural history exposition that is both illuminating and absorbing.

ENQUIRY INTO PLANTS

Theophrastus—c. 300 B.C.

Reprinted by permission of the publisher and the Loeb Classical Library from Theophrastus: Enquiry into plants, Volumes I and II, translated by Sir Arthur Hort. Cambridge, Mass., Harvard University Press, 1916.

Perhaps not so imaginative nor conceptually creative as Aristotle, his teacher and predecessor as head of the Lyceum, Theophrastus was a much more careful observer of nature. Most of his botanical writings were based on material brought to him by those who accompanied Alexander on his expeditions. The following selection, with its obvious anthropomorphisms, shows strong ecological orientation in its consideration of plant associations and the dynamic and causal relationships of plants with their environment.

OF THE IMPORTANCE OF POSITION AND CLIMATE

I. The differences between trees of the same kind have already been considered. Now all grow fairer and are more vigorous in their proper positions; for wild, no less than cultivated trees, have each their own positions: some love wet and marshy ground, as black poplar, abele, willow, and in general those that grow by rivers; some love exposed and sunny positions; some prefer a shady place. The fir is fairest and tallest in a sunny position, and does not grow at all in a shady one; the silver-fir on the contrary is fairest in a shady place, and not so vigorous in a sunny one.

Thus there is in Arcadia near the place called Krane a low-lying district sheltered from wind, into which they say that the sun never strikes; and in this district the silver-firs excel greatly in height and stoutness, though they have not such close grain nor such comely wood, but quite the reverse,—like the fir when it grows in a shady place. Wherefore men do not use these for expensive work, such as doors or other choice articles, but rather for ship-building and house-building. For excellent rafters beams and yard-arms are made from these, and also masts of great length which are not however equally strong; while masts made of trees grown in a sunny place are necessarily short but of closer grain and stronger than the others.

Yew *pados* and joint-fir rejoice exceedingly in shade. On mountain tops and in cold positions odorous cedar grows even to a height, while silver-fir and Phoenician cedar grow, but not to a height,—for instance on the top of Mount Cyllene; and holly also grows in high and very wintry positions. These trees then we may reckon as cold-loving; all others, one may say in general, prefer a sunny position. However this too depends partly on the soil appropriate to each tree; thus they say that in Crete on the mountains of Ida and on those called the White Mountains the cypress is found on the peaks whence the snow never disappears; for this is the principal tree both in the island generally and in the mountains.

Again, as has been said already, both of wild and of cultivated trees some belong more to the mountains, some to the plains. And on the mountains themselves in proportion to the height some grow fairer and more vigorous in the lower regions, some about the peaks. However it is true of all trees anywhere that with a north aspect the wood is closer and more compact and better generally; and, generally speaking, more trees grow in positions facing the north. Again trees which are close together grow and increase more in height, and so become unbranched straight and erect, and the best oar-spars are made from these, while those that grow far apart are of greater bulk and denser habit; wherefore they grow less straight and with more branches, and in general have harder wood and a closer grain.

Such trees exhibit nearly the same differences, whether the position be shady or sunny, windless or windy; for trees growing in a sunny or windy position are more branched shorter and less straight. Further that each tree seeks an appropriate position and climate is plain from the fact that some districts bear some trees but not others; (the latter do not grow there of their own accord, nor can they easily be made to grow), and that, even if they obtain a hold, they do not bear fruit—as was said of the date-palm, the sycamore, and others; for there are many trees which in many places either do not grow at all, or, if they do, do not thrive nor bear fruit, but are in general of inferior quality. And perhaps we should discuss this matter, so far as our enquiries go. . . .

OF DISEASES AND INJURIES DONE BY WEATHER CONDITIONS

. . . there are certain affections due to season or situation which are likely to destroy the plant, but which one would not call diseases: I mean such affections as freezing and what some call 'scorching.' Also there are winds which blow in particular districts that are likely to destroy or scorch; for instance the 'Olympian' wind of Chalcis in Euboea, when it blows cold a little before or after the winter solstice; for this wind scorches up the trees and makes them more dry and withered than they would become from the sun's heat even in a long period; wherefore its effect is called 'scorching.' In old times it occurred very frequently, and it recurred with great violence in the time of Archippus, after an interval of forty years.

The places which suffer most in this way are hollow places, valleys, the ground near rivers, and, in general, places which are least open to wind; the tree which suffers most is the fig, and next to that the olive. The wild olive, being stronger, suffered more than the cultivated tree, which was surprising. But the almonds were altogether unscathed, as also were the apples pears and pomegranates; wherefore this too was a surprising fact. The tree gets scorched by this wind right down to the trunk, and in general the upper are caught more and earlier than the lower parts. The effects are seen partly at the actual time of budding, but in the olive, because it is evergreen, they do not appear till later; those trees therefore which have shed their leaves come to life again, but those that have not done so are completely destroyed. In some places trees have been known, after being thus scorched and after their leaves have withered, to shoot again without shedding their leaves, and the leaves have come to life again. Indeed in some places, as at Philippi, this happens several times.

Trees which have been frost-bitten, when they are not completely destroyed, soon shoot again, so that the vine immediately bears fruit, for instance in Thessaly. In Pontus near Panticapaeum the frost-bite occurs in two ways, either just from cold, if the season is wintry, or from long spells of frost; in either case this generally occurs in the forty days after the winter solstice. The frosts occur in fine weather, but the cold spells, which cause the frost-bite, chiefly when in fine weather the 'flakes' fall; these are like filings, but broader, and can be seen as they fall, but when they have fallen, they disappear—though in Thrace they freeze solid. . . .

OF THE EFFECTS OF CLIMATE, SOIL, AND MANURING

For growth and nourishment the climate is the most important factor, and in general the character of the season as a whole; for when rain, fair weather and storms occur opportunely, all crops bear well and are fruitful, even if they be in soil which is impregnated with salt or poor. Wherefore there is an apt proverbial saying that "it is the year which bears and not the field."

But the soil also makes much difference, according as it is fat or light, well watered or parched, and it also makes quite as much difference what sort of air and of winds prevails in that region; for some soils, though light and poor, produce a good crop because the land has a fair aspect in regard to sea breezes. But, as has been repeatedly said already, the same breeze has not this effect in all places; some places are suited by a west, some by a north, some by a south wind.

Again the working of the soil and above all that which is done before the sowing has an important effect; for when the soil is well worked it bears easily. Also dung is helpful by warming and ripening the soil, for manured land gets the start by as much as twenty days of that which has not been manured. However manure is not good for all crops; and further it is beneficial not only to corn and the like but to most other things, except fern, which they say it destroys if it is put on. (Fern is also destroyed if sheep lie on it, and, as some say, lucerne is destroyed by their dung and urine.). . .

HISTORY OF PLANTS

Linnaeus—1750

Reprinted from The Elements of Botany, Chapter XI, translated by Hugh Rose. Published by T. Cadell, 1775.

The renascence of the Greek spirit of inquiry in natural history writing reached its acme in the work of Gesner and Aldrovandi in the sixteenth century, and in Linnaeus, Reáumur, and Buffon in the eighteenth century. In addition to his significant contributions to taxonomy, Linnaeus' writings show considerable perceptions in ecological matters, notably regarding the phenology and geography of plants. Unlike the herbalists, he recognized the influence of environmental factors in promoting seasonal progression and plant distribution. This feature is evident in the following passage which is a portion of a chapter detailing what the Swedish botanist considered important for a complete understanding of plants.

SECT. 334

The native places or stations of plants respect the country, climate, soil, and situation, nature of the ground, earth, and mould. The only true foundation of gardening, and the right cultivation of plants, depends on the knowledge of the native places of their production, from whence the rules and principles of the art ought to be derived. Miller's Gardener's Dictionary lays down the particular culture of every plant; but this method of gardening through all the known species of plants would be too tedious, diffuse, and burdensome. From the natural place of their growth we know where to find the different species of plants for gardens, herbals of dried plants, medicinal and economic uses. The country respects the kingdom, provinces, districts; and, when the plants are very rare and scarce, the places of their growth ought to be most particularly mentioned. The climate respects the latitude, longitude, and altitude of the place, which last is its perpendicular height above the level of the sea. Vaillant was the first who introduced the climates in describing the native places of plants, and this he did with regard to the latitude only. But that the latitude alone is not sufficient, and much less the longitude, appears from this; that places very remote from each other, but under the same latitude, produce plants very different. Rome in Italy, Pekin in China, and New York in America, are situated nearly under the same degree of North latitude; Rome being 41:51, Pekin 39:55, and New York 41:0. In like manner Palestine and Florida on the North, and the Cape of Good Hope and Chile on the South, are nearly under the same latitudes; but those countries produce plants very different from one another. It is much more proper to observe the altitude of the place in describing the habitations of plants; thus the aquatic plants of India often agree with those of Europe, as the hooded milfoil, the sun-dew, the water-lily, the arrow-head, and *Aldrovanda*. The Alpine plants of Lapland, Greenland, Siberia, Switzerland, Wales, Scotland, the Pyrenean mountains, Olympus, Ararat, and Brazil, are often the same, though growing in places so remote from each other. Suppose a meadow a little higher than the sea, and full of such plants as commonly grow in meadows, and the adjacent ground a little higher still, and further from the sea; this last will produce other plants very different from the meadow; examples of which may be seen everywhere. In describing the habitations of plants, we ought always particularly to mention the soil, situation, nature of the ground, earth, mould, etc. in which they grow. This is very various, being either in the sea, on the sea shore, about fountains or springs, in rivers, or on the banks of rivers, in lakes, ditches, water-pits, ponds, pools, fens, marshes, bogs; on the tops of very high mountains, and in thick forests on their sides; on little hills, declivities, cliffs, rocks, stones, caverns, old high walls; groves, woods, hedges, and shady places; heaths, commons, fields, fallows, closes, plowed lands, gardens, dunghills, rubbish, meadows, pastures, loam, sand, gravel, clay, chalk or marl; or lastly, on the roots, trunks, and branches of trees or other plants. In this respect plants may be arranged into six general divisions, according to their places of growth above recited, viz. aquatic, Alpine, hilly, shady, campaign, and parasitic plants, each of which contains several subdivisions. We shall give examples of each in their order. . . . From what has been said it appears that the nature of any ground or soil may be readily known from the bare inspection of the plants that grow in the same. Thus, the *Potentilla argentea*, tormentil cinquefoil, indicates clay under the surface; *Melampyrum cristatum*, crested cow-wheat, grows only in hilly ground; *Melampyrum arvense*, purple cow-wheat, in plowed land; *Melampyrum nemorum*, wood cow-wheat, in groves or shady places; *Melampyrum pratense*, meadow cow-wheat, in meadow or pasture ground; *Melampyrum sylvaticum*, yellow cow-wheat, in woods;

Pedicularis sylvatica, common lousewort, in spungy [sic.] or spouty ground; *Aira cerulea*, purple hair-grass, in turfy ground.

SECT. 335

The time of the whole duration of plants, or the years of their age, the time of their germination, that is, their sprouting or springing out of the ground after sowing, the time of their foliation, or leafing, flowering, sleeping, watching, fruiting, and shedding their leaves, plainly indicates the climate, or points out to us how one climate differs from another. And first of germination, which is the time that seeds require to spring out of the ground, or to put forth their seminal leaves after sowing. And in this respect the seeds of plants differ amazingly, from one or two days to as many years. Thus, e.g., the millet and wheat come up in one or two days; the navew, rocket, blite, mustard, turnip, spinache, and kidney-bean, in three or four days; the dill, lettuce, cucumber, gourd, and cresses, in four or five days; the beet and radish in six days; barley in seven days; orrach in eight days; cabbage in ten; beans require from fifteen to twenty; the onion comes up in nineteen or twenty days; the hyssop in thirty days; parsley seed in forty days; smallage in forty or fifty days; the peach, almond, walnut, chestnut, and piony [sic], in one year; the cornel and hazle-nut in two years after sowing. The foliation or leafing of plants is the time of the spring or summer they unfold, expand, or put out their first leaves. . . .

The watching or vigils of plants are the precise times of the day that their flowers open and shut. Such flowers as observe a determinate time of opening and shutting are called solar; and are of three sorts, viz., I. Meteorical, which observe the hour of expanding with less accuracy, but open sooner or later according to the degree of shade, moisture, dryness, greater or lesser pressure of the atmosphere. 2. Tropical, are those which open in the morning and shut up before night, but the time of their opening is sooner or later as the days increase or decrease; therefore they observe the Turkish or unequal hours. 3. The third sort of solar flowers is called the Equinoxial. These open precisely at a certain hour of the day, and generally shut up every day at a determinate hour, and therefore observe European or equal hours. . . .

Of the sleep of plants (as we may call it) in the night, we have spoken somewhat in chapter V, sect. 133. This sleep of plants is a certain position or situation of their leaves very different from that they have by day, and takes place almost in every species of plants. . . .

Now this nocturnal change in the position of the leaves of plants, which we call sleep, may be ascribed by some, partly to the darkness, and partly to the cool air, of the night. But that these are not the sole cause of this phenomenon appears from hence, that the same plants, though placed in a stove, where the degree of heat is the same both day and night, do not withstanding at their usual hours in the evening contract their leaves, and go to sleep, and open or expand them again very early in the morning; and, which is very remarkable, that they observe the same vicissitudes of contracting and expanding their leaves, whether the window shutters of the stove are shut or open. Let it be observed, that as animals while young and tender sleep most, so also do plants in their young state, but when grown up they indulge less in this respect.

The next thing to be observed, is the time that that plants ripen their fruits and seeds. Common barley sown in Lapland May 31, 1732, was cut July 28, consequently ripened in 58 days. The same sort of barley sown at Upsala

Mar. 6, 1750, was cut Aug. 4, and ripened in 151 days. And we find that at Upsala the medium is 110 days, in Scania 90 days, and in Lapland 60 days. For as eggs require a fixed time for the exclusion of the young, so the barley does in different provinces to ripen the seed, as appears by the above examples. And thus should observations be made on other plants as to the time of ripening their seeds.

Defoliation is the time of autumn, when trees shed their leaves, and thereby point out the progress of autumn, and the approach of the ensuing winter. The ash is among the first that sheds, and the last that puts out its leaves. The first fall of the leaves of trees with us is about the autumnal equinox. We ought carefully to observe also the first blowing of the meadow saffron. . . .

Botanists, having been hitherto taken up in acquiring the knowledge of plants, and confounded, or as it were overwhelmed, with the prodigious number and vast variety which nature everywhere presented to their view, have not been at leisure to make a regular course of observations in the manner of astronomers, although, in my opinion, such observations would have been of far greater utility to the public. Calendars of *Flora* should be made out in every province yearly, according to the time of plants coming into leaf, flower, fruit, and shedding their leaves; observing also the climate, that the difference of one country from another might from thence appear. The time also of solar flowers opening and shutting should be made out in every climate, that anyone, without the help of a clock, or seeing the sun, might know the time of the day. Maps of the plants also should be formed, which would point out everywhere the country, climate, and soil. Such observations would be highly useful in discovering more clearly the nature of the earth in general. The progress of the year from the putting out to the fall of the leaves of trees would show the climate, and also the greatest heat and cold of the place. In our botanic thermometer the freezing point is 0, and that of boiling water 100. The autumnal plants are those of Virginia, which flower kindly with us in Sept. and Oct. but rarely produce ripe seeds. The winter plants are those of the Cape of Good Hope, that flower with a gentle heat in the middle of winter, which is midsummer time in their native places. The spring or vernal plants are all those called the Alpine, which produce their flowers and fruit very early. The plants which flower twice a year, to wit, in spring and autumn, are all the Indian ones between the Tropics. The cold plants, such as the Alpine, etc., will scarcely bear the heat of 30 degrees on our thermometer. The temperate plants, such as those of Spain, Italy, etc. will scarce bear the cold of 8 degrees. The warm plants will bear the heat of 40 degrees, but the cold of 10 degrees will kill them. The cold plants placed in a stove, at first grow very luxuriant, but in a short time grow weak and die. The warm plants in a cold situation do first cease to grow, then lose their leaves, and produce neither flowers nor fruit. . . .

THE NATURAL HISTORY OF ANTS

René Antoine Ferchault de Réaumur—c. 1742

Reprinted by permission of the publisher from The Natural History of Ants, an unpublished manuscript translated by William Morton Wheeler. New York, Alfred A. Knopf, pp. 161–168, 1926.

Although best known for his Mémoires pour servir à l'Histoire des Insectes, *Réaumur dealt quite competently with industrial arts and physics as well, making substantial contributions to these fields. This less well known discourse on ants, presumed by Wheeler to have been written as part of the uncompleted* Memoires, *provides an excellent example of naturalistic writing. Disregarding the diffuseness of Réaumur's style, which Wheeler suggests is "due to a desire for completeness of description," the thoroughness and perspicacity evidenced in this selection were characteristic of the great naturalists. It was this tradition which was carried on in the nineteenth century by Charles Darwin, Alfred Wallace, and Henry Bates.*

Are there then in a formicary two kinds of females, winged and wingless? No, there is only one kind; both of them are the same individuals seen at different seasons. There constantly happens to the winged ants what happens to no other known animal of the class of those that bear wings: they lose theirs. . . .

. . . When we follow the ants through their various stages we see that those that are born without wings pass their lives without having them, whereas those that are to be winged have wings from the moment of their birth, like the other flies and the butterflies; that is, after the transformation which enables us to recognize them as ants. . . .

Now if we observe a formicary at certain seasons we find in it certain very large ants which we might regard as having lost their wings, and which are actually such individuals. We find also others quite as large that still possess wings. Both kinds are females, though their number is always far inferior to that of the wingless ants of medium size, which are the ones that carry on most of the work. We also find some very small wingless females and finally some winged individuals as small as the latter. If the female ants have need of males—for this is a question we may ask, since we know that plant-lice are fecund without copulation—it is natural to suspect that the small winged ants are the males. The great disproportion in size by no means conflicts with this presumption, since the general rule among insects requires that the males should be smaller than the females. . . .

Perhaps I should have learned nothing from the first chance opportunity of seeing two ants mating, if I had been less familiar with the ways of these small insects. Being on the road to Poitou and finding myself on the levée of the Loire, very near Tours, on one of the first days of the month of September, 1731, I descended from my berlin, enticed to stroll about by the beauty of the spot and the mild temperature of the air, which was the more agreeable because the earlier hours of the day had been warm. The sun was within about an hour of setting. During my stroll I noticed a lot of small mounds of sandy and earthy particles rising above the openings that led the ants to their subterranean abode. Many of them were at that time out of doors; they were red, or rather reddish, of medium size. I stopped to examine several of these earthen monticules and noticed on each among the wingless ants a number of winged ones of two very different sizes. Some of them had abdomens no larger than those of the wingless ants, and to judge from unaided vision one of the larger winged individuals must have weighed more than two or three times as much as one of the smaller. Over the beautiful levée, where I was enjoying my walk, there appeared in the air in places not very far apart small clouds of large flies which flew about in circling paths. They might have been taken for gnats or craneflies or may-flies. Often the small cloud hung in the air at a height within reach of the hand. I used one of mine to capture some of these flies and succeeded repeatedly in doing so. All I secured were without difficulty recognized for what they were, for they were winged ants like those I had found at every step on the small mounds of earth. But I observed—and the observation was as important as it was easy to make—that I almost invariably captured them in pairs. Not only did I almost always find in my hand one large and one small ant, but most frequently I took them copulating and held them for some time before they separated. The small ant was resting on the large one just as among common flies the male while mating rests on the female. The posterior end of the small ant was curved downward so as to apply itself to that of the female and it adhered so firmly that force was necessary to separate the pair. The abdomen of this small male was scarcely half as long as that of the large female, so that it could cover only the posterior portion of the latter's abdomen. I compressed the abdomen of some of the large ants and caused clusters of eggs to exude.

In order, therefore, to see ants copulating it is not necessary to know the place in which they hide during the act. Since I first took in the air the pairs of red ants of which I have just spoken, it has been easy for me to secure copulating ants of nearly all the species of this country. The fine days of summer and autumn, those especially that are bright and sunny, and during which various kinds of flies form small swarms in the air, are also the days on which the winged ants take flight. But they are not always congregated in the air in a kind of vortex; more frequently they are found dispersed, though occasionally they are present in the air in such great numbers as to be visible far and wide over very great areas. Even when they are flying and are difficult to observe near at hand, they can be distinguished nevertheless, at least during copulation, from several flies that differ but little from them in size and shape. This is indicated by a peculiarity that has never deceived me. When what looks like a fly about the size of an ant, with a posterior enlargement from which something seems to be dangling, is seen in the air, it is almost certain that what is taken to be a single fly is really a pair of ants. If the fly that seems to have this kind of tassel at its hind end passes within reach of the hand and is successfully captured it will be found that the hand holds two insects, a large winged female and another very small but also winged individual, whose posterior end is hooked to that of the former.

It is therefore in mid-air that the nuptials must be celebrated of those ants that pass the greater portion of their lives underground and the remainder of their lives crawling on its surface or at most on walls, plants or trees. I have sometimes stood near a formicary, part of whose inhabitants were winged, at about two or three o'clock in the afternoon while it was still being warmed by the sun's rays.

Then the winged individuals of the two different sizes issued from the earth, betook themselves, so to speak, to the roof of their abode and there, after being thoroughly warmed, strolled about in various directions, without, so far as I could see, any teasing of the large by the small winged individuals; that is, without any tender preludes to mating. Then one by one both the large and the small ones took flight. Soon the surrounding air was seen to be filled with them, and the large ones were seen each to have a small one dangling from its posterior end. Not only, therefore, do they remain aloft while they are copulating, but they actually begin the act in the air. Usually the female does not long remain alone. I have reason to believe this because along with the female and attached male which I expected to capture, and which I captured without their separating from each other, I havc sometimes secured at the same time two or three additional males which, jealous of the good fortune of the first, apparently wished to supplant him, or were, perhaps, waiting till he left vacant the place that was the object of their desires.

Furthermore, I have always seen the ants return one by one to their formicary as they left it. Thus it is in the air that mating begins and continues. Then it is the task of the female to support the male, contrary to what is found in the flies called demoiselles, among which the male carries the female. Nature seems to have varied her combinations in all possible ways. The female ant flies in divers directions without being abandoned by her male, and sometimes carries him out of sight. Since it is impossible to follow continuously with the eyes even those that fly lowest, and since others crossing them cause them to be lost to view, I have never been able to ascertain how long the flight and the mating may continue. I have seen some that alighted very near the formicary before separating.

It has therefore been established that the wings are necessary to the ants, both male and female, in order that they may mate, and it would seem that these organs have been given them solely for this purpose. At least it is certain that the females do not long retain their wings after they have been fecundated. The males also shed theirs, but it would seem that they retain them much longer. Their wings are not useless, except on occasions when they fly through the air without succeeding in encountering females of their own formicary; for all appearances indicate that mating occurs only among ants born together, that is, among those of the some formicary. . . .

THE PHYSICAL AND CHEMICAL ENVIRONMENT

The various physical and chemical forces impinging upon an organism can be analyzed quite apart from any consideration of the organism. This was as obvious a truth in a period when earth, air, fire, and water were considered to be the major environmental principles as it is today when sundry physical and chemical phenomena are acknowledged to be of significance. Concomitant with this recognition of a wider diversity of environmental agents has been the development of increasingly complex and sophisticated methodology and instrumentation to aid in their analysis.

Environmental analysis without consideration of the organism is relatively meaningless for the ecologist. Life is a unit of interaction, and ecology is concerned essentially with those interactions which occur at the individual, population, and community levels of organization.

Interaction may take the form of the environment regulating the organism—its distribution in time and space, its physiognomy and phenology, among other peculiarities; it may involve compensatory and behavioral adaptations on the part of organisms; it may consist of regulation and modification of the abiotic environment by organisms through the release of excrements and as agents of decomposition. This section deals with the analysis of environmental factors and certain aspects of their regulatory effect on organisms; the converse situation of organisms regulating environment is treated in the section on ecosystems. In reality, all the readings represent some aspect of organism-environment interaction.

ORGANIC CHEMISTRY IN ITS APPLICATION TO VEGETABLE PHYSIOLOGY AND AGRICULTURE

Justus Liebig—1840

Reprinted from Professor Liebig's complete works on chemistry. Philadelphia, T. B. Peterson, pp. 9, 36, 39–43, 70–71, 1841.

There are likely few contemporary chemists who would concur with the first sentence of the following passage. Ecology, however, benefited immensely from this orientation and its major by-product, the delineation of the limiting role of a minimal supply of minerals in the growth and development of plants. Thereby, Liebig laid the foundation for increased understanding of the role of the environment in the regulation of organisms.

The peculiar object of organic chemistry is to discover the chemical conditions essential to the life and perfect development of animals and vegetables, and generally to investigate all those processes of organic nature which are due to the operation of chemical laws. Now, the continued existence of all living beings is dependent on the reception by them of certain substances, which are applied to the nutrition of their frame. An inquiry, therefore, into the conditions on which the life and growth of living beings depend, involves the study of those substances which serve them as nutriment, as well as the investigation of the sources whence these substances are derived, and the changes which they undergo in the process of assimilation.

A beautiful connection subsists between the organic and inorganic kingdoms of nature. Inorganic matter affords food to plants, and they, on the other hand, yield the means of subsistence to animals. The conditions necessary for animal and vegetable nutrition are essentially different. An animal requires for its development, and for the sustenance of its vital functions, a certain class of substances which can only be generated by organic beings possessed of life. Although many animals are entirely carnivorous, yet their primary nutriment must be derived from plants; for the animals upon which they subsist receive their nourishment from vegetable matter. But plants find new nutritive material only in inorganic substances. Hence one great end of vegetable life is to generate matter adapted for the nutrition of animals out of inorganic substances, which are not fitted for this purpose. . . .

Many of the inorganic constituents vary according to the soil in which the plants grow, but a certain number of them are indispensable to their developement. All substances in solution in a soil are absorbed by the roots of plants, exactly as a sponge imbibes a liquid, and all that it contains, without selection. The substances thus conveyed to plants are retained in greater or less quantity, or are entirely separated when not suited for assimilation. . . .

The examples cited above, in which the quantity of oxygen contained in the bases was shown to be the same, lead us to the legitimate conclusion that the developement of certain plants is not retarded by the substitution of the bases contained in them. But it was by no means inferred that any one base could replace all the others which are found in a plant in its normal condition. On the contrary, it is known that certain bases are indispensable for the growth of a plant, and these could not be substituted without injuring its developement. Our inference has been drawn from certain plants, which can bear without injury this substitution; and it can only be extended to those plants which are in the same condition. It will be shown afterwards that corn or vines can only thrive on soils containing potash, and that this alkali is perfectly indispensable to their growth. Experiments have not been sufficiently multiplied so as to enable us to point out in what plants potash or soda may be replaced by lime or magnesia; we are only warranted in affirming that such substitutions are in many cases common. The ashes of various kinds of plants contain very different quantities or alkaline bases, such as potash, soda, lime, or magnesia. When lime exists in the ashes in large proportion, the quantity of magnesia is diminished, and in like manner according as the latter increases the lime or potash decreases. In many kinds of ashes not a trace of magnesia can be detected.

The existence of vegetable alkalies in combination with organic acids gives great weight to the opinion that alkaline bases in general are connected with the developement of plants. . . .

Let us consider the composition of the ashes of two fir-trees as analysed by an acute and most accurate chemist. One of these grew in Norway, on a soil the constituents of which never changed, but to which soluble salts, and particularly common salt, were conveyed in great quantity by rain-water. How did it happen that its ashes contained no appreciable trace of salt, although we are certain that its roots must have absorbed it after every shower?

We can explain the absence of salt in this case by means of the direct and positive observations referred to, which have shown that plants have the power of returning to the soil all substances unnecessary to their existence; and the conclusion to which all the foregoing facts lead us, when their real value and bearing are apprehended, is that the alkaline bases existing in the ashes of plants must be necessary to their growth, since if this were not the case they would not be retained.

The perfect developement of a plant, according to this view, is dependent on the presence of alkalies or alkaline earths; for when these substances are totally wanting its growth will be arrested, and when they are only deficient it must be impeded.

The roots of plants are constantly engaged in collecting from the rain those alkalies which formed part of the sea-water, and also those of the water of springs, which penetrates the soil. Without alkalies and alkaline bases most plants could not exist, and without plants the alkalies would disappear gradually from the surface of the earth.

When it is considered, that sea-water contains less than one-millionth of its own weight of iodine, and that all combinations of iodine with the metallic bases of alkalies are highly soluble in water, some provision must necessarily be supposed to exist in the organization of sea-weed and the different kinds of Fuci, by which they are enabled during their life to extract iodine in the form of a soluble salt from sea-water, and to assimilate it in such a manner, that it is not again restored to the surrounding medium. These plants are collectors of iodine, just as land plants are of alkalies; and they yield us this element, in quantities such as we could not otherwise obtain from the water without the evaporation of whole seas.

We take it for granted that the sea-plants require metallic iodides for their growth, and that their existence is dependent on the presence of those substances. With equal justice, then, we conclude, that the alkalies and alkaline earths, always found in the ashes of land-plants, are likewise necessary for their developement. . . .

In order not to form an erroneous conclusion regarding the processes of vegetable nutrition, it must be admitted that plants require certain salts for the sustenance of their vital functions, the acids of which salts exist either in the soil (such as silicic or phosphoric acids) or are generated from nutriment derived from the atmosphere. Hence, if these salts are not contained in the soil, or if the bases necessary for their production be absent, they cannot be formed, or in other words, plants cannot grow in such a soil. The juice, fruit, and leaves of a plant cannot attain maturity, if the constituents necessary for their formation are wanting, and salts must be viewed as such. These salts do not, however, occur simultaneously in all plants. Thus, in saline plants, soda is the only alkali found; in corn plants, lime and potash form constituents. Several contain both soda and potash, some both potash and lime; whilst others contain potash and magnesia. . . . The respective quantities of the salts required by plants are very unequal. The aptitude of a soil to produce one, but not another kind of plant, is due to the presence of a base which the former requires, and the absence of that, indispensable for the developement of the latter. Upon the correct knowledge of the bases and salts requisite for the sustenance of each plant, and of the composition of the soil upon which it grows, depends the whole system of a rational theory of agriculture; and that knowledge alone can explain the process of fallow, or furnish us with the most advantageous methods of affording plants their proper nourishment. . . .

OPTIMA AND LIMITING FACTORS

F. F. Blackman—1905

Reprinted by permission of the publisher from Annals of Botany **19**:281–295, 1905.

Blackman's major contribution to ecology was extending Liebig's "law of the minimum" to encompass the limiting effects of the maximum as well. This "law of limiting factors" as it came to be known, is developed in this selection. In the latter part of the paper, Blackman suggests but does not develop the concept which much later came to be known as "factor interaction."

In this article it is proposed to subject to critical consideration the conception of the 'optimum' as a primary general relation between physiological processes and the external or internal conditions which affect them.

In treating physiological phenomena, assimilation, respiration, growth, and the like, which have a varying magnitude under varying external conditions of temperature, light, supply of materials, &c., it is customary to speak of three cardinal points, the *minimal* condition below which the phenomenon ceases altogether, the *optimal* condition at which it is exhibited to its highest observed degree, and the *maximal* condition above which it ceases again.

As the maximum temperature for most metabolic processes is very near to the death point, exact location of it is attended with considerable experimental uncertainty and precise data are generally wanting. In practice, attention is usually concentrated upon the optimum of the condition and upon the general form of the middle part of the simple curve, which is usually accepted as a satisfactory graphic expression of the relation between the function and the condition.

In the treatment of the assimilation of carbon dioxide in all textbooks we find mention of optima of temperature, of light, and of carbon dioxide-supply for this process. After some years of experimental study of the effect of external conditions upon carbon-assimilation the writer has demonstrated that much of this treatment is quite incorrect, and from this position has passed to the general conviction that there is much that is misleading in that treatment of the effect of an external condition which involves giving definite values to its cardinal points.

We will at present confine our attention to the condition of temperature and will begin with certain *a priori* considerations derived from chemical dynamics.

The rate at which all normal chemical change takes place is increased by a heightened temperature condition.

Most reactions *in vitro* take place so quickly that it is impossible to measure their rate, but with all that go slowly in aqueous solution and resemble the processes of the organism, such as the saponification of esters, the inversion of sugar by acids, and others, it has been found that the acceleration produced by increased temperature is about the same. This has been generalized by van't Hoff into the rule that for every rise of 10°C. the rate of reaction is about doubled or trebled.

If this rule of chemical dynamics does not hold good for chemical reactions within the organism it is the duty of the physiologist to attempt, at any rate, to explain the aberration. Now it is interesting to note that this relation has actually been found to hold, as regards medium temperatures, say from 10°C. to 27°C., for quite a number of cases in animal and vegetable organisms so diverse in nature that the law clearly is *primarily* applicable to chemical change in the cell as well as the test-tube. Thus the respiration numbers of Clausen, for lupine seedlings and for *Syringa* flowers, show between 0° and 20°C., an increase of two and a half times for a rise of 10°C., the assimilation numbers obtained by Miss Matthaei and the writer for cherry-laurel leaves a coefficient of 2.1, and for sunflower leaves 2.3, while to come to more complex metabolic changes, the times required for spore-formation in *Saccharomyces pastorianus* (Herzog) and for the development of frogs' eggs (as calculated by Cohen from Hertwig's data. . .) at different medium temperatures both proceed within the limits of this rule.

As regards the rate of metabolic chemical change in the organism at high temperatures, this law clearly does not express the whole truth. If it did we should expect, with increasing temperature, all vital processes to proceed with ever-increasing velocity till the fatal temperature was reached at which some essential proteid coagulated or some other connexion was dislocated, and the whole metabolic machinery came suddenly to a standstill.

What then does happen as we approach the upper temperature-limit of the working of the organism? An important new factor, the *time-factor*, comes into play.

In later years this factor hardly receives the attention that it deserves. Sachs, however, clearly pointed out that the higher the temperature the more quickly the fatal effect ensues, and that short exposure to a very high temperature may not kill, when a prolonged exposure to a slightly lower temperature is fatal. . . .

The optimum has by some investigators been regarded as the highest temperature which can be permanently sustained without depression of function, but more usually a real optimum is held to be characterized by this, that the retardation produced by exposure to super-optimal temperature must not be of the nature of permanent injury, and that therefore on cooling again to the optimum temperature there must be a return of the function to its highest value.

There has been little attempt to apply this principle experimentally, and it looks as if everything would depend on the *time* of exposure to the super-optimal temperature. Rather than by direct experiment, it is probable that the high transient values will in future have to be estimated by the convergence of the lines of evidence that we have already indicated. . . .

We start this section with the following axiom.

When a process is conditioned as to its rapidity by a number of separate factors, the rate of the process is limited by the pace of the 'slowest' factor.

I think one may fairly express surprise at the extent to which this principle has been overlooked by those who have proposed to work out the relation between a function and some *single* one of the various factors that control it.

This desirable end often cannot be really accomplished without taking deliberate thought to the other factors, lest surreptitiously one of *them*, and not the factor under investigation, becomes the real limiting factor to an increase of functional activity.

We will consider in some detail the application of this axiom to assimilation, and briefly its application to respiration and growth.

Carbon assimilation furnishes the most instructive case for the consideration of the inter-relation of conditioning factors, because these factors are largely external ones, whereas in growth they are internal and less under control.

Let us then consider first the case of assimilation. We can recognize five obvious controlling factors in the case of a given chloroplast engaged in photosynthesis.

(1) The amount of CO_2 available,
(2) the amount of H_2O available,
(3) the intensity of available radiant energy,
(4) the amount of chlorophyll present,
(5) the temperature in the chloroplast.

In theory any one of these five might be the limiting factor in the total effect, and it is comparatively easy to experiment with (1), (3), or (5) successively as limiting factors.

Many experimenters have indeed done this without premeditation. The experiments of Reinke, in which with increasing light the rate of assimilation (as measured by the bubbling of *Elodea*) suddenly ceased its proportional increase and remained stationary while the light increased yet another tenfold, I interpret as probably a case in which the supply of carbon dioxide was the limiting factor: its limit of arrival by osmosis being once reached no further increase of assimilation was possible.

The experiments of Kreusler on the effect of temperature on the assimilation of a shoot of *Rubus* gave, as higher and higher temperatures were used, at first a steady rise of assimilation up to 15°C., but after this the assimilation practically never rose further. This state of things has been shown by Miss Matthaei to be a case in which inadequate illumination limited the assimilation to that obtained at 15°C., and so further heating produced no increase. There are also contemporary examples of such misinterpretation which will be discussed elsewhere.

When the rate of a function exhibits, in experiment, a sudden transition from rapid increase to a stationary value, it becomes at once probable that a 'limiting factor' has come into play. . . .

PHYSIOLOGICAL ANIMAL GEOGRAPHY

Victor E. Shelford—1911

Reprinted by permission of the author and publisher from Journal of Morphology **22**:551–618, 1911.

Blackman's concept of limiting factors was developed from the perspective of control exerted by the environment. It is the organism, however, which responds to minimum and maximum factors; thus, the investigation of the ecological and physiological attributes of organisms assumes significance in explaining their geography. Professor Shelford's "law of toleration" incorporates both the geographic environment and the ecological physiology of organisms. This brief report does not at all suggest the significant impact Professor Shelford has had in ecology through his own work and that of his students. The duration of his productive work is recognized in the publication of The Ecology of North America (University of Chicago Press) in 1964, almost sixty years following the first paper from his graduate student days.

3. THE RELATION OF PHYSIOLOGICAL CHARACTERS TO GEOGRAPHIC RANGE

Our studies of animal distribution usually consist of a list of names of species with a statement of the distribution of each, followed by such interpretation as suits our particular purposes. Attempts actually to study the environment in any detail, or the reactions of animals to the conditions of environment are rare indeed. Furthermore, the groups most studied (higher vertebrates) are probably least dependent upon their environmental complexes; they are often decidedly migratory and because of their size least adapted to experimental study.

Some quite extensive attempts to correlate geographic range with meteorological conditions have been made but always with only implied reference to the physiological character of the organisms themselves, and usually with the use of *species* as an *index of conditions*. A few factors have been emphasized, and these usually in the sense of barriers. Merriam emphasizes temperature; Walker atmospheric moisture.

Heilprin, like most paleontologists, emphasizes food. There appears to be no adequate basis for the idea that the same single factor governs the distribution of most animals. Such a conclusion probably results from leaving the organism out of consideration.

Since the environment is a complex of many factors, every animal lives surrounded by and responds to a complex of factors, at least in its normal life activities within its normal complex. Can a single factor control distribution?

A large amount of physiological study of organisms has been conducted with particular reference to the analysis of the organism itself, but with little reference to natural environments. Many of the factors and conditions employed in such experiments are of such a nature that the animal never or rarely encounters them in its regular normal life. Other experiments are, however, attempts to keep the environment normal, except for one factor. These have demonstrated that in ordinary reactions an animal responds to the action of a single stimulus. Certain general laws govern the reaction of animals to different intensities of the same stimulus.

a. Laws governing the reactions of animals. The laws governing the stimulation of animals in the experiments of the laboratory are familiar subjects in the textbooks of physiology. With respect to a given factor used in the experiment, it has been found that there is a range of conditions within which the activities of the animal proceed without marked stimulative features. These are called optimal conditions. Take, for example, temperature. There is in most animals which have been subjected to experimentation with temperature, a range of several degrees in which the animal is not markedly stimulated (optimum). As the temperature is raised or lowered from such a condition, the animal is stimulated. If the temperature be continuously raised, a point is reached at which the animal dies. The temperature condition just before death occurs is called the maximum. The lowering of temperature produces results comparable in a general way to those of high temperature. The condition just before the death point is reached is called the minimum. With various limitations, unimportant in this connection, the same is true with respect to each of the various factors which an animal encounters in nature. Which factor determines the limitations of occurrence of an animal on the earth's surface? The answer to this is suggested in Liebig's Law of Minimum.

b. Law of minimum. Liebig's law of minimum is summarized by Johnstone:

> A plant requires a certain number of food stuffs if it is to continue to live and grow. Each of these food substances must be present in a certain proportion. If it is absent the plant will die; if present in a minimal proportion the growth will also be minimal. This is true no matter how abundant the other food stuffs may be. The growth is then dependent upon the amount of food stuff present in minimal quantity.

In nature this law applies both geographically and locally. As applied to animals it includes both food and material for abode. The presence, absence and success of a species is determined by the necessary material which is absent or present in minimal quantity.

c. Law of toleration of physical factors. We have noted in the case of the tiger beetles, that for the egg-laying to take place the surrounding temperature and light must both be suitable, the soil must be moist, probably also warm, and must satisfy the ovipositor tests with respect to several factors. Egg-laying, the *positive reaction*, is then probably a response to several factors.

Furthermore, after the eggs are laid, the conditions favorable for egg-laying must continue for about two weeks if the eggs are to hatch and the larvae reach the surface of the ground. The success of reproduction depends, then, upon the qualitative and quantitative *completeness* of the complex of conditions. The *negative reaction*, on the other hand, appears to be different. The absence of eggs, the number of failures to lay and therefore the number of eggs laid in any situation can be controlled by qualitative or quantitative deficiency or excess with respect to *any one of several factors*. The presence, absence, or number of eggs laid is, then, determinable by a single factor, according as it is near the optimum or near either the maximum or minimum tolerated by the species. It is, however, not necessary that a single factor deviate; the effect is similar or more pronounced if several deviate.

In nature the presence or absence, or success of a species or group of species, its numbers and sometimes its size, etc., are largely determined by the degree of deviation of a factor or factors from the range of optimum of the species or group of species. The cause of the deviation in the factor or factors is not of importance. For example, in the case of a soil-inhabiting species such as Cicindela tranquebarica, to which considerable moisture is necessary, the cause of the deficiency in one case may be climatic deficiency in rainfall, in another a rapid drainage due to steep slope and porosity of soil. The former is what we have called a climatic (geographic) condition and the latter a local condition. The evidence for the law of toleration as applying to distribution is good so far as the local distribution is concerned and, since the same factors are involved in the geographic, there is no difficulty in the application of the law to geographic distribution also. The fact that in so far as our observation can go at present, the tiger beetles are found in similar conditions throughout their ranges, is also good evidence for the application of both the laws of minimum and toleration to geographic distribution. In fact the *law of minimum* is but a special case of the *law of toleration*. Combinations of the factors which fall under the law of minimum may be made, which makes the law of toleration apply quite generally; for example: food and excretory products may be taken together as constituting a single factor. From this point of view the law of toleration applies, the food acting on the minimum side, excretory products on the maximum.

d. Application of the law of toleration to geographic distribution. The so-called centers of distribution are often only areas in which conditions are optimum for a considerable number of species. The relation of the law to centers of distribution is shown in the diagram below; above the line is the scale of stimulation with the limits of toleration shown and below the parallel relation of the distribution and relative abundance.

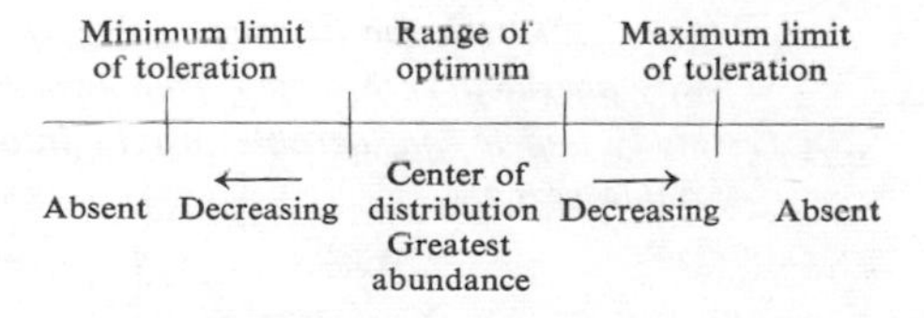

On account of the nature and distribution of climatic and vegetation conditions, it follows that as we pass in one direction from a center, one factor may fluctuate beyond the range of toleration of a species under consideration; but as we pass in another direction it is very likely to be a *different* factor. The divisions of Merriam's zones into arid and humid portions is an illustration of this, and seems to constitute a begging of the temperature question.

4. TENTATIVE LAWS OF DISTRIBUTION

On this general basis tentative laws of distribution may be formulated.

a. Governing the limit of geographic range. The geographic range of any species is limited by the fluctuation of a single factor (or factors) beyond the limit tolerated by that species. In non-migratory species the limitations are with reference to the activity which takes place within the narrowest limits. In migratory species this activity limits the range only during a part of the life cycle.

b. Governing distribution area. The distribution area of a species is the distribution of the complete environmental complex within which it can live as determined (1) by the activity which takes place within the narrowest limits and (2) by the animal's power of migration. Barriers in which some one factor of the complex fluctuates beyond the limits of toleration of the species at all periods of its life-history may prevent the animal from reaching all the suitable habitats, but this is the result of the working of the laws rather than an exception, and faunistic animal geography begins where physiological animal geography ends.

WATER—GENERAL CONSIDERATIONS; THERMAL PROPERTIES

Lawrence J. Henderson—1913

Reprinted by permission of Lawrence J. Henderson, Jr. from The fitness of the environment. New York, The Macmillan Co., 1913.

In this "inquiry into the biological significance of the properties of matter" Henderson, a biochemist, defends the hypothesis that ". . . the actual environment is the fittest possible abode of life." In doing so, the ecologist was provided with a new framework of reference for more circumscribed study and a considerable insight into environmental influences of an overriding sort.

GENERAL CONSIDERATIONS

It was assuredly not chance that led Thales to found philosophy and science with the assertion that water is the origin of all things. Whether his belief was most influenced by the wetness of animal tissues and fluids, or by early poetic cosmogonies, or by the ever present importance of the sea to the Ionians, however vague his conception of water may, indeed must, have been, he at least expressed a conclusion which proceeded from experience and serious reflection. . . . And it is especially worthy of note that of earth, air, fire, and water the last is the only one which happens to be an individual chemical compound. From that day to this the unique position of water has never been shaken. It remains the most familiar and the most important of all things. . . .

. . . In physics, in chemistry, in

geology, in meteorology, and in biology nothing else threatens its preëminence. . . and the physiologist has found that water is invariably the principal constituent of active living organisms. Water is ingested in greater amounts than all other substances combined, and it is no less the chief excretion. It is the vehicle of the principal foods and excretory products, for most of these are dissolved as they enter or leave the body. Indeed, as clearer ideas of the physico-chemical organization of protoplasm have developed it has become evident that the organism itself is essentially an aqueous solution in which are spread out colloidal substances of vast complexity. As a result of these conditions there is hardly a physiological process in which water is not of fundamental importance. . . .

All of these circumstances. . . depend in great part upon the quantity of water which is present outside the earth's crust, and upon its often unique physical and chemical properties. . . .

Of the total extent of the earth's surface the oceans make up about three fourths, and they contain an amount of water sufficient, if the earth were a perfect sphere, to cover the whole area to a depth of between two and three miles. This corresponds to about 0.2 per cent of the volume of the globe. The occurrence of water is, moreover, not less important and hardly less general upon the land. In addition to lakes and streams, water is almost everywhere present in large quantities in the soil, retained there mainly by capillary action, and often at greater depths. The atmosphere also contains an abundance of water as aqueous vapor and as clouds. Now the very occurrence of water upon the earth, and especially its permanent presence, is due in no small degree to its chemical stability in the existing physical and chemical conditions. This stability is of great moment in the various inorganic and organic processes in which water plays so large a part. In the first place the chemical reactions in which it is concerned during the process of geological evolution, though they are no doubt in the total of great magnitude, are both slow and far from violent. Long since any very active changes of this sort, so far as the superficial part of the crust is concerned, have run their course. In the second place water is really, at the temperature of the earth and in comparison with most other chemical substances, an extremely inert body, for the union of hydrogen with oxygen is so firm that it is not readily dissolved.

Thus water exists as a singularly inert constituent of the atmosphere, as a liquid nearly inactive in chemical processes on the surface and in the soil, and everywhere as a mild solvent which does not easily attack the substances which in great variety dissolve in it. The chemical changes which do follow upon solution are not such as to produce substantial chemical transformations, and most substances can pass through water unscathed. The nature of water, then, is a great factor in the chemical stability, which, no less than the physical stability of the environment, is essential to the living mechanism. But it may be questioned if such stability would not necessarily be ultimately attained in greater or less degree with almost any other substance, as a result of the general tendency of chemical processes to reach a condition of equilibrium, and it will therefore be well to turn to more secure fields of inquiry.

THERMAL PROPERTIES

Specific heat. First among these is the heat capacity or, as it is more commonly termed, the specific heat of water. This quantity has the value of

1.000 for the interval between 0° and 1° centigrade, a number which is due to the choice of water in defining the calorie or fundamental unit of heat. The calorie, small calorie, or gram calorie is that quantity of heat which is required to raise the temperature of one gram of water through 1° centigrade, and it varies slightly with the temperature, having the relative values 1.000 for the interval from 0° to 1°, 0.998 for the interval from 4° to 5°, 0.992 for the interval from 15° to 16°, and its mean value for the interval from 0° to 100° is 1.004. The heat capacity of water is then 1.000, in that 1.000 calorie is required to raise the temperature of 1.000 gram of water through 1.000 degree centigrade. . . .

The most obvious effect of the high specific heat of water is the tendency of the ocean and of all lakes and streams to maintain a nearly constant temperature. This phenomenon is of course not due to the high specific heat of water alone, being also dependent upon evaporation, freezing, and a variety of circumstances which automatically mix and stir water. But in the long run the effect of high specific heat is of primary importance. It will be convenient to postpone consideration of the regulation and importance of the constant temperature of the ocean until the other properties of water which contribute thereto have been discussed.

A second effect of the high specific heat of water is the moderation of both summer and winter temperatures of the earth. It is not easy to estimate the total magnitude of this effect, but the manner in which it comes about is well illustrated by the differences between seaboard and inland climates or between the climate of a large part of the United States, which is a continental climate, and that of Western Europe, which is essentially an insular climate. In the most extreme form such moderation of climate is to be observed on the high seas and upon small islands. There are found the smallest known differences between the mean temperatures of different months of the year and of different hours of the day, and the least tendency to violent changes of temperature. The calculation of Zenker regarding normal temperatures may be cited as a good illustration of the nature of the case.

Latitude	Continental Climate	Marine Climate	Difference
Degrees	Degrees	Degrees	Degrees
0	34.6	26.1	−8.5
10	33.5	25.3	−8.2
20	30.0	22.7	−7.3
30	24.1	18.8	−5.3
40	15.7	13.4	−2.3
50	5.0	7.1	2.1
60	−7.7	0.3	8.0
70	−19.0	−5.2	13.8
80	−24.9	−8.2	16.7
90	−26.1	−8.7	17.4

It is unnecessary to discuss the effects upon living organisms of the equable temperature of the ocean and of the moderation of climate, for obviously we are here confronted by a true instance of regulation of the environment.

The high heat capacity of water operates in still another manner to regulate temperature upon the land and at the same time to increase the mobility of the environment of marine organisms. For directly or indirectly it is involved in the formation and duration of ocean currents, especially the movement of water in the depths from the polar to the tropical seas, and it determines the amount of heat carried by such currents. A similar and even more important "function" is the direct promotion of winds, with the resulting distribution of aqueous vapor throughout the atmosphere, a primary factor in the dissemination of water by means of the rainfall. Here the essential thing is the existence of a vast warm reservoir in the tropics and of two similar cold reservoirs at the poles.

Under these circumstances the circulation of winds, bearing away water vapor from the tropical oceans, is inevitable, and the process is intensified by the high specific heat of water.

The living organism itself is directly favored by this same property of its principal constituent, because a given quantity of heat produces as little change as possible in the temperature of its body. Man is an excellent case in point. An adult weighing 75 kilograms (165 pounds) when at rest produces daily about 2400 great calories, which is an amount of heat actually sufficient to raise the temperature of his body more than 32° centigrade. But if the heat capacity of his body corresponded to that of most substances, the same quantity of heat would be sufficient to raise his temperature between 100° and 150°. In these conditions the elimination of heat would become a matter of far greater difficulty, and the accurate regulation of the temperature of the interior portion of his body, especially during periods of great muscular activity, well-nigh impossible. Extreme constancy of the body temperature is, of course, a matter of vital importance, at least for all highly organized beings, and it is hardly conceivable that it should be otherwise. In the first place marked influence of change of temperature upon chemical reaction is almost universal, and as a rule an increase of 10° centigrade in temperature will more than double the rate of a chemical change. Secondly all living organisms contain both chemical substances and physico-chemical structures or systems which begin to be altered, and usually irreversibly altered, at a temperature which is very little above that of the human body. It is perhaps imaginable that conditions might be otherwise in beings of a very different kind, but to-day every chemist well knows that if he is to control a chemical process, almost the first desideratum is rigid regulation of the temperature at which the process takes place.

It is therefore incontestable that the unusually high specific heat of water tends automatically and in most marked degree to regulate the temperature of the whole environment, of both air and water, land and sea, and that of the living organism itself. Likewise the same property favors the circulation of water by facilitating the production of winds, besides contributing to the formation of ocean currents. Here is a striking instance of natural fitness, which in like degree is unattainable with any other substance except ammonia.

HEAT EXCHANGE NEAR THE GROUND; COLD AIR FLOODS AND COLD AIR DAMS

Rudolf Geiger—1941

These excerpts are typical of the direction that the German meteorologist Geiger brought to ecology—namely that the environment immediately associated with the organism, the microclimate, is the critical factor, not the gross, or macroclimate typically measured. This distinction is extensively treated by J. N. Wolfe, R. T. Wareham and H. T. Scofield (1949. Microclimates and macroclimate of Neotoma, a small valley in central Ohio. Ohio Biological Survey Bulletin **41**: *1–267). An excellent application of the microclimate approach in ecology is that by John Cantlon (1953. Vegetation and microclimates on north and south slopes of Cushetunk Mountain, New Jersey. Ecological Monographs* **23**: *241–270). David Gates has written a concise, sophisticated and ecologically oriented treatment of energy exchange (1962. Energy exchange in the biosphere. New York, Harper and Row.)*

MIDDAY HEAT EXCHANGE AT THE GROUND SURFACE

THE INCOMING RADIATIONAL TYPE

At the upper limit of its atmosphere the earth receives a vertical solar radiation amounting to about 2 calories per square centimeter each minute. This value is called "solar constant." At European latitudes normal incidence does not occur. There the horizontal surface receives at the border of the atmosphere only a portion of the solar constant. When this radiation penetrates the earth's atmosphere it suffers a series of losses. . . .

A considerable portion of the enormous incoming sun energy is reflected by the surface of the clouds and is ineffective concerning the heat economy of air and ground. As an average for the northern hemisphere and the year, this amount is 33% of the incoming radiation. In the atmosphere another portion of radiation is scattered in all directions diffusely by the air molecules themselves and by substances suspended in the atmosphere (dust, plankton). The radiation does not suffer a loss in the true sense of the word but only a deflection from its original direction. But because a portion of the scattered radiation goes back to universal space also this portion is eliminated with regard to the terrestrial heat exchange. Reflections from clouds and diffuse scattering into universal space make together 42%. The reflecting power (albedo) of the earth, therefore, is 0.42; for the inhabitant of universal space the earth looks about as bright as Venus does for our eyes.

The third loss is the absorption of radiation caused by ozone, water vapor, and carbonic acid; this is a true loss in that the radiation energy is used to increase the temperature of the absorbing gases and, therefore, is eliminated from the insolation economy. What happens with this portion is not discussed in this book.

Despite the enormous distance the sun rays have to pass through from the limit of the atmosphere down to the bottom of the atmosphere, a mighty radiation flux penetrates down to the earth's surface partly as direct sun radiation, partly as scattered radiation from the sky. The two together represent the main portion of the solar heat at the disposal of the heat economy of earth and air. Wherever this immense energy current strikes upon the surface of the solid ground the radiation cannot penetrate this obstacle. A portion is reflected from the surface. Most of it is absorbed, changed into heat, and serves to raise the temperature of the ground.

The earth's surface, then, plays the most important part in midday heat exchange, but the layer of air next to the ground is that part of the atmosphere whose temperature relationships are most directly determined by the relationships of the surface itself. Observations of this lowest layer of air are therefore indispensable to studies of heat transfer. . . .

The temperature conditions of the layer near the ground are determined by the immense amount of heat which the surface of the ground absorbs. In summer, this surface is heated in our region up to 60°C, sometimes to 70° and 80°. . . . The temperature of the surface would be increased even much more if a heat loss—caused and maintained by the temperature contrasts—did not take place upwards and downwards. . . . One portion of the heat is conducted from the surface to the deeper layers of the ground. . . . The greater portion serves to heat the air layer near the ground and thus, indirectly, to heat the atmosphere. Partly also here, heat conduction is effective, but. . . . it does not play an important role as far as quantity is concerned. Primarily, convection and radiative pseudo conduction come into consideration. . . .

Furthermore, the ground loses much heat as a consequence of evaporation since the surface is deprived of 600 gcal if one gram of water evaporates; this is an amount of heat which would suffice to heat 6 g water from 0°C to the boiling point.

From the significance of the earth's surface for heat exchange it can be concluded that the highest temperature at about noon is at the boundary between ground and air; starting from here, the temperature decreases upward and downward. This kind of temperature distribution at noon time is called "*Incoming Radiation Type*." The real character of this type will be demonstrated by an extreme example.

Fig. 2 gives the temperature distribution which J. G. Sinclair observed at the Desert Laboratory at Tucson on June 21, 1915, at 1 PM. As we approach the ground from above, the temperature rises continuously and at an

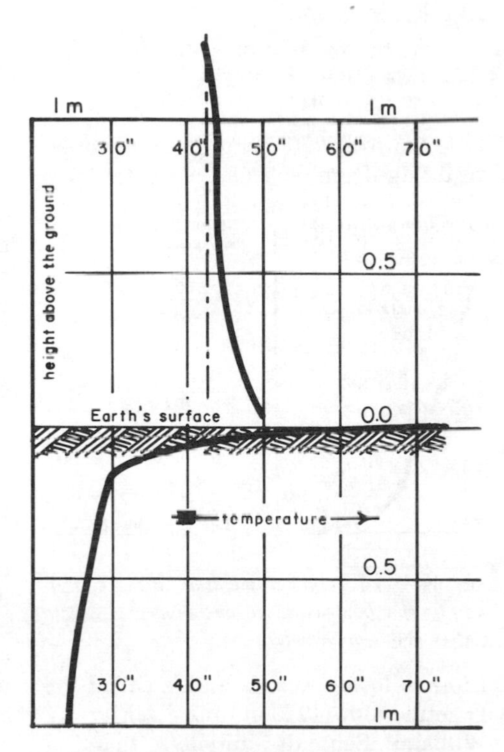

FIG. 2. *The incoming-radiation (insolation) type. (Tucson, 21 June 1915)*

increasingly rapid rate. At the surface there is a temperature discontinuity between air and earth. The surface itself possesses the highest temperature, not measured here, but in any case far above 71.5°, the measurement at a depth of 4 mm in the ground. In the first 10 cm of earth the temperature decreases with extraordinary rapidity, so that at a depth of 7 cm it is already several degrees below the air temperature. The effect of the time of day, the temporary noon-time heating, extends to a depth of only about 10 cm, as the break in the temperature curve indicates. In the lower earth layers the temperature falls again slowly.

Extremely high midday temperatures are therefore, as the illustration indicates, limited to the air and soil layers immediately bordering the earth's surface. Even under our mild climatic conditions the same holds true, though to a lesser extent. . . .

COLD AIR FLOODS AND COLD AIR DAMS

Fig. 89 is a cross-section of a "sink hole," a rock kettle shut in on all sides, resulting from subsidence. It is near

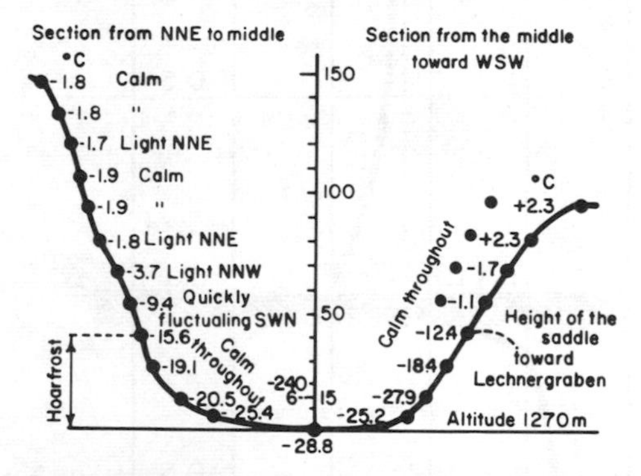

FIG. 89. *Temperature distribution in the Gstettneralm sink hole near Lunz on January 21, 1930. (After Wilhelm Schmidt)*

Lunz in lower Austria and is called the Gstettneralm (1270 m above sea level). Wilhelm Schmidt initiated there a great bioclimatic cooperative project of temperature measurements on the slopes of the sink hole and was able to demonstrate relatively very low night temperatures in the kettle. The cross-section shown in Fig. 89 exaggerates the altitude somewhat. The temperatures which were taken with an Assmann aspiration psychrometer before sunrise on Jan. 21, 1930 are entered at the points of observation. Simultaneous data on wind relationships are given as well. The left side of the illustration gives the section from north-northeast to the middle of the sink hole. On the upper part of the slope for some 70 m down the temperatures are from 1° to 2° below zero. As we descend still further the temperature drops with extraordinary rapidity and on the floor of the kettle reaches −28.8°C. The cold air from the slopes accumulates there and cannot escape. The heavy frost which formed in the lowest 40 m was a visible evidence of this stratification.

In the right hand half of Fig. 89 is a cross-section from the middle toward the west-southwest. Here the sink hole is intersected by a saddle. Temperatures below freezing prevail up to the height of this saddle. Inasmuch, however, as the cold air can flow over the saddle at this point, the temperatures above the saddle increase rapidly. If we look across at the left half of the illustration we can recognize the effect of this overflow on that side of the sink hole.

The Gstettneralm and Schmidt's measurements have attained fame in that during the well-known severe winter of 1928–29 the lowest minimum temperatures of all middle Europe were observed there, −48°C. A microclimatic phenomenon has here, as so often elsewhere, taken the record away from the macroclimate. It is significant, also, that during the following winters as low as −51° was observed at the same place—an indication that it is not so much the winter weather conditions as a whole, as it is the local, temporary conditions which lead to such extreme temperatures. In the work of W. Schmidt mentioned above, we see in particular the peculiarly conclusive thermogram from the bottom of this sink hole.

Even in midsummer temperatures below freezing are reached in the sink hole, and it is self-evident that the plant world and the animal world must adapt themselves to these local conditions. At the bottom of the sink hole the plant growth consists of only a few hardy grasses and a few herbaceous plants which can maintain themselves under protection of the snow cover in winter, while in midsummer they hurry through their growing season in a few weeks. As one ascends the side of the sink hole, dwarf pines appear first, then stunted spruces and snow roses. Farther up the spruces become larger and are mingled with alpine roses. At the upper rim of the sink hole is a normal forest. The reversal of normal temperature stratification resulting from the flood of cold air is thus reflected in a reversed plant stratification. Whereas the forest usually ceases as we go upward, it comes to an end here as we descend into the sink hole. Even in the animal world there appears a similar dependence of kind and number of kinds on the relative height in the sink hole. . . .

THE UTILIZATION OF SOLAR ENERGY BY AQUATIC ORGANISMS

George L. Clarke—1939

In discussing the variation in amount and nature of light with depth and kind of body of water, Clarke demonstrates the modification of one environmental factor (light) by another (water). In the latter half of the paper, the regulatory effect of light in limiting the distribution and photosynthesis of organisms is emphasized. Dr. Clarke's long association with the Woods Hole Oceanographic Institution (since 1931) provided the strong marine flavor to his text (1954. Elements of ecology. New York, John Wiley & Sons, Inc.).

. . . . Research in this field falls roughly into two parts, namely, (1) the determination of the amount and nature of the light actually present at various depths in all types of water bodies, and (2) the measurement of the extent to which submerged organisms are able to utilize the light present. From the biological point of view we need to know not only the range of light intensity at any point but also its spectral composition, its angular distribution, and its distribution in time.

The solar energy which falls upon a body of water is subject first of all to a "surface loss" which in the case of the ocean may amount to as much as 60 per cent in rough weather. Only about 3 to 9 per cent of this is ordinarily due to reflection (for solar altitudes greater than 30°) and the remainder has been found to be caused by a greatly increased rate of extinction in the uppermost meter of water. . . .

As the light passes from the surface downward into the water, it is reduced in intensity according to the following equation:

$$\frac{I}{I_0} = e^{-kL}$$

where I_0 is the initial intensity, I is the final intensity, k is the extinction coefficient, L is the thickness of the layer in meters, and e is 2.7. When this relationship between the reduction in the light and the thickness of water through which it has passed is expressed graphically on a semilogarithmic plot, a straight line is obtained (Fig. 1).

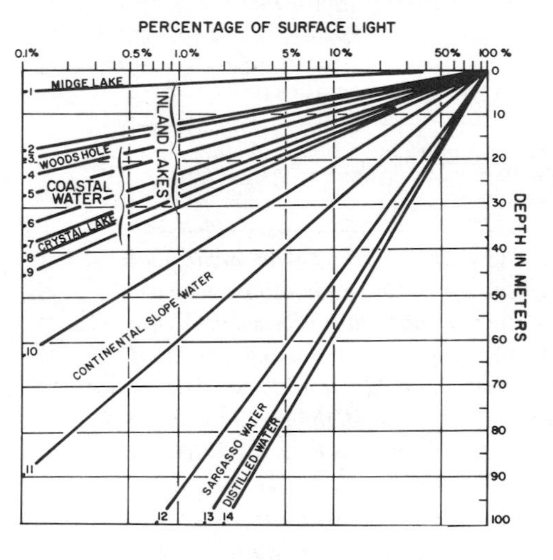

FIG. 1. *Comparison of the rates of penetration of the yellow-green component of daylight into natural waters (Photometer sensitive to wave lengths 5000–6000 Å). Curves show the relation between depth and illumination expressed as a percentage of the light at the surface. The curves represent the* average *value of the extinction coefficient for each series and no "surface loss" is included.*

The slope of the line is determined by the value of the extinction coefficient, k, which is thus an index of transparency. The extinction coefficient varies widely in the different parts of the spectrum—even for pure water—and its actual value depends upon the precise wavelength considered. In Fig. 1 the rate of absorption of red light by distilled water is seen to be very high, that for yellow light lower, and that for blue light very much lower. For example, after traversing 70 meters of distilled water blue light has suffered only a slight reduction to 70 per cent of its initial value, whereas yellow light has been reduced to 6 per cent. In the case of red light a reduction to 6 per cent has already taken place after passing through less than 3 meters of water.

Now the energy of the sun as it reaches the surface of a natural body of water is not equal in all parts of the spectrum. . . . We therefore start with unequal quantities of energy at the different wavelengths and these are absorbed at unequal rates as the light penetrates into the water. The result is that after passing through successive meters of water the spectral composition of the light present becomes rapidly and profoundly altered. The infrared and red components are reduced to small quantities within a very few meters and the ultraviolet, which was initially of small magnitude, soon drops to a minute fraction of the whole. As a consequence, after sunlight had traversed 100 meters of distilled water nothing but the blue component with a little green and violet would remain. . . .

In most natural waters the rate at which light penetrates is further decreased by the presence of varying amounts of suspended particles and dissolved material. The great diversity which results in the transparency of natural waters may be appreciated by comparing the curves of light penetration for certain typical lakes and oceanic areas in various parts of the world (Fig. 3). As will appear presently, only those measurements can be fairly compared which were made within the same part of the spectrum. In the figure observations with photometers sensitive to the yellow-green region (maximum 5500Å) are presented. Sargasso water is seen to be nearly as transparent as distilled water in this spectral region and light is reduced to 1 per cent of its surface value at about 100 meters. Beyond the edge of the continental shelf 100 miles or more from the coast in both the Atlantic and the Pacific the transparency is such that the 1 per cent value is reached at about 50 meters. In coastal waters the same value occurs at between 30 and 15 meters. Although there are a few inland lakes which are as clear as typical coastal waters, the majority of them are more turbid. In Midge Lake, for example, the illumination has been reduced to 1 per cent of its surface value at 3 meters. The extreme range of possible transparency in natural waters is thus very great.

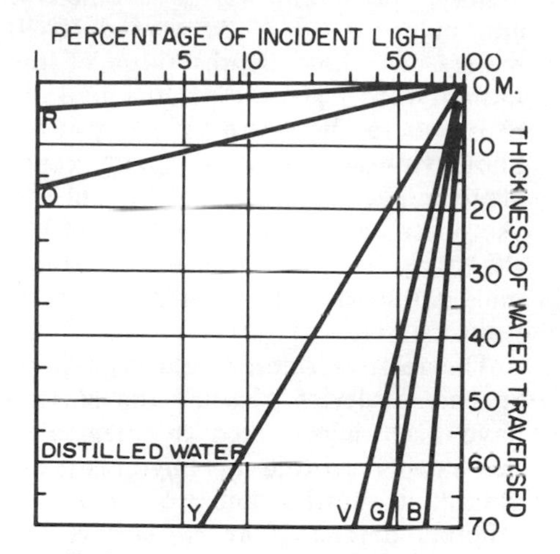

FIG. 3. *Transmission of light by distilled water at 6 wave lengths within the visible spectrum. Curves show the percentage of incident light (logarithmic scale) which would remain after passing through the indicated thickness of water.*

In the various natural waters we find that the *relative* rates of absorption of *different parts of the spectrum* are not the same as those characterizing distilled water. This situation is brought about by the fact that both the suspended and the dissolved material present have a *selective* action on light beyond that of the water itself, and the nature of the selective effect varies widely from one body of water to another. As a result it becomes necessary to measure separately the rate of penetration of each spectral region for each lake or oceanic area. . . .

The distribution in time of the illumination at any point is controlled by changes in the length of day and by seasonal variation in transparency. The latter is of vital importance since it has been shown to be chiefly responsible for the tremendous differences in amount of light received daily by organisms at only moderate depths—as much as 10,000 × at 30 meters. The agents causing changes in transparency, however, are not adequately known and present another opportunity for research.

In dealing with the utilization of the light energy by aquatic animals and plants, separate consideration will be given to the major subdivisions of the solar spectrum to which the following magnitudes may be roughly assigned: Infrared, 41 per cent; ultraviolet, 7 per cent; and visible, 52 per cent. . . . the infrared radiation is almost entirely absorbed in the uppermost meter. The chief importance of the infrared is, therefore, the rapid heating of the surface stratum.

Ultraviolet light in large amounts is injurious to plankton and other organisms, but according to ZoBell and McEwen virtually no bactericidal radiations penetrate sea water to as great a depth as 3 meters. The beneficial effects of ultraviolet in vitamin formation and in other poorly understood ways call for exact measurements of its rate of penetration. Yet serious disagreement exists on the rate of absorption of ultraviolet light even for distilled water!

. . . . Previously it had been supposed that ultraviolet was absorbed very rapidly by pure water itself, but the observations of James and Birge indicate a much lower absorption at least as far as 3600Å. It is essential to know whether this low rate continues to hold for the shorter, and more important, wavelengths or whether there is an abrupt upward turn. . . .

Turning now to the visible component of the spectrum, we find that many observations exist on the degree of activity of fish and of plankton animals in relation to its intensity. The information obtained, however, has not yet been adequately applied to the ecological relationships of the species concerned. A prominent case in point is the diurnal migration of plankton. Although research in this field has shown conclusively that the daily change in illumination is primarily responsible for the migration, the internal physiological reactions which control direction and speed of swimming are poorly understood. . . . Even less clear are the reasons why the vertical migration of one species differs from that of another and why the behavior of the same species varies profoundly from time to time and from place to place. . . .

The intensity of illumination controls photosynthesis and hence limits the depth of growth of both bottom-living and pelagic plants. For example, the lower limits for fixed plants in the following oceanic areas are: in Baltic, 20 meters; off Iceland, 50 meters; and in Mediterranean, 130–160 meters. In lakes the lower limits are: Trout Lake, 10–12 meters; Crystal Lake, 15–20 meters; and in Crater Lake, 12 meters. The maximum abundance of phytoplankton has been reported at the following depths: off Syracuse, 50 meters; off California, 25–55 meters; and in north European waters, 10–30 meters. At these depths most of the radiant energy present is in the green or blue, but red light is most effective for photosynthesis. Diatoms and other algae appear, however, to be able to use other parts of the visible spectrum effectively. The mechanism which makes this possible requires elucidation.

The relative rates of photosynthesis at various levels beneath the surface have been investigated by measuring the oxygen evolved by phytoplankton placed in bottles and suspended at different depths. Near the surface the illumination has sometimes been found sufficiently strong to inhibit photosynthesis, although the exact explanation for this is wanting. . . . Below the point of maximum photosynthesis the rate drops off to a depth at which no appreciable reaction takes place, but respiration continues at all levels to which living cells may be distributed. The intensity of light at which photosynthesis just balances respiration is termed the compensation intensity, the value of which has been reported in two recent investigations as 500 lux and 350 lux (or 0.3 per cent of noon sunlight) respectively. . . . Since the compensation intensity will naturally vary from species to species, further determinations for types important ecologically are seriously needed. The depth at which the compensation intensity is found, known as the compensation point, has been located (for short intervals) in a number of cases: Sargasso Sea, greater than 100 meters; English Channel, 45 meters; Gulf of Maine, 24–30 meters; East Sound (W. coast of Canada), 10–19 meters; Trout Lake, Wis., 8–16 meters; Woods Hole

Harbor, 7 meters. The depth of the compensation point over an average 24 hour period is, however, the significant value from the point of view of the continued growth and ecological role of each species. Marshall and Orr, working in the Clyde Sea area, found that on this basis the depth varied from 2 meters to 30 meters according to the season. . . .

It thus appears that most of the light incident on the surface of lakes or oceanic areas is absorbed by the water itself or by detritus and that only a very small part can be utilized by plants or animals. We conclude that aquatic organisms are existing under very unfavorable circumstances in regard to the utilization of solar energy. It is for this reason that the intensity, amount, and composition of the light are so frequently found to be limiting or highly significant factors in the aquatic environment. . . .

FACTORS EFFECTING VEGETATIONAL ZONATION ON COASTAL DUNES

Henry J. Oosting and W. Dwight Billings—1942

Reprinted by permission of the author and publisher from Ecology **23**:131–142, 1942.

This paper is an excellent example of procedure and interpretation in environmental analysis. The first portion considers several factors which might determine the distribution of plants on a local scale. Field measurements and observations are the basis for eliminating all but one of the various agents. Direct experimentation is then used to corroborate that factor as being of major regulatory significance in zonation. In addition to the substantial investigations of both authors, Dr. Oosting is the author of a widely used text (1956. The study of plant communities. San Francisco, Freeman and Co.).

The coast of North Carolina is discontinuously paralleled by a series of narrow, usually elongate islands. These low-lying sand "banks" may support a sclerophyllous forest in which live oak (*Quercus virginiana* L.) predominates and which includes numerous characteristic species of southern affinity. . . .

Because of the full exposure to almost constant wind from the ocean, a slight disturbance of the vegetative cover may result in extensive "blow outs" of the unconsolidated soil. Once initiated, the shifting of the sand may not be checked naturally for years. Man's activities have contributed materially to the destruction of cover. Grazing has been particularly serious, for it has indirectly transformed several of the banks into almost barren seas of shifting sand.

Today, grazing has been largely discontinued and, on government controlled areas particularly, much time and effort have been expended in attempts to stabilize the shifting dunes. Miles of brush barriers have been constructed and thousands of acres have been planted with grasses. The success of these attempts cannot yet be evaluated.

One of the most effective native sand-binding grasses is sea oats (*Uniola paniculata* L.) which is found in abundance on these coastal dune areas. The importance of this species and its associates as natural stabilizers prompted an investigation of the environmental factors governing their distribution. A portion of Bogue Bank near old Fort Macon at the entrance to Beaufort harbor, North Carolina, was chosen for intensive study. The area has been relatively undisturbed in recent years and illustrates all degrees of stability and vegetational development. The exposed position of the bank subjects it to the full sweep of the ocean wind and the pounding surf.

The ocean side of the bank is bordered by a sand beach of varying width which terminates at a low (5–15 ft.) foredune. Behind this is an extensive depression sometimes covered with small dunes in all stages of development and stability, sometimes blown out to a depth very near the water table. This area may be only 150 feet wide but is often 600 feet or more in width, and it terminates inland at a relatively high rear dune which may be 40 feet high. The rear dune forms a ridge down the center of the bank and obviously affords shelter to the leeward, for here vegetation is much less disturbed and woody species predominate, usually forming dense thickets whose tops rarely extend above the crest of the dune. . . .

THE VEGETATION

. . . Size and habit make *Uniola paniculata* and *Andropogon littoralis* the most conspicuous plants on the area. They may grow intermixed but where one is relatively abundant the other is not important. One of the objectives of the transect mapping was to determine the relative abundance of the two species in different positions on the dunes. The transect data. . . show that these two species far exceed all others in number and cover and that there are certain zonal concentrations which are probably general. Uniola exceeds Andropogon on the foredune (zones I and II) and on the crest of the rear dune (zone V). Andropogon is more abundant in the protected depression between the large dunes (zone III). On the windward slope of the rear dune (zone IV) either may predominate. On transect 1, Uniola is more important in this zone, but whenever the slope is fairly stable, as on transect 2, Andropogon predominates, especially on the lower portion bordering zone III. . . .

THE ENVIRONMENT

Soil factors. . . . It seemed plausible that soil moisture might be a factor in determining differences in vegetation. Field water content, therefore, was determined at three different times during the study. Duplicate samples were taken at depths of 10 cm. and 20 cm. at each of the 10 stations and also in the blowout area (zone IIIa). . . .

There seem to be no significant differences between the moisture contents at the various stations except for the obviously higher percentages recorded from the moist depression at station 3A on transect 1. Usually there is somewhat more moisture at the 20 cm. depth than at 10 cm. The lowest values are exhibited at the first and last stations on each transect. . . .

Observation of a visible spray of salt water from the surf suggested the possibility that wind-deposited salt on the surface of the soil might be rain-leached into the soil increasing the osmotic concentration of the soil solution. Absorption of water, transpiration rates, and water requirements have all been shown to be reduced as the salt content of the soil increases. . . . If concentrations of salts in the dune sand are sufficiently different at different stations, this might serve as a selective factor in determining the distribution of dune plants.

Soil samples of one hundred grams each were taken at the transect stations from the upper 10 cm. and the second 10 cm. Each sample was soaked in 200 ml. of distilled water for one hour and then 50 ml. portions of the water were titrated and salt calculated as NaCl. The highest salt content found was 1.81 mg. per 100 gm. of soil, which is only 0.0018 per cent of dry weight. There seems to be no reason to suppose that such minute quantities of salt could chemically or osmotically affect the growth or distribution of plants on the dunes.

Considering the amount of salt spray carried over the dunes, it is obvious that leaching must be very rapid to maintain the low salt concentrations at root depths. A possibility also exists that the dune plants may absorb some of this soil salt. Our limited data indicate a variation from day to day in the salt content of the soil and that the concentration at 20 cm. is rather consistently less than at 10 cm. (2 to 40 per cent). There is likewise variation from station to station which is paralleled on the two transects. The windward side of the foredune has the highest concentrations, the crest of the foredune the next highest. This is as might be anticipated in terms of wind-borne salt spray. The crest of the rear dune, which yields the third highest salt spray catches, is lowest in soil salts (0.94 mg. per 100 gm. of soil). . . .

Soil pH throughout the dunes area ranges from 7.4 to 7.9. Usually there is a greater amount of shell material in samples with the higher values. No consistent differences between stations or depths are apparent. . . .

Surface soil temperatures of 125–127° F. are not uncommon in the early afternoon sometime after the sun has reached its peak but at the same time air temperatures do not exceed 95–100° F.

Soil temperatures at 4 and 10 inches likewise respond to fluctuations of atmospheric temperature, but the magnitude of variation is much less than at the surface and the lag is greater. Highest temperatures recorded at a depth of four inches are 95° F. at 2:00 P. M. and at the same time 89° F. at ten inches. . . .

No soil temperature variations were noted which can be interpreted as factors in the zonal distribution of a species. . . .

ATMOSPHERIC FACTORS

Hourly determinations of air temperature taken simultaneously at all stations during a day show much variation, with no apparent correlations with zones or topography. . . .

. . . Evaporation is consistently somewhat higher at stations on transect 2 than at those on transect 1. At all stations, evaporation rates are three to four times as great by day as by night.

The greatest overall loss on both transects is at station 5 atop the rear dune, and the loss at station 2 on the foredune is almost as great. This suggests a possible correlation with the distribution of Uniola, for the species has its best development at or near these stations. The least evaporation takes place at station 3 sheltered by the foredune. Losses on the windward side of the foredune and rear dune (stations 1 and 4) are all of about the same magnitude.

By day the greatest evaporation is on the foredune (station 2) followed in decreasing order by stations 5, 4, 3 and least of all on the windward side of the foredune (station 1). The night rates of loss indicate a quite different pattern, for station 5 has the highest values followed by stations 1, 2, 3, and 4. The greater daytime evaporation in the exposed situations may contribute to the presence of Uniola and the absence of Andropogon in such places. . . .

. . . On these dunes, the relative humidity decreases from the foredune inland to the top of the rear dune. On transect 1, the humidity is invariably lower on the beach than on the foredune but the reverse is true on transect 2.

The data suggest no strong relationship between the distribution of vegetation and relative humidity on the dunes.

Both evaporation and relative humidity are profoundly influenced by the more or less constant wind from the direction of the sea. Other factors being equal, places in the lee of sheltering dunes will lose less water by evaporation than exposed positions in front of or on the crests of dunes. . . .

That the effect of this wind on dune vegetational zonation is not confined to its evaporational influence is clearly shown by the results obtained with the salt spray traps described above. The amount of salt spray and the distance it is transported are largely determined by wind. The total NaCl intercepted by 5 traps on a transect for any single run ranged from 29 mg. on a calm day to 121 mg. on a windy day when breakers were rolling. Again, the relative amount of spray striking at a station varies from day to day, and this too depends upon wind velocity.

Regardless of weather and the amount of salt transported by the wind, the salt catch values for the windward side of the foredune (station 1) are always 40 to 50 per cent of the total salt intercepted on the transect during an exposure of the traps. Then, ordinarily, the crest of the foredune is exposed to the next highest amount of spray and, surprisingly, the crest of the rear dune receives the next highest amount. Successively, the leeward side of the foredune receives relatively much less and the base of the rear dune the very least (only about 15 per cent of the total).

Apparently much of the salt spray is dropped on the foredune as the wind rises from the water. Then as it passes over the depression behind the foredune, there is no obstruction until the rear dune is reached. Some of the spray is lost between the two dunes, perhaps by gravity. However, it would appear that the real force of the wind is deflected upward by the foredune and its first obstruction thereafter is the crest of the rear dune.

Here, then, is a factor which shows some correlation with the distribution of the two major dune species. Uniola is invariably found in areas of greatest exposure, whether the soil be stable or not. Andropogon predominates on protected areas and on the seaward slope of the rear dune but not on its crest. Assuming that salt spray is the factor limiting or controlling the two species, one may suppose that the lower portion of the windward slope of the rear dune consistently receives a minimum of salt spray (as at station 4) and that only the crest of the dune is subjected to the heavy spray content of the wind rising from the foredune. . . .

PHYTOMETER STUDIES

In table V a summary is presented of the relative responses of the three grass species during the phytometer treatments. Detailed observations were made at the time of transplanting (August 1), and again 12 days after treatment was begun, 8 days later, and finally when the experiment was terminated (September 1). The symbols used in the table indicate the condition of the plants relative to that of the last preceding observation. . . .

The phytometer experiments suggest several generalizations. Andropogon and Uniola are relatively unaffected by low soil moisture over considerable periods of time but, because of a probable lower moisture requirement, Uniola is capable of longer survival under extreme conditions. Under comparable low moisture conditions Spartina will die before the other two species show much indication of suffering. Andropogon cannot live for long when salt water is added to the soil but Uniola is much less affected. Daily watering is less favorable to all three species than watering on alternate days. Probably better growth is possible under wider intervals of watering. Salt spray is seriously injurious to Andropogon, affects Uniola only slightly, if at all, and has no effect on Spartina.

TABLE V. *Responses of plants of three dune species to watering and spraying treatments at intervals during a month. The symbols indicate: (○) unaffected, (+) improved in appearance, either in color or new growth; (−) declining, unhealthy or dying. The first symbol in each group compares the plants to their field condition, the second is compared to the first, and the third to the second*

	Uniola	Andropogon	Spartina
No treatment	○ ○ +	○ + −	○ ○ −
Water daily	○ ○ ○	○ + ○	− ○ ○
Water alternate days .	○ ○ +	○ + +	− ○ +
Seawater daily	− ○ −	− − −	− ○ +
Water daily and seawater spray daily . .	○ ○ ○	− − −	○ ○ ○

DISCUSSION AND CONCLUSIONS

The transect data serve to corroborate the zonal distribution of the major species on the Ft. Macon dune area and to show the relationship of these zones to topographic features. Such a distribution is usually explainable on the basis of exposure, soil, temperature, or moisture relationships. Here, however, the usual factors do not seem to control the situation. The soil is uniform or nearly so, soil moisture does not seem to vary characteristically for the zones nor sufficiently to have any strong influence. Temperature of the soil and air varies widely and inconsistently. Relative humidity and evaporation rates are greatest at the crests of the fore and rear dunes. None of these factors seems to be strongly correlated with the distribution of the dominant species.

The phytometer studies show that Uniola and Andropogon require very little moisture to survive and, in fact, do better under low soil moisture conditions than when watered daily. Thus, the deep depressions are left to more mesophytic species. If the depressions are periodically flooded with salt water *Spartina patens* is dominant. If moist with seepage water, the low places are predominantly occupied by *Fimbristylis castanea.* The phytometer experiments further show that the water requirement of Uniola is less than that of Andropogon. This may be a factor contributing to the predominance of Uniola on the crests of the dunes where evaporation is greatest and may partially explain its success as a pioneer dune former in dry and shifting sand. However, the relative tolerance of the two species to salt spray is such that Andropogon dies under exposures which scarcely affect Uniola. Apparently, the general distribution of the two species on the dunes is largely controlled by the extent of exposure of the habitat to wind-borne spray. . . .

FURTHER STUDIES IN PHOTOPERIODISM, THE RESPONSE OF THE PLANT TO RELATIVE LENGTH OF DAY AND NIGHT

W. W. Garner and H. A. Allard—1923

Reprinted from Journal of Agricultural Research **23**: 871–920, 1923.

The regulatory action of an environmental factor is perhaps no better illustrated than in plant photoperiodism, the study of which was pioneered by Garner. The response of organisms to periodic environmental oscillations (tides, lunar changes, etc.,) has yielded an extensive literature and considerable polemic. The opposing viewpoints concerning the operation of these "biological clocks" are ably summarized by F. A. Brown (1959. Living clocks. Science **130**: *1535–1544) and C. S. Pittendrigh (1958. Perspectives in the study of biological clocks. Perspectives in marine biology. Berkeley, University of California Press, pp. 239–268).*

In an earlier paper considerable data were presented tending to show that the length of day exercises a remarkable regulatory action in initiating or inhibiting sexual reproduction in plants. In a number of species studied it was found that ordinarily the plant can attain the flowering and fruiting stages only when the length of day falls within certain limits, so that in such cases flowering and fruiting occur only at certain seasons of the year. In this respect some species and varieties respond to relatively long days while others respond to short days. Moreover, some plants are much more sensitive to change in length of day than are others. In the absence of the particular day length favorable to sexual reproduction vegetative development may continue for a more or less indefinite period, thus frequently leading to the phenomenon of gigantism. It was discovered, also, that exposure to a daily light period intermediate between that favorable only to vegetative development, on the one hand, and that favoring only flowering and fruiting on the other hand, tends to cause both forms of activity to progress simultaneously. This combined form of activity constitutes what is commonly known as the "everflowering" or "everbearing" behavior. It was suggested that probably the seasonal range in length of day is an important factor in the natural distribution of plants and that in agricultural practise the correct time for planting many crop plants may be largely conditioned by the prevailing length of day. To designate the response of the plant to length of day the term "photoperiodism" was suggested. . . .

LONG-DAY AND SHORT-DAY PLANTS AND THE CRITICAL LENGTH OF DAY FOR FLOWERING

. . . the plants studied tend to arrange themselves into two groups. One of these groups consists of species that are caused to flower by the action of short days while the other includes those species that are forced into flowering through the action of long days. For convenience the first named group are spoken of as short-day plants while the second group are designated as long-day plants. At first sight it would seem that these two groups of plants are diametrically opposed in their response to length of day, but detailed study of the two groups indicates that the difference is one of degree rather than of kind. In fact, classification into the two groups is more or less arbitrary. In the case of such plants as Cosmos and Bidens, flowering is inhibited by a daily light exposure much in excess of 12 hours' duration, while vegetative development promptly gives way to flowering when the light period is reduced to 12 hours or less. These plants will flower even when receiving only a few hours of light daily; in other words, it is not possible to reduce the light duration sufficiently to prevent flowering without killing the plants. On the other hand, Solidago and Hibiscus are readily prevented from flowering by reducing the light period to something less than 12 hours, although under these conditions they may continue to live and may even continue development in certain directions. These plants are not inhibited from flowering by increasing the light duration beyond the normal. The important point is that the inhibition of flowering in the first case by a long light period is not of the same sort as the inhibiting effect of a short light period in the second case; that is, the inhibition in the two cases results in different alternative forms of vegetative activity, as will be shown in later paragraphs. There are, moreover, plants which may be said to occupy an intermediate position in that it is possible to have a day length too long as well as one too short to induce flowering. *Mikania scandens* L., briefly discussed in our former paper, is an example of this type. In the wild state Mikania regularly flowers in late July and through August, and if kept in the greenhouse through the winter it also usually flowers very sparsely in the spring. Seedlings from a planting made December 10 were unable to flower under the influence of the lengthened daily light period in the electrically illuminated greenhouse, while similar plants in the control greenhouse flowered at the usual time in August of the following summer. On the other hand, this species was unable to flower through the summer or fall under day lengths of 5, 10, and 13 hours' duration. The Biloxi variety of soybeans (*Soja max* (L,) Piper), discussed in detail in the former paper, occupies a position slightly below the intermediate position of Mikania in response to day length. In this case flowering is readily inhibited by a day length in excess of 13 hours. On the other hand, with very short day lengths only a very few cleistogamous flowers and fewer seed are developed but the reproductive phases apparently can not be entirely suppressed. . . .

Not only do plants differ markedly as to the particular length of day most favorable for flowering but they also differ widely as to the narrowness of the range in day length which will permit of flowering. Experiments with Mikania, referred to above, indicate that under ordinary conditions this plant will readily flower only under a day length ranging but little beyond an hour on either side of 14 1/2 hours, which is approximately the optimum for flowering. Buckwheat flowers readily under a daily illumination period ranging at least from 5 hours up to 18 or 20 hours and probably even under continuous illumination, notwithstanding the fact that the extent of vegetative development and life duration are profoundly affected by this range in the length of the light period. While there is a certain degree of antagonism or incompatibility between the vegetative and reproductive phases of activity, the two obviously are not necessarily affected to the same degree by a given change in duration of the light period. *Viola papilionacea* Pursh will flower under all lengths of day met with in temperate regions except for a short period in midwinter. In the broadest sense the plant will flower continuously for about 10 months of the year, a conspicuous example of everblooming. During the summer months, however, only the cleistogamous type of flower is seen while in spring and fall only the showy blue, chasmogamous blossoms develop. By maintaining a light period equivalent to the long summer days the cleistogamous flowering continues indefinitely and, similarly, a considerably shorter light period will maintain the open type of flowering indefinitely, thus illustrating a narrower type of everblooming. In this case the whole effect of the range in length of day from February to the summer solstice is merely to change the type of blossom (involving change in relative fertility).

Thus, beginning with the equatorial length of day of 12 hours as the standard, it may be said that a group of plants normally will flower under any range downward to less than 6 hours, while another group will flower under any range upward to at least 18 hours and probably up to continuous illumination. Other plants will flower only within a comparatively narrow range on either side of the 12-hour standard. Still others are capable of flowering throughout these ranges, their response being quantitative rather than qualitative in character. . . .

SPRING FLOWERING AND FALL FLOWERING

The facts brought out in the preceding discussion of the relation between long-day and short-day plants and the balance between the vegetative and the reproductive types of activity throw light on the relationships existing between spring-flowering and fall-flowering plants. As is well known, many plants normally flower only during the spring, while many others regularly flower only in the fall. There are a number of plants, however, which flower in both spring and fall, although usually there is a marked difference in the extent of the flowering during the two seasons. Finally, there is a large group of plants which blossom in midsummer and a smaller group which under favorable conditions flower in winter. It is well known that in a very large number of perennials the flower buds are organized during the summer or early fall of the year preceding that in which the blossoms finally open, so that, in considering the effects of light duration, it is necessary to avoid confusing the action on the laying down of primordia and that on the final unfolding of the blossom.

Broadly speaking, in cool temperate regions short-day plants will flower chiefly in the fall rather than in the spring because of the lag in temperature rise in spring as compared with the lengthening of the day. In other words, in spring the day length is likely to become too long for flowering of short-day plants before the temperature has risen sufficiently to permit plants to become active. This is true more particularly of the annuals and those herbaceous perennials which require considerable vegetative development as an antecedent to flowering. That plants of these types which regularly flower in the fall will actually flower in the spring when the obstacle of low temperature is removed has been demonstrated in a number of cases. As a specific illustration Peking soybeans germinating in the greenhouse March 31 showed first open blossoms on May 12, or 42 days after appearance above ground, while a second lot germinating April 13, just two weeks later than the first planting, did not show open blossoms till July 16, 90 days after germination. Plantings of the Biloxi soybeans made on the same dates failed to flower till September, since the day length was already above the critical for flowering in this variety. The Biloxi quickly flowers, however, if planted in winter or early spring in the greenhouse. Indirectly, the many experiments already described in which various plants have been forced into flowering out of season by shortening the light period or inhibited from flowering in the normal season by increasing the light period furnish proof of this relationship of spring and fall flowering in the short-day plants. As the critical light period for flowering becomes longer the chances for spring flowering of the species are increased till finally spring flowering merges with summer flowering in those species which are intermediate between the more typical short-day and long-day plants. Again, sparse flowering in spring is to be looked for in those of the short-day plants which are able to flower at all, for the reason that the change in day length is toward the optimum for vegetative activity and away from the optimum for flowering. It is under these conditions, also, that various modifications and abnormalities in flowering and fruiting, quantitative as well as qualitative, are most likely to occur. On the other hand, the short-day plants as a whole will have their energies thrown into flowering and fruiting more or less quantitatively, as it were, through the change in day length in the fall when the change is away from the optimum for vegetative activity and toward the optimum for sexual reproduction. One important qualification must be made to this principle, namely, that it holds good only so long as the day length does not become too short for the flowering and fruiting processes.

The long-day plants, on the other hand, through late spring and early summer are subjected to a changing day length which is approaching the optimal for sexual reproduction, hence it is to be expected that these plants would flower and fruit abundantly during this period. A large proportion of spring flowering plants consists of woody and herbaceous perennials in which the flower primordia are organized during the summer preceding the spring in which the blossoms unfold. In this case it seems probable that the optimal day length for flower development following the summer solstice passes by before the embryonic flower buds have made much progress in their development and the direction of the change in day length through late summer and the fall is away from this optimum for flowering and fruiting and toward or through the optimum for vegetative activity. Under these conditions further development of the flower buds would be attended with difficulty so that their growth would be slow. If the onset of cold weather is delayed, some species may flower in the fall instead of in the normal spring season. In some, and probably in most instances, however, flowering would be inhibited by the short days of late fall and winter. On the other hand, the cold weather of winter may exercise a distinctly helpful influence on the completion of the flowering process by establishing a favorable balance of income over outgo. Consequently, the earliness of flowering in the spring will depend largely on how soon the temperature rises to the point where development can actively proceed. The necessary internal conditions for flowering having been established, it remains for rise in temperature in spring to speed up the unfolding of the blossoms. Nevertheless, the increasing length of the day in the spring undoubtedly remains a factor, particularly in those species which do not unfold their blossoms till spring is well advanced. . . .

COMPENSATION FOR TEMPERATURE IN THE METABOLISM AND ACTIVITY OF POIKILOTHERMS

Theodore H. Bullock—1955

Reprinted by permission of the author and publisher from Biological Reviews **30**:311–342, 1955.

The adaptation to an environmental variable, in this instance temperature, and the ecological significance of this compensation is one of the points developed by Bullock in this paper. This aspect of ecological physiology provides yet another dimension to the concept of tolerance and suggests caution in the assessment of the role of any given factor in the ecology of any given group.

. . . It is generally assumed that poikilotherms operate at lower rates in colder habitats and seasons. It is the purpose of this article to call attention to evidence, old and new, supporting the thesis that many cold-blooded animals are, on the contrary, relatively independent of temperature, within limits, in nature. This is to say that these species tend to maintain a certain level of metabolism and other characters measured as rates, compensating for different temperatures by homoeostatic mechanisms of various kinds.

The phenomena of temperature races and of acclimation are familiar to geneticists and physiologists, but the numerous indications in the literature that these are probably operating in ecology on a grand scale have been overlooked to such a degree that standard treatises on ecology may contain no reference to compensatory differences in metabolism or activity in different habitats or seasons. Usually there is mentioned only the phenomenon of change in tolerance to extremes, e.g. winter hardiness. Since the common examples of the latter phenomenon are species unable to maintain full activity in winter, the impression is reinforced that cold-blooded forms are victims of the environmental temperature. Many species, perhaps whole habitat groups, may fail characteristically to show compensatory adaptation of rates of activity or metabolism over a large part of the range of temperatures to which they are exposed naturally. But it will be shown below, after reviewing some of the facts already known, that a great variety of animals do show compensation normally, thereby affecting their ecologic, geographic and seasonal status—and consequently evolution—to a major degree. . . .

II. THE FACT OF COMPENSATION

. . . Moore first showed that several species of the genus *Rana* could be arranged in a series such that the more northern-ranging breed earlier at a given latitude, develop faster, have lower temperature coefficients (Q_{10}) and limits of heat tolerance. What is more pertinent in the present connexion, he later showed that the same is true of latitudinally separated populations of one wide-ranging species, *R. pipiens*. More stenotopic species like *R. catesbeiana* and *R. clamitans* do not show such physiological differentiation among their populations. Moore's data show clearly the importance of making comparisons only in the physiological temperature range or of otherwise avoiding the extremes where excessive heat or cold greatly change the rate-temperature curve. Similarly,

Volpe found certain species of toads (*Bufo fowleri* and *B. americanus*) which show geographic temperature adaptation at least in the lower portion of the physiological temperature range. . . .

In this laboratory a series of studies has been directed toward the physiological ecology of temperature adaptation, and three of them bear upon the latitudinal comparison within a species. Roberts found compensatory differences in the standard metabolism between populations of a shore crab, *Pachygrapsus crassipes*, from different points on the coast. Rao reported the same with respect to the rate of ciliary pumping of water in a mussel, *Mytilus californianus*, from Puget Sound to Los Angeles. These cases, in contrast to most earlier ones, were controlled as to weight, which has a large effect. Moreover, in *Mytilus* size has a different effect in the different populations—less in the cold-adapted, more in the warm-adapted—so that northern animals can grow bigger without the activity per gram being depressed too far. Dehnel has found in three species of gastropods (*Thais emarginata*, *Crepidula nummaria*, *Lacuna carinata*) that larvae growing within capsules on their own yolk, in samples at Sitka, Alaska, grow from two to nine times faster than in samples in southern California at any given temperature, between 10 and 16°C.

In short, adaptation of metabolism and other rate functions to latitude, as though it were compensation for temperature, is widespread, within and between species.

(2) *Microgeographic physiological differences within the species.* The discovery of precisely similar differences between individuals separated by less than a metre deserves a separate heading. This was discovered recently in a student project on intertidal invertebrates by James, confirmed by Wemple, and has been reported in a preliminary note by Segal, Rao & James. Limpets (*Acmaea limatula*) have a consistently faster heart beat in samples taken from lower intertidal levels than from higher levels. The species ranges vertically less than 1.5 m. but individuals probably do not move outside of a territory extending only a fraction of this distance in height, over considerable periods. The significant parameter of the intertidal difference appears to be temperature; the higher tide specimens act as though adapted to higher average temperatures which is probable in this locality. Transplantation of limpets in the field indicates that complete acclimation is possible in a few weeks. Not only heart rate but also condition of gonads reflects the intertidal position and is reversible within a month. *Mytilus edulis* and *M. californianus* both show similar vertical differentiation, in pumping rate and in shell/body ratio. In a certain case, 75 cm. vertically is equivalent to about 330 miles latitudinally in the pumping-rate compensation of *M. californianus* of 20 g. soft parts at 16°C., as between the given geographic localities. . . .

(a) *Distribution and types of adaptation.* The distribution [of temperature compensation] among species is apparently wide but far from universal. But this statement can apply only to a given measure of the tendency. It is quite uncertain whether there is complete absence of regulatory adaptation in any organism, that is, passive submission to the role of 'Spielball der Umgebung.'

The known instances are widely scattered among the groups of animals and plants. There is considerable evidence that terrestrial and possibly fresh-water forms are relatively poorer in instances or in the degree of compensation than marine poikilotherms. Interestingly and inevitably, the terrestrial forms are the ones which exhibit *par excellence* winter hardiness (acclimation of tolerance), long known and studied but only recently analysed metabolically by Scholander, Flagg, Hock & Irving. However, several cases have been cited above among insects, pulmonates, and amphibians, as well as fresh-water fish, of metabolic adaptation to temperature by one or another measurement so that a generalization like that above must at the least be qualified. I feel confident in predicting that reptiles will also yield examples of physiological adaptation, although as Prof. R. B. Cowles has pointed out to me, these animals accomplish in part the same result behaviourally by controlling their microclimate, e.g. sunning and shading themselves, and this may be in lieu of some physiological adaptation.

We may recognize various types of animals on the basis of this tendency, at least for a given physiological character. There are the non-acclimating, the partially-, completely-, over-, and reverse-acclimating cases. Precht has formalized these as types IV, III, II, I and V, respectively. There are only a few cases of types I and V. We may distinguish slow- and fast-acclimating instances (measured in days) and as a separate group those in which 'immediate' compensation or 'temperature-independence' is manifest (measured in minutes). There appear to be species in which various genotypes exist, each adapted to a certain temperature but unable to acclimate, and others in which adaptation is phenotypic, that is, the genotype permits a wide range of acclimation. The facts at hand do not allow a simple statement as to the greater importance of the one or the other among eurythermal species. . . .

(b) *Mechanisms and levels*. . . . Consideration of these differences also suggests the probability that the separate regulatory processes are not always proportional so as to preserve the balance of the organism. Thus we have seen dehydrogenase activity altered without concomitant change in catalase. We may propose that it is the factor of balanced alteration which is the crucial one limiting the extent of acclimation in a species and its frequency among species. One might ask, if a winter-adapted animal can metabolize faster than a summer-adapted one, at summer temperature, then why does it instead normally slow down, when it could be feeding, reproducing and dominating its habitat faster? The simplest answer appears to be balance; something is not proceeding as fast as oxygen consumption, so that the whole machine is unable to keep up the high rate. Indeed, it is tempting to speculate that the hazards of balance, or the proportional change in various mechanisms, conceal the answer to the general biological question: Why are not eurythermal species more common or why are not most species distributed more widely than they are? But we must not mistake this facile statement for a fact; the actual fact of an imbalance which is sufficient to be effective in nature in limiting acclimated individuals must first be demonstrated. . . .

(c) *Significance in ecology and evolution*. The extent or adequacy of the compensatory change varies greatly. Although frogs and cunners (*Tautogolabrus adspersus*) exhibit seasonal acclimation, it is not enough to prevent them, at least in some typical habitats, from being nearly immobilized in winter. This is not to say, however, that the physiological changes are without significance.

It is easier to recognize the significance in those cases where the degree of adaptation is enough to insure almost or quite as high a rate in the one habitat or season as in the other. It is difficult to estimate the completeness of compensation based on the habitat temperatures because the latter are difficult to specify, except in certain cases such as the Arctic and tropical oceans. Without further work we cannot assume that the monthly average, daily average or any given measure short of the complete curve of temperature against time, is biologically appropriate, since we do not know how the organism weights equal departures from the average in the two directions or for different lengths of time.

One approach which offers some advantages is to plot an acclimated *R-T* curve (each point being the rate after acclimation to that temperature) superimposed on the same ordinates with the usual, acutely measured curve. The latter will typically be steeper, departing in both directions—above the acclimated at high temperatures and below it at low temperatures (Fig. 5)—at least when the animal

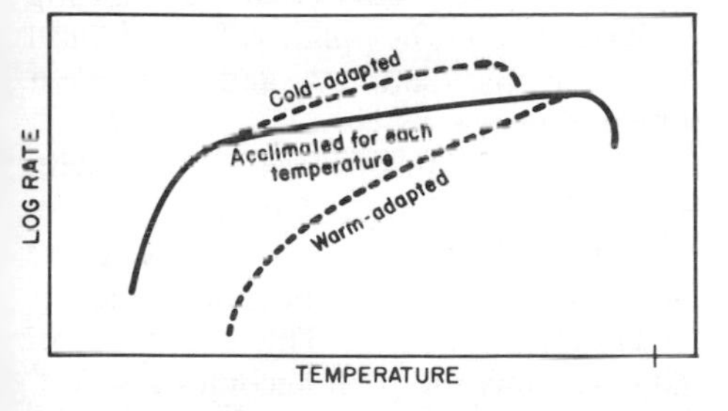

FIG. 5. *Hypothetical R-T curves showing the relation between the usual, acutely measured, temperature effect on cold-adapted and on warm-adapted individuals and the possibly more natural curve when temperature is changed slowly or time for acclimation is available at every temperature.*

acutely measured is one used to a non-extreme temperature. Perfect acclimation would then be shown by a horizontal, acclimated *R-T* slope and would obtain over a definite, limited temperature range. We possess data sufficient only for a few points on the acclimated *R-T* curve in any of the cases discussed above. Fry & Hart present an acclimated *R-T* curve of goldfish activity, showing a moderate degree of compensation.

This acclimated *R-T* curve should be of great biological interest as a means of comparing species in an ecologically significant way. The curve can in particular be expected to show not only a slope indicating the degree of sensitivity to temperature but a length indicating temperature range and a shape at the ends indicating the sharpness of geographic or ecological limits. This sharpness of transition from physiological to lethal temperatures might well be typically more abrupt than has been indicated by considering only the acutely measured *R-T* curve.

The acclimated curves will also show whether there is proportionally more compensatory change in adapting to low temperatures than to high. This is the result which Rao & Bullock believe to be most common though not at all universal, as shown by a higher Q_{10} in general for comparable portions of the warm-acclimated curve than for the cold-acclimated curve (i.e. portions of equal rates or ordinate levels). It is as though either curve were derived from the other, not by simple displacement (lateral or vertical or a combination) but by pivoting around a point off-scale to the right.

It is to be hoped that studies will be forthcoming permitting the plotting of acclimated *R-T* curves. But even now the large number of cases that have been cited in which adaptation has been demonstrated at two or a few places, seasons or acclimation temperatures permit the general conclusion that the phenomenon of compensatory regulation must be of great importance in extending the ecological, geographic and seasonal limits of the species. . . .

THE METHOD OF TRIAL AND ERROR IN THE BEHAVIOR OF LOWER ORGANISMS

Herbert S. Jennings—1904

Reprinted from Contributions to the study of behavior in lower organisms. Carnegie Institution of Washington Publication 16, 1904.

The chief response of lower organisms to changes in environmental factors, i.e., stimuli, was, according to Jennings, the method of trial and error. This adaptive behavioral response was in marked opposition to the nonadaptive tropistic concept advanced chiefly by Jacques Loeb (see p. 47). The considerable polemic elicited by adherents of each hypothesis subsequently lessened as the incompleteness of each became apparent and their complementarity was realized.

. . . [Trial and error] has been found by Lloyd Morgan, Thorndike, and others to play a large part in the development of intelligence in higher animals. Intelligent action arises as follows: The animal works by the method of trial and error till it has come upon the proper method of performing an action. Thereafter it begins with the proper way, not performing the trials anew each time. Thus intelligent action has its basis in the method of "trial and error," but does not abide indefinitely in that method.

Behavior having the essential features of the method of "trial and error" is widespread among the lower and lowest organisms, though it does not pass in them so immediately to intelligent action. But like the dog bringing the stick through the fence the first time, they try all ways, till one shows itself practicable.

This is the general plan of behavior among the lowest organisms under the action of the stimuli which pour upon them from the surroundings. On receiving a stimulus that induces a motor reaction, they try going ahead in various directions. When the direction followed leads to a new stimulus, they try another, till one is found which does not lead to effective stimulation.

This method of trial and error is especially well developed in free-swimming single-cell organisms—the flagellate and ciliate infusoria—and in higher animals living under similar conditions, as in the Rotifera. In these creatures the structure and the method of locomotion and reaction are such as to seem cunningly devised for permitting behavior on the plan of trial and error in the simplest and yet most effective way.

These organisms, as they swim through the water, typically revolve on the long axis, and at the same time swerve toward one side, which is structurally marked. This side we will call *X*. Thus the path becomes a spiral. The organism is, therefore, even in its usual course, successively directed toward many different points in space. It has opportunity to try successively many directions though still progressing along a definite line which forms the axis of the spiral. At the same time the motion of the cilia by which it swims is pulling toward the head or mouth a little of the water from a slight distance in advance. The organism is, as it were, continually taking "samples" of the water in front of it. This is easily seen when a cloud of India ink is added to the water containing many such organisms.

At times the sample of water thus obtained is of such a nature as to act as a stimulus for a motor reaction. It is hotter or colder than usual, or contains some strong chemical in solution, perhaps. Thereupon the organism reacts in a very definite way. At first it usually stops or swims backward a short distance, then it swings its anterior end *farther than usual toward the same side X to which it is already swerving*. Thus its path is changed. After this it begins to swim forward again. The amount of backing and of swerving toward the side *X* is greater when the stimulus is more intense.

This method of reaction seems very set and simple when considered by itself. It is almost like that of a muscle which reacts by the same contraction to all effective stimuli. The behavior of these animals seems, then, of the very simplest character. To practically all strong stimuli they react in a single definite way.

But if we look closely at this simple method of reacting, we find it, after all, marvelously effective. The organism, as we have seen, is revolving on its long axis. When, as a consequence of stimulation, it swings its anterior end toward the side *X*, this movement is combined with the revolution on the long axis. As a consequence, the anterior end is swung about in a wide circle; the organism tries successively many widely differing directions. From each of these directions, as we have seen, a sample of water is brought to the sensitive anterior end or mouth. Thus the reaction in itself consists in trying the water in many different directions. As long as the water coming from these various directions evinces the qualities which caused the reaction—the greater heat or cold or the chemical—the reaction, with its swinging to one side, continues. When a direction is reached from which the water no longer shows these qualities, there is no further cause for reaction; the strong swerving toward the side *X* ceases, and the organism swims forward in the direction toward which it is now pointed. It has thus avoided the region where the conditions were such as to produce stimulation. . . .

. . . Not until recently, it must be confessed, has the real significance of this type of behavior been fully perceived. The results seemed to a large degree negative; the reaction method clearly did not agree with the prevailing tropism theory, nor with any other of the commonly held theories as to the reactions of lower organisms. Just what the organism did was, indeed, fairly clear, but the plan of it all, the general relations involved in all the details, was *not* clear. This was partly due, perhaps, to overemphasis of certain phases of the reaction and to a tendency to consider other features unimportant. The behavior under stimuli is a unit; each factor must be considered in connection with all the others; then the general method running through it all becomes strikingly evident. . . .

In general terms we find that through this reaction by trial and error the organisms are kept in conditions favorable to their existence, and prevented from entering unfavorable regions. Through it they keep out of hot and cold regions and collect in regions of moderate temperature. Through it they tend to keep out of strong or injurious chemicals and out of regions where the osmotic pressure is much above or below that to which they are accustomed. Through it they gather in regions containing small amounts of certain chemicals, not leaving them for regions where there is either more or less of these chemicals. When oxygen is needed they collect through this reaction in regions containing oxygen; when the oxygen pressure is high, they do not react with reference to oxygen, or through this reaction they avoid regions containing much oxygen. Through this reaction organisms which contain chlorophyll, and therefore need light, gather in lighted regions or move toward the source of light; through the same reaction the same organisms avoid very powerful light. In all these cases, when there is error the organism goes back and tries a new direction, or a whole series of new directions. . . .

Examination shows that error from the standpoint of this behavior is as a rule *error* also from the standpoint of the general interests of the organism, considering as the interests of the organism the performance of its normal functions, the preservation of its existence, and the production of posterity. In general the organism reacts as error to those things which are injurious to it, while in those conditions which are beneficial it continues its normal activities. There are some exceptions to this, but in a general view it is clearly evident. There is no common thread running through all the different agents which constitute "error" in the reactions, save this one, that they *are* error from the standpoint of the general interests of the organism. . . .

This method of trial and error, which forms the most essential feature of the behavior of these lower organisms, is in complete contrast with the tropism schema, which has long been supposed to express the essential characteristics of their behavior. The tropism was conceived as a fixed way of acting, forced upon the organism by the direct action of external agents upon its motor organs. Each class of external agents had its corresponding tropism; under its action the organism performed certain forced movements, usually resulting in its taking up a rigid position with reference to the direction from which the stimulus came. Whether it then moved toward or away from the source of stimulus was determined by accidental conditions, and played no essential part in the reaction. There was no trial of the conditions; no indication of anything like what we call choice in the higher organisms; the behavior was stereotyped. Doubtless such methods of reaction do exist. In the reactions of infusoria to the electric current (an agent with which they never come into relation in nature), there are certain features which fit the tropism schema, and in the instincts—the "Triebe"—of animals there are features of this stereotyped character. The behavior of animals is woven of elements of the most diverse kind. But certainly in the lower organisms which we have taken chiefly into consideration the behavior is not typically of the stereotyped character expressed in the tropism schema. The method of trial and error is flexible; indeed, plasticity is its essential characteristic. Working in the lowest organisms with very simple factors, it is nevertheless capable of development; it leads upward. The tropism leads nowhere; it is a fixed, final thing, like a crystal. The method of trial and error on the other hand has been called the "method of intelligence" (Lloyd Morgan); it involves in almost every movement an activity such as we call choice in higher organisms. With the acquirement of a *finer perception of differences* the organism acting on the method of trial and error rises at once to a higher grade in behavior. Combining this with the development of sense organs and the differentiation of motor apparatus, the path of advancement is wide open before it. . . .

FORCED MOVEMENTS, TROPISMS AND ANIMAL CONDUCT

Jacques Loeb—1918

Reprinted by permission of the publisher from Forced movements, tropisms, and animal conduct. Philadelphia, J. B. Lippincott Co., pp. 13–18, 1918.

***According to Loeb, the reaction of an animal to a stimulus is a "forced movement" owing to differences in tension of symmetrical muscles. This concept of behavior conflicted with that of Jennings' "trial and error" hypothesis** (**see p. 44 for added comment**).*

INTRODUCTION

The analysis of the mechanism of voluntary and instinctive actions of animals which we propose to undertake in this volume is based on the assumption that all these motions are determined by internal or external forces. Our task is facilitated by the fact that the overwhelming majority of organisms have a bilaterally symmetrical structure, *i.e.*, their body is like our own, divided into a right and left half.

The significance of this symmetrical structure lies in the fact that the morphological plane of symmetry of an animal is also its plane of symmetry in physiological or dynamical respect, inasmuch as under normal conditions the tension in symmetrical muscles is the same, and inasmuch as the chemical constitution and the velocity of chemical reactions are the same for symmetrical elements of the surface of the body, *e.g.*, the sense organs.

Normally the processes inducing locomotion are equal in both halves of the central nervous system, and the tension of the symmetrical muscles being equal, the animal moves in as straight a line as the imperfections of its locomotor apparatus permit. If, however, the velocity of chemical reactions in one side of the body, *e.g.*, in one eye of an insect, is increased, the physiological symmetry of both sides of the brain and as a consequence the equality of tension of the symmetrical muscles no longer exist. The muscles connected with the more strongly illuminated eye are thrown into a stronger tension, and if now impulses for locomotion originate in the central nervous system, they will no longer produce an equal response in the symmetrical muscles, but a stronger one in the muscles turning the head and body of the animal to the source of light. The animal will thus be compelled to change the direction of its motion and to turn to the source of light. As soon as the plane of symmetry goes through the source of light, both eyes receive again equal illumination, the tension (or tonus) of symmetrical muscles becomes equal again, and the impulses for locomotion will now produce equal activity in the symmetrical muscles. As a consequence, the animal will move in a straight line to the source of light until some other asymmetrical disturbance once more changes the direction of motion.

What has been stated for light holds true also if light is replaced by any other form of energy. Motions caused by light or other agencies appear to the layman as expressions of will and purpose on the part of the animal, whereas in reality the animal is forced to go where carried by its legs. For the conduct of animals consists of forced movements.

The term forced movements is borrowed from brain physiology, where it designates the fact that certain animals are no longer able to move in a straight line when certain parts of the brain are injured, but are compelled to deviate constantly toward one side, which is (according to the species and the location of the injury in the brain) either the side of the injury or the opposite side. The explanation of these forced movements is that on account of the one-sided injury of the brain the tension of the symmetrical muscles is no longer the same. As a consequence, the impulses for locomotion which are equal for symmetrical muscles will cause greater contraction in certain muscles of one side of the body than in the symmetrical muscles of the other side, and the animal will no longer move in a straight line. The only difference between the forced movements induced by unequal illumination of the two eyes and by injury to the brain is that in the latter case the forced movements may last for days or throughout the whole life, while in the former case they last only as long as the illumination on the two sides of the body is unequal. If we bring about a permanent difference in illumination in the eyes, *e.g.*, by blackening one eye in certain insects, we can also bring about permanent circus motions. This shows that animal conduct may be justly designated as consisting of forced movements.

The idea that the morphological and physiological symmetry conditions in an animal are the key to the understanding of animal conduct demanded that the same principle should explain the conduct of plants, since plants also possess a symmetrical structure. The writer was able to show that sessile animals behave toward light exactly as do sessile plants; and motile animals like motile plants. The forced orientations of plants by outside sources of energy had been called tropisms; and the theory of animal conduct based on the symmetrical structure of their body was, therefore, designated as the *tropism theory of animal conduct*. . . .

Although the tropism theory of animal conduct was offered thirty years ago its acceptance was delayed by various circumstances. In the first place, the majority of the older generation of biologists did not realize that not only the methods of the physicist are needed but also the physicist's general viewpoint concerning the nature of scientific explanation. In many cases the problem of animal conduct is treated in a way which corresponds more to the viewpoint of the introspective psychologist than to that of the physicist. The attempts to explain animal conduct in terms of "trial and error" or of vague "physiological states" may serve as examples. None of these attempts have led or can lead to any exact quantitative experiments in the sense of the physicist. Other biologists have still more openly adopted an anthropomorphic method of explanation. If pleasure and pain or curiosity play a role in human conduct, why should it be otherwise in animal conduct? The answer to this objection is that typical forced movements when produced in human beings, as, *e.g.*, in Ménière's disease or when a galvanic current goes through the brain, are not accompanied by sensations of pleasure or pain, and there is no reason to attribute the circus movements of an animal, after lesion of the brain or when one eye is blackened, to curiosity or thrills of delight. An equally forcible answer lies in the fact that plants show the same tropisms as animals, and it seems somewhat arbitrary to assume that the bending of a plant to the window or the motion of swarmspores of algæ to the window side of a vessel are accompanied or determined by curiosity or by sensations of joy or satisfaction. And finally, since we know nothing of the sentiments and sensations of lower animals, and are still less able to measure them, there is at present no place for them in science.

The second difficulty was created by the fact that the Aristotelian viewpoint still prevails to some extent in biology, namely, that an animal moves only for a purpose, either to seek food or to seek its mate or to undertake something else connected with the preservation of the individual or the race. The Aristotelians had explained the processes in the inanimate world in the same teleological way. Science began when Galileo overthrew this Aristotelian mode of thought and introduced the method of quantitative experiments which leads to mathematical laws free from the metaphysical conception of purpose. The analysis of animal conduct only becomes scientific in so far as it drops the question of purpose and reduces the reactions of animals to quantitative laws. This has been attempted by the tropism theory of animal conduct. . . .

INSTINCT, WITH ORIGINAL OBSERVATIONS ON YOUNG ANIMALS

Douglas A. Spalding—1872

Reprinted by permission of the publisher from British Journal of Animal Behavior 2:2–11, 1954. This is a reprint of the original which appeared in MacMillan's Magazine in 1872.

In spite of its diffuseness of style and frequent philosophical overtones, Spalding's paper is a classic in the study of instinctive behavior. It is remarkable for its approach, techniques and insights. An overriding theoretical framework of instinctive behavior came later in the work of Lorenz (see p. 53) but one finds there much which is first described here.

The only theory of instinct, of the nature of an explanation, is that put forward by Mr. Herbert Spencer as part of his philosophy of evolution; but, as a theory, it is only beginning to be understood and appreciated among scientific men; while some eminent thinkers question the reality of the phenomena to be explained. Professor Bain, our other psychologist, and his able following of trained disciples, simply discredit the alleged facts of instinct. Unfortunately, however, instead of putting the matter to the test of observation and experiment, they have contented themselves with criticising the few accidental observations that have been recorded, and with arguing against the probability of instinctive knowledge. . . . The position of psychologists of the too purely analytical school, however, is not that the facts of instinct are inexplicable; but that they are incredible. . . . And it is held, that all the supposed examples of instinct may be—for anything that has yet been observed to the contrary—nothing more than cases of rapid learning, imitation, or instruction.

Thus it would appear that with regard to instinct we have yet to ascertain the facts. With a view to this end, I have made many observations and experiments, mostly on chicken. The question of instinct, as opposed to acquisition, has been discussed chiefly in connection with the perceptions of distance and direction by the eye and the ear. Against the instinctive character of these perceptions it is argued, that as distance means movement, locomotion, the very essence of the idea is such as cannot be taken in by the eye or ear; that what the varying sensations and feelings of sight and hearing corrrespond to, must be got at by moving over the ground—by experience. On the other hand, it is alleged that, though as regards man the prolonged helplessness of infancy stands in the way of the observer, we have only to look at the young of the lower animals to see that as a matter of fact they do not require to go through the process of learning the meaning of their sensations in relation to external things; that chickens, for example, run about, pick up crumbs, and follow the call of their mother *immediately* on leaving the shell. For putting this matter to the test of experiment, chickens, therefore, are most suitable and convenient subjects. I have observed and experimented on more than fifty chickens, taking them from under the hen while yet in the eggs. But of these, not one on emerging from the shell was in a condition to manifest an acquaintance with the qualities of the outer world. On leaving the shell they are wet and helpless; they struggle with their legs, wings, and necks, but are unable to stand or hold up their heads. Soon, however, they may be distinctly seen and felt pressing against and endeavouring to keep in contact with any warm object. They advance very rapidly. I have seen them hold up their heads well, peck at objects, and attempt to dress their wings when only between four and five hours old. But there is no difficulty in conceiving that, with great spontaneity and a strong power of association, much might be learned in four or five hours. Professor Bain is of opinion, from observations of his own on a newly dropped lamb, that "a power that the creature did not at all possess naturally, got itself matured as an acquisition in a few hours." Accordingly, in the absence of precautions, the time that must elapse before chickens have acquired enough control over their muscles to enable them to give evidence as to their instinctive power of interpreting what they see and hear, would suffice to let in the contention that the eye and the ear may have had opportunities of being educated. To obviate this objection with respect to the eye, I had recourse to the following expedient. Taking eggs just when the little prisoners had begun to break their way out, I removed a piece of the shell, and before they had opened their eyes drew over their heads little hoods, which, being furnished with an elastic thread at the lower end, fitted close round their necks. The material of these hoods was in some cases such as to keep the wearers in total darkness; in other instances it was semi-transparent. Some of them were close at the upper end, others had a small aperture bound with an elastic thread, which held tight round the base of the bill. In this state of blindness—the blindness was very manifest—I allowed them to remain from one to three days. The conditions under which these little victims of human curiosity were first permitted to see the light were then carefully prepared. Frequently the interesting little subject was unhooded on the centre of a table covered with a large sheet of white paper, on which a few small insects, dead and alive, had been placed. From that instant every movement, with the date thereof, as shown by the watch, was put on record. Never in the columns of a Court Journal were the doings of the most royal personage noted with such faithful accuracy. This experiment was performed on twenty separate chickens at different times, with the following results. Almost invariably they seemed a little stunned by the light, remained motionless for several minutes, and continued for some time less active than before they were unhooded. Their behaviour, however, was in every case conclusive against the theory that the perceptions of distance and direction by the eye are the result of experience, of associations formed in the history of each individual life. . . .

It would be out of place here to attempt to indicate the full psychological bearing of these facts. But this much may be affirmed, that they put out of court all those who are prepared only to argue against the instinctive perception by the eye of the primary qualities of the external world. When stripped of all superflous learning, the argument against this and every other alleged case of instinctive knowledge is simply that it is unscientific to assume an instinct when it is possible that the knowledge in question may have been *acquired* in the ordinary way. But the experiments that have been recounted are evidence that prior to experience chickens behave as if they already possessed an acquaintance with the established order of nature. A hungry chick that never tasted food is able, on seeing a fly or a spider for the first time, to bring into action muscles that were never so exercised before, and to perform a series of delicately adjusted movements that end in the capture of the insect. This I assert as the result of careful observation and experiment; and it cannot be answered but by observation and experiment at least as extensive. It is no doubt common for scientific men to discredit new facts, for no other reason than that they do not fit with theories that have been raised on too narrow foundations. . . .

If now it be taken as established that in the perceptions of the eye and the ear, chickens at least manifest an instinctive knowledge of the relations and qualities of external things, the popular belief that the special knowledge, the peculiar art and skill, so marked in the various species of animals, come to them mostly without the labour of acquisition, is at once freed from all antecedent improbability. In the way of direct evidence, the little that I have been able to observe in this wide field goes to prove that the current notions are in accordance with fact. We have seen that chickens follow the call of their mother before they have had any opportunity of associating that sound with pleasurable feelings; and one or two observations, which must be taken for what they are worth, support the general opinion that they have an equally instinctive dread of their more deadly enemies. When twelve days old one of my little *proteges*, while running about beside me, gave the peculiar chirr whereby they announce the approach of danger. I looked up, and behold a sparrow-hawk was hovering at a great height over head. Having subsequently procured a young hawk, able to take only short flights, I made it fly over a hen with her first brood, then about a week old. In the twinkling of an eye most of the chickens were hid among grass and bushes. . . .

A few manifestations of instinct still remain to be briefly spoken of. Chickens as soon as they are able to walk will follow any moving object. And, when guided by sight alone, they seem to have no more disposition to follow a hen than to follow a duck, or a human being. Unreflecting on-lookers, when they saw chickens a day old running after me, and older ones following me miles and answering to my whistle, imagined that I must have some occult power over the creatures, whereas I simply allowed them to follow me from the first. There is the instinct to follow; and, as we have seen, their ear prior to experience attaches them to the right object. The advantage of this arrangement is obvious. But instincts are not conferred on any principle of supplying animals with arts very essential to them, and which they could not very well learn for themselves. If there is anything that experience would be sure to teach chickens, it would be to take care when they had got a piece of food not to let their fellows take it from them, and from the very first they may be seen to run off with a worm, pursued by all their companions. But this has been so stamped in their nature that, when they have never seen one of their kind, nor ever been disturbed in the enjoyment of a morsel, they nevertheless, when they get something larger than can be swallowed at once, turn round and run off with it. . . .

The only theory in explanation of the phenomena of instinct that has an air of science about it, is Mr. Spencer's doctrine of Inherited Acquisition. The laws of association explain our intellectual operations, and enable us to understand how all our knowledge may be derived from experience. A chicken comes on a bee, and, imagining it has found a dainty morsel, seizes the insect, but is stung, and suffers badly. Henceforth bees are avoided; they can be neither seen nor heard without a shudder of fear. Now, if we can realize how such an association as this—how that one individual learns by experience may, in any degree, be transmitted to the progeny of that individual—we have a key to the mystery of instinct. Instinct in the present generation is the product of the accumulated experiences of past generations. The plausibility of this hypothesis, however, is not appreciated by the majority of even the educated portion of the community. But the reason is not far to seek. Educated men, even materialists—their own positive statements to the contrary notwithstanding—have not yet quite escaped from the habit of regarding mind as independent of bodily organization. Hence it is, that while familiar with the idea of physical pecularities passing by inheritance from one generation to another, they find it difficult to conceive how anything so impalpable as fear at the sight of a bee should be transmitted in the same way. Obviously, this difficulty is not consistent with a thorough belief in the intimate and invariable dependence of all kinds of mental facts on nervous organization. . . .

TAXIS UND INSTINKTHANDLUNG IN DER EIROLLBEWEGUNG DER GRAUGANS. I.

Konrad Lorenz and Niko Tinbergen—1938

Reprinted by permission of the authors and publisher from Zeitschrift für Tierpsychologie **2**: 1–29, 1938. Translated by Ursula Stechow, 1964.

Animal behavior studies began as an integral component of ecology; currently certain of such investigations appear to be unwanted stepchildren owing to their peculiar orientation. The thrust of animal behavior studies identified with Lorenz has led to a highly analytic approach in which the ecological context is often completely obscured. A critique of Lorenz' theory of instinctive behavior is given by D. S. Lehrman (1953. Quarterly Review of Biology **28**: *337–363).*

A. TOPOTAXIS

Most aspects of the process which we have, with A. Kühn, called taxis—and specifically topotaxis—contain side by side with directional reaction also rigid instinct patterns undergoing compulsive motion formulae, above all that of locomotion. Nevertheless, the essential criterion of topotaxis remains some singularly specific motion (the turning of an animal's entire body or of one of its parts, as for example, its eyes or head) directed and with its intensity determined by outside stimuli. . . .

The turning motion, characteristic of any kind of taxis in the widest sense of that word, and which orients the animal within its space, was called "related orientation turning" (*orientierte Bezugswendung*) by K. Bühler. The very ample term comprises any change in posture relating an organism to the spatial data of its environment. It thus includes the simplest turning "toward" or "away-from" as well as any spatial reaction resulting from cognizance of outside stimuli through highly complex mental achievements. . . .

. . . Without getting involved in the purely ideological question of whether an animal is subject, actively steering itself according to such stimuli, or object, passively directed by them, we can state that we have here objective evidence of the establishment, through outside stimuli, of purposeful activity expedient in the preservation of the species. In the simplest and best analyzed cases, this process is most certainly one of reflex activity in the true sense of that term. But even in orientation reaction, brought about by so-called higher mental processes, the activity of the central nervous system is essentially answering to, and utilizing external stimuli, and thus, at least in function, reflex-like as a phenomenon.

B. INSTINCT ACTIVITY

Instinct activities, too, show relationships to reflexes, namely in the fact that, like them, they are brought about by specific outside stimuli. Closer scrutiny, however, reveals that merely the trigger mechanism and not the further development of a formal activity is truly one of reflex. The total form of a once initiated activity seems to be independent not only of external stimuli but even altogether of the receptoral equipment of the animal. Instinct activities are not, like any form of taxis, native reaction norms, but rather native motion norms.

Improbable though it seems upon first glance, there are a number of weighty reasons for the assumption that the whole series of well-coordinated, highly expedient, species-preserving activities of an animal should be brought about, like the doings of a tabetic, without involvement of receptors (in other words, that they should not be a string of reflexes). By eliminating in various organisms all receptors of the central nervous system, E. von Holst has succeeded in bringing totally convincing evidence that in it are lodged stimulus-producing, rhythmo-automatic processes touched off through impulses coordinated already in the central nervous system and passed on as a series—and in perfect species-preserving form—to the animal's muscular system without the aid of the peripheral system or its receptors. . . .

. . . If it seems a bit premature today to equate altogether the motion automatisms investigated by von Holst to instinct activities, it must be stated with all possible emphasis that two of the most important phenomena which clearly outline instinctive behavior and which offer to any other kind of explanation well-nigh insurmountable difficulties, do allow themselves an easy berth within the assumption of such rhythmo-automatic stimulus production and the central coordination of impulses. These two phenomena are the lowering of the threshold of trigger stimuli and the thus facilitated voidance of an instinct action in a situation where not even the physico-mechanical conditions of its species-preserving purpose are met.

Even where the instinct activity is triggered by an unconditioned reflex, which would normally react only to a certain, often highly specific combination of outside stimuli, we see, occasionally quite closely, that the form of the resulting motion is independent of that of the stimuli bringing it about. If the latter fail to appear for any time longer than normal to conditions in the accustomed span of time, then very soon, diminuation will occur in the selectivity of that particular instinct activity; the animal will now, in a similar pattern, respond also to other stimulus situations merely resembling the truly adequate one previously known; the resemblance of the now activating stimuli to the ones previously alone effective, need be the less evident the longer the reaction "stoppage" lasts. In cases where the kind of stimuli triggering a specific instinct activity makes a quantitative evaluation possible at all, we find that with the increased duration of the rest period the threshold value of the necessary stimulus intensity goes into continual decline. Since both phenomena are evidently founded upon the same process in the central nervous system, I have [previously] incorporated both under the concept "threshold lowering" (*Schwellerniedrigung*). Now in many, if not even fundamentally in all instinct activities, the threshold value can literally reach the zero point where, upon a shorter or longer stoppage period, the whole series of motions is executed to perfection without appreciable influence of any outside stimuli. This we call "idling reaction" (*Leerlaufreaktion*). Threshold-lowering and *Leerlaufreaktion* speak doubly in favor of the premise of rhythmo-automatic stimulus production and central coordination of impulses.

The threshold-lowering phenomenon suggests the idea of an inner accumulation of a reaction-specific incentive—von Holst expects this to be enzyme (*Erregungsstoff*) activity—which is being continually produced by the central nervous system and which increases to the higher potential the longer the detention (which the actual execution of a particular instinct activity would bring) fails to come about. The higher the attained tension, the more intense the instinct activity when finally launched and the more difficult then for the superior instance, which is the central nervous system, to stem the instinct activity and keep it from breaking forth at the "wrong time." These ideas, as presented here in gross simplification, were developed earlier and in ignorance of von Holst's findings. . . .

For all these reasons it seems justified to raise to the status of working hypothesis our assumption that, through coordination of single acts, instinct activity is independent of each and all receptors and that it is not to be influenced by them. This may be an overly crude simplification of facts and may mean to the concept of instinct activity an uncommon narrowing down, especially since we are aware through von Holst's investigations that an impulse sent out by centrally coordinated automatism can be superseded by the reflex contraction of even one muscle. . . ,

SUMMARY AND RESULTS

We investigated the question, in what way an instinct activity (in the sense of receptor-independent, centrally coordinated motion processes) might be co-functioning with one or more receptor-guided, topotactic acts and, in the united effect, produce in an animal species-preserving, purposive behavior. In the activity series by which the grey goose restores to the nest an egg that has rolled away from it, taxis as well as instinct patterns are involved, whether simultaneously or in sequence. As an initiating orientation reaction, the directional stretching of the neck sets up the stimulus situation in which instinct activity is triggered and simultaneously, the topographic placement created which is the prerequisite of the species-preserving functioning of its course, a typical case therefore of "appetence behavior" in Craig's manner of thinking. The now initiated instinct activity is a bending down and inward of neck and head by which motion the egg, lying close against the lower surface of the beak, is shoved toward the nest. Beginning with the first moment of this motion series and lasting all the way to its completion, this process runs entirely in the sagittal plane, with an additional orientation reaction participating in the general process. By thigmotactically directed lateral motion, the egg is held in balance and kept to its direction at the underside of the shoving beak.

Our assumption that the motion within the sagittal plane should be a pure instinct activity is founded upon the following facts as found: 1. It shows the phenomenon of the *Leerlaufreaktion*, characteristic of receptor-independent instinct acts. 2. The form of the motion remains continually the same. We did not succeed in obtaining marked, receptor-directed adjustments to physically changed environmental factors. Neither the details of the path over which the egg was to be rolled, nor the shape of the object to be rolled produced appreciable variety in motion activities. Wherever variations were sought by force (as for example by oversized objects) the motion jammed and was broken off. 3. The power behind the sagittal movement is, within the narrowest confines, found to be constant. Even if the object-produced touch stimuli create a small tonus effect upon the muscle that executes the motion, this effect seems, nevertheless, always to be the same regardless of the different weights of objects involved. The motion thus stops upon even the slightest overweighting of the object. 4. The activity shows the reaction-specific fatigue factor which, in contrast to taxis, is the mark of instinct activity.

The assumption that, contrary to the motions occurring in the sagittal plane, the lateral motions giving balance should be stimulus-directed orientation reactions is founded upon the following facts: 1. Lateral motions do not occur when, devoid of an object, the sagittal ones continue in an idling process. 2. Lateral motions do not come about with objects that do not allow a straying from their path. 3. Objects whose diversion occurs in a way different from that normally happening to the goose egg show a perfect adjustment of the lateral motion to the motion peculiarities of the object in question. . . .

DISCRIMINATION OF STREAM ODORS BY FISHES AND ITS RELATION TO PARENT STREAM BEHAVIOR

Arthur D. Hasler and Warren J. Wisby—1951

Reprinted by permission of the senior author and publisher from the American Naturalist **85**: 223–238, 1951.

Orientation, especially as it occurs in homing and migratory behavior, has offered considerable challenge to the student of animal behavior and provided ample opportunity for far-ranging speculation. A wide variety of forces (gravitation, rotation) and agents (sun, stars) and processes (sound emission, color discrimination) have been proposed as homing stimuli for different groups of animals. In this paper, olfaction is identified as being of significance in the recognition pattern of fish.

The role of sensory mechanisms in orientation of fishes, especially in relation to homing, remains a mystery notwithstanding many efforts to solve this problem. It is the object of this paper to point up again the possibility that the sense of smell may play an important part in directing fishes to their home waters. The primitive character of this sensory system, its evolutionary constancy, its extreme sensitivity in comparison to other receptor processes, and its capacity to serve as a memory-evoking mechanism, all point to a working hypothesis—that olfactory stimuli may be factors in the homing of migrating fishes. . . .

In the above observations, it could not be clearly proved that fishes orient on the basis of olfaction; nor has the idea been proposed that the home water carries a distinctive odor which through discrimination and memory may serve as a directing guide to the fishes in orienting toward and reaching its original habitat. The chief objective of our experiments was to determine whether streams do have characteristic odors and if fishes can discriminate between them, and whether they can retain in memory habits of orientation learned with respect to these odors.

It may be desirable, at this point, to define clearly the requirements of an odor which is to serve as a "sign-post" for returning salmon. First of all, it must remain relatively constant in any one stream over a period of years because an interval of three to five years may elapse between original learning of the olfactory controlled reaction and its reinstatement, upon return to the vicinity of the home water to spawn. . . .

The second condition which must be placed upon the odor is that it must have significance only to those returning migrants which had been conditioned to it during their freshwater sojourn; while being neutral to all others for it would seem that any odor, or substance, which was an attractant or repellent would induce salmon to enter a stream or tributary irrespective of whether or not they were native to the stream.

There is yet another restriction which must be placed upon a homing odor. It must remain detectable even though the stream be changed severely in chemical and physical characteristics, for salmon will continue to attempt to return to a stream even though that stream may have been seriously polluted, or gutted by floods, during the time the salmon were at sea. . . .

It was the immediate intent of this experiment to determine if it were possible to obtain an olfactory discrimination between Otter Creek and Honey Creek by the bluntnose minnow. The minnows were trained in such a manner that they learned to associate the odor of one of the streams with food and the odor of the other with punishment.

The equipment used by the authors [in] 1949 and 1950 was suitable for conducting this series of training tests. It consisted of several seven gallon aquaria, each with a siphon-airlift circulation system installed in both ends. Water was siphoned from the aquarium, returned by air pressure, and discharged into a 6-inch funnel which was suspended above the tank. The funnel was connected to a glass tube which lay across the end of the aquarium. Perforations in the tube directed the incoming water across the bottom of the aquarium. Water from the jet on one side flowed only about halfway across, because there it met the stream from the other end, and both were deflected upward. This produced two currents or convection cells, each of which involved one half of the tank. Water samples containing the odors were introduced into the aquarium by means of a separatory funnel, which was connected to the siphon tube after it left the tank.

An objection to the two-electrode punishment system, as described by the authors (*l.c.*), was overcome by introducing a third electrode. Formerly, it was difficult to punish a fish which entered the end zone more than two to four centimeters above the electrodes. Also, a fish between the electrodes was apt to be injured, as a shock was administered. With a third electrode, located about two inches above the one in the corner, it was possible to punish, without injuring, any fish entering the end zone below the level of the new electrode. Thus, a region (2″ × 2″ × 6″) bounded on the bottom by the two electrodes on the floor of the aquarium was designated as the "end zone," that is, the place where the fish were fed or punished by electric shock (2.3 volts; 20 milliamperes) depending on which odor was being introduced. Also, higher voltages could be used without adversely affecting the fish, thereby impressing the training to the negative odor.

The fish were rewarded by introducing food, pressed on perforated celluloid strips, into the end zone. Since, in this method of training, hunger is the principal motivating force, tests were timed at those intervals when hunger motivation was at its greatest. An attempt was made to test at different times each day, and to feed no more than was necessary for the well-being of the experimental animals. The fish were fed very heavily every sixth day, and tests omitted on the seventh, because a mere subsistence diet such as this would, in time, have harmed them. . . .

Fishes of two aquaria received positive training to water of Otter Creek, that is, fish were fed immediately after the test, and negative training to water of Honey Creek, that is, fish were punished by a light electrical current if they entered the end zone during the time this water was being introduced. Two other aquaria were trained to the same two odors, but with opposite meanings; Honey Creek was the positive odor; Otter Creek, the negative. If training were accomplished the fish should eventually associate food with the positive scent, and therefore enter the end zone. The negative scent would be associated with punishment and the fish should stay out of the end zone.

It should be pointed up that the fish were fatigued to the natural odors of the aquarium so that introduction of an unfamiliar water was immediately detected if in a perceptible concentration. In order to assure a forceful stimulus the creek water was diluted only by one-half when it was put into the separatory funnel. A minimal detectable concentration was not established. . . .

At the outset the fishes showed natural unlearned orientative responses for the odor of either creek, that is, they entered the end zone more often during the introduction of the odor on either the negative or the positive test than during the pretest. Not until later in the training sequence did they discriminate between them.

. . . The minnows learned equally well irrespective of whether Otter Creek (draining quartzite watershed) was positive or negative. A noticeable degree of discrimination was accomplished in a month of training. . . .

After reaching the discrimination level. . . training was continued for two more months in order to attain the maximum level of discrimination, or the plateau in the learning curve.

RETENTION OF LEARNING

. . . An attempt was. . . made to determine the length of retention of discrimination in the bluntnose minnow. Daily training was stopped and odors were presented weekly, without reward or punishment. After six weeks the fish were confusing the two odors so completely it was apparent that discrimination no longer existed.

That this method of testing does not produce a clear-cut measure of actual retention is well known to psychologists. The procedure followed involves detraining through repeated testing, and through interference habits set up by routine daily feeding between tests. That is, an animal which has been trained to associate food with an odor, will be subjected to the reverse of this training process if fed without prior introduction of the odor. Thus, the minnows, during these tests, were actually being detrained, and the results of the tests can only be considered to be an absolute minimum indication of true retention.

It should be kept in mind that the life span of the bluntnose minnow is only two years. Hence, training was started at the senile stage, whereas salmon would be conditioned to the stream odor while young. . . .

SEASONAL INFLUENCE ON CHARACTER OF ODOR

. . . To test the possibility of seasonal changes in odor, samples were collected during winter and presented to fish that had been trained to water from the same streams which had been collected in summer. The fish responded equally well to this water, indicating that the odor characteristics recognized by the fish in these two streams did not lose their identity with the change in season.

EVIDENCE OF OLFACTORY DETECTION OF STREAM ODORS

To determine if these differences in water are perceived by tissues of the fish's nose, the olfactory capsules of trained fishes were destroyed by heat cautery. After the wound had healed, these fish were again tested with the training odors. There was no response; nor did they participate in the reaction when placed in an aquarium with normal, trained minnows. It can thus be seen that a reaction to the substance is dependent on the olfactory system and on individual perception of the odor, and is not a "follow the leader" phenomenon.

That the latter is true can also be shown by placing a blinded, but otherwise normal, fish, which has received positive training to one odor and negative training to the other, in an aquarium with fishes which have received the reverse training. When one of the training odors is then introduced into the aquarium, the odd fish exhibits a response which is the opposite of that being demonstrated by the resident fishes.

NATURE OF THE ODOR

With this proof that the olfactory receptors were stimulated by a property of the creek water, it was logical to wonder what the substance was. . . .

Differences in total organic nitrogen of the two streams were quite marked. Since most odorous compounds are organic in nature, it seems quite likely that the elements detected by the minnows may be located in this fraction. . . .

SIGNIFICANCE AND APPLICATION

Most of the evidence for the reliability of parent stream behavior in fishes is found in the literature on the salmon. When it was decided to initiate a series of experiments to attempt to discover the mechanism behind parent stream behavior, therefore, they were designed to lead eventually to a series of actual tests in the field with salmon.

In this research, one major barrier to the hypothesis that fish orient to their home streams, has been explored. That is, it was shown that some streams, at least, have odor characteristics which can serve to produce persisting differential responses in certain fishes. Furthermore, the results of generalization tests indicate strongly that the odors of streams are aromatic substances present in the volatile organic fraction. However, our evidence for olfactory discrimination of stream water by fishes does not constitute proof that parent stream behavior is not also controlled by other factors. . . .

One of the characteristics which a stream must have to fulfill the conditions of our thesis is that the substance, to which the fishes are responding on their return journey, must remain detectable even though the stream be changed severely in chemical and physical characteristics. Salmon continue to return regardless of pollution, floods, and changes in weather. These things do alter the materials in the stream, but on the basis of our evidence it appears that aromatics derived from the vegetation and soils of the watershed lend a distinctive odor which can be perceived, learned and recognized again after a protracted period of non-exposure. The aromatic characteristic of a watershed, filtering into the stream, might be surmised to remain constant over long periods.

Additional collateral indications of the importance of the sense of smell in the life of a fish comes from a large series of studies by von Frisch and his students. Their results attest the extreme sensitivity of the fish nose to natural substances, for they show that fish have been found capable of recognizing one another by scent, and that they may be alarmed at extremely dilute emanations (Schreckstoff) from injured fish skin. It would seem too that the acuity of the sense of smell in fishes is of similar sensitivity as that of dogs and insects where but a few molecules stimulate the end organ. In contrast, the common chemical sense and the ability to discriminate temperature differences are crude senses when compared with the olfactory system.

Techniques have been developed whereby it is now possible to hatch and maintain salmon through the fingerling stage in aquaria at Madison. Preliminary results from a set of experiments currently in progress indicate that the olfactory system of salmon is very acute, and that they can discriminate between stream odors.

A set of field experiments must also be undertaken to furnish final proof of the hypothesis herein contained. Of a number of possible methods of solution, one promises to be of some practical value. The hypothesis could be tested by exposing salmon to a constant, artificial odor through the fingerling stage and then determining if the fish conditioned in a hatchery could be decoyed to a neighboring stream upon return from the sea. Should this be the case, it would aid in salvaging the declining salmon runs where new dams may obstruct passage to their parent streams. . . .

THE STUDY OF POPULATIONS

Discrete populations of a species are sufficiently unit-like in their characteristics and responses to permit their being objectified. Among the many facets of a population, ecologists are concerned with aspects of their growth (natality, mortality, growth form, etc.), regulation (fluctuations, oscillations, dispersal, etc.), and inter- and intraspecific interactions (cooperation, competition, etc.).

Since its inception, this field has had a strong mathematical orientation in formulating and testing descriptive and predictive models. Much of its empirical and theoretical development has had an animal focus based on data derived largely from laboratory populations of relatively few diverse kinds of organisms. The original anthropocentric orientation given the field continues, for in spite of the more esoteric and academic aspects of population ecology, the implications regarding the human population are not easily avoided.

AN ESSAY ON THE PRINCIPLE OF POPULATION AS IT AFFECTS THE FUTURE IMPROVEMENT OF SOCIETY

Thomas Robert Malthus—1798

Reprint of the first and second chapters of the first edition. *London, Johnson*, 1798.

This is the most significant essay on population ever written and perhaps one of the most influential essays in all literature. Malthus' practical and realistic analysis demonstrated the principle that a population will outstrip its means of subsistence owing to inherent differences in their rates of increase and that under such stress vice and misery will operate to restrain population growth. This principle shattered a prevalent utopian aura in which man was to enjoy unlimited progress and infinite perfectibility. The second, and subsequent, editions of the essay lacked the forcefulness of the first, being mitigated in the proposing of "moral restraint," i.e., chastity, as a preventive check on population growth.

. . . In entering upon the argument I must premise that I put out of the question, at present, all mere conjectures, that is, all suppositions, the probable realization of which cannot be inferred upon any just philosophical grounds. A writer may tell me that he thinks man will ultimately become an ostrich. I cannot properly contradict him. But before he can expect to bring any reasonable person over to his opinion, he ought to shew, that the necks of mankind have been gradually elongating, that the lips have grown harder and more prominent, that the legs and feet are daily altering their shape, and that the hair is beginning to change into stubs of feathers. And till the probability of so wonderful a conversion can be shewn, it is surely lost time and lost eloquence to expatiate on the happiness of man in such a state; to describe his powers, both of running and flying, to paint him in a condition where all narrow luxuries would be condemned, where he would be employed only in collecting the necessaries of life, and where, consequently, each man's share of labour would be light, and his portion of leisure ample.

I think I may fairly make two postulata.

First, That food is necessary to the existence of man.

Secondly, That the passion between the sexes is necessary and will remain nearly in its present state.

These two laws, ever since we have had any knowledge of mankind, appear to have been fixed laws of our nature, and, as we have not hitherto seen any alteration in them, we have no right to conclude that they will ever cease to be what they now are, without an immediate act of power in that Being who first arranged the system of the universe, and for the advantage of his creatures, still executes, according to fixed laws, all its various operations.

I do not know that any writer has supposed that on this earth man will ultimately be able to live without food. But Mr. Godwin has conjectured that the passion between the sexes may in time be extinguished. As, however, he calls this part of his work a deviation into the land of conjecture, I will not dwell longer upon it at present than to say that the best arguments for the perfectibility of man are drawn from a contemplation of the great progress that he has already made from the savage state and the difficulty of saying where he is to stop. But towards the extinction of the passion between the sexes, no progress whatever has hitherto been made. It appears to exist in as much force at present as it did two thousand or four thousand years ago. There are individual exceptions now as there always have been. But, as these exceptions do not appear to increase in number, it would surely be a very unphilosophical mode of arguing, to infer merely from the existence of an exception, that the exception would, in time, become the rule, and the rule the exception.

Assuming then, my postulata as granted, I say, that the power of population is indefinitely greater than the power in the earth to produce subsistence for man.

Population, when unchecked, increases in a geometrical ratio. Subsistence increases only in an arithmetical ratio. A slight acquaintance with numbers will shew the immensity of the first power in comparison of the second.

By that law of our nature which makes food necessary to the life of man, the effects of these two unequal powers must be kept equal.

This implies a strong and constantly operating check on population from the difficulty of subsistence. This difficulty must fall some where and must necessarily be severely felt by a large portion of mankind.

Through the animal and vegetable kingdoms, nature has scattered the seeds of life abroad with the most profuse and liberal hand. She has been comparatively sparing in the room and the nourishment necessary to rear them. The germs of existence contained in this spot of earth, with ample food, and ample room to expand in, would fill millions of worlds in the course of a few thousand years. Necessity, that imperious all pervading law of nature, restrains them within the prescribed bounds. The race of plants, and the race of animals shrink under this great restrictive law. And the race of man cannot, by any efforts of reason, escape from it. Among plants and animals its effects are waste of seed, sickness, and premature death. Among mankind, misery and vice. The former, misery, is an absolutely necessary consequence of it. Vice is a highly probable consequence, and we therefore see it abundantly prevail, but it ought not, perhaps, to be called an absolutely necessary consequence. The ordeal of virtue is to resist all temptation to evil.

This natural inequality of the two powers of population and of production in the earth and that great law of our nature which must constantly keep their effects equal form the great difficulty that to me appears insurmountable in the way to the perfectibility of society. All other arguments are of slight and subordinate consideration in comparison of this. I see no way by which man can escape from the weight of this law which pervades all animated nature. No fancied equality, no agrarian regulations in their utmost extent, could remove the pressure of it even for a single century. And it appears, therefore, to be decisive against the possible existence of a society, all the members of which should live in ease, happiness, and comparative leisure; and feel no anxiety about providing the means of subsistence for themselves and families.

Consequently, if the premises are just, the argument is conclusive against the perfectibility of the mass of mankind.

I have thus sketched the general outline of the argument, but I will examine it more particularly, and I think it will be found that experience, the true source and foundation of all knowledge, invariably confirms its truth. . . .

NOTICE SUR LA LOI QUE LA POPULATION SUIT DANS SON ACCROISSEMENT

P. F. Verhulst—1838

Reprinted from Correspondence mathematique et physique **10**:113–121, 1838. Translated by Lawrence Wilson, 1964.

The first mathematical formulation of population growth was made in this essay. The logistic equation which Verhulst derived describes the nature of population increase as it occurs under limiting conditions. A plot of the equation is the familiar S-shaped population curve. Not unlike other discoveries in science, Verhulst's contribution was not widely recognized until some time after Pearl and Reed (see p. 66) independently derived the same equation in 1920.

It is generally known that Malthus established as his first principle that the human population tends to grow in geometrical progression according to which it will double after a certain period of time, for example, every twenty-five years. This proposition is incontrovertible if the continually increasing difficulty of guaranteeing subsistence once the population has reached a certain density or the resources upon which the population draws in growing, even when the society is still nascent (e.g., the greater division of labor, the existence of a stable government and means of defense assuring public order, etc.) are kept in mind.

Indeed, *all things being equal*, if one thousand individuals have become two thousand after twenty-five years, these two thousand will become four thousand after the same lapse of time.

In our old European societies where the fertile land had been cultivated for a very long time, the labor expended in improving acreage already under cultivation can result only in a constantly decreasing amount compared to what it originally produced. Assuming that the production of the soil has been doubled, it is not very likely that one will succeed in making it produce a third more in the second period. The virtual increase in population thus finds a limit in the area and fertility of the country, and the population tends, consequently, to become stationary.

The same is not true in certain truly exceptional cases—for example, when a civilized people cultivate a fertile territory, previously uninhabited, or when it expends an industriousness which results in great temporary benefits. A numerous family then becomes an asset and the second generation finds it easier to establish itself since it does not have to struggle like the first generation against the odds with which the native state of the land confronted the first settlers.

To judge the rapidity with which the population grows in a given country, the yearly increase in population must be divided by the figure of the original population. This relationship being independent of the absolute size of the population, it can be regarded as the measure of this rapidity. If it is constant, the population increases geometrically; if it is growing, the progression is more than geometrical, and less than geometrical if it is decreasing.

Various hypotheses concerning the resistance or the sum of the obstacles put in the way of the indefinite development of the population can be made.

Mr. Quetelet suggests that it is proportional to *the square of the rapidity with which the population tends to grow.*

This amounts to making the change in the population that of a moving body which falls in going through a resistant milieu. The results of this comparison agree in a satisfactory manner with the statistical data and the results I have obtained with my own formulae, when an indefinitely increasing density is granted in passing through the strata of the milieu.

Population growth has, of necessity, a limit if only in the area of land indispensable for accommodating that population. When a nation has consumed all the fruits of its fields, it can indeed obtain foodstuffs from outside through the exchange of its other products, and can thus support a new increase of population. But it is obvious that these imports must be limited and be halted even long before the surface of the entire country is taken up with cities. All the formulae by which an attempt will be made to represent the law of population must therefore satisfy the condition of admitting a *maximum* which will be attained only at an infinitely remote time. This *maximum* will be the figure of the population when it has become stationary.

I have long tried to determine by analysis what the probable law of population is; but I have abandoned this kind of research because the data provided by observation are too few to permit verification of the formulae in such a way as to leave no doubt as to their exactness. However, since the path I have followed seems to me to lead to the discovery of the true law, once there is sufficient data, and since the results I have obtained may be of interest, at least as a matter for speculation, I felt myself obliged to accept Mr. Quetelet's invitation to make them public.

Let p be the population and let us represent by dp the infinitely small increase it makes within the infinitely short time dt. If the population grew geometrically, we would have the equation $dp/dt = mp$. But since the rate of growth is retarded by the increase in the number of inhabitants itself, we shall have to remove from mp an unknown function of p, so the formula to be integrated will become

$$\frac{dp}{dt} = mp - \varphi(p).$$

The simplest hypothesis that one could make on the nature of the function φ, is to assume $\varphi(p) = np^2$. The integral of the above equation then becomes

$$t = \frac{1}{m}[\log. p - \log.(m - np)] + \text{constant}.$$

and it will require three observations to determine the two coefficients m and n and the arbitrary constant.

In solving the last equation for p, it becomes

$$p = \frac{mp'e^{mt}}{np'e^{mt} + m - np'} \qquad (1)$$

in designating by p' the population which exists at $t = 0$, and by e the base of the Napierian logarithm. If $t = \infty$, then the corresponding value of p is $p = m/n$. Such is therefore the upper limit of the population.

Instead of assuming $\varphi p = np^2$, one can make $\varphi p = np^\alpha$, α being any number, or $\varphi p = n \log. p$. Each of these hypotheses equally well satisfies the observed facts, but by the same token they yield very different values for the upper limit of the population.

I have assumed successively

$$\varphi p = np^2, \quad \varphi p = np^3, \quad \varphi p = np^4, \quad \varphi p = n \log. p;$$

and the differences between the calculated population and those which provide the observation are found to be essentially the same.

When the population increases more or less in geometrical progression, the term $-\varphi p$ becomes $+\varphi p$; the differential equation is then integrated as in the preceding case but one imagines that it can no longer be the maximum population. . . .

ON THE RATE OF GROWTH OF THE POPULATION OF THE UNITED STATES SINCE 1790 AND ITS MATHEMATICAL REPRESENTATION

Raymond Pearl and Lowell J. Reed—1920

Reprinted by permission of the publisher from Proceedings of the National Academy of Sciences **6**:275-288, 1920.

In this paper the logistic curve of population growth under limiting conditions is derived and applied to the population of the United States. The paper is of interest not alone for the independent discovery of a mathematical formulation described a century earlier by Verhulst (see p. 64) but also because of the influence the senior author had in promoting the use of statistical analysis in ecology. The limitations of the sigmoid growth model have been increasingly recognized; L. B. Slobodkin discusses this point (1961. Growth and regulation of populations. New York, Holt, Rinehart and Winston).

It is obviously possible in any country or community of reasonable size to determine an empirical equation by ordinary methods of curve fitting, which will describe the normal rate of population growth. Such a determination will not necessarily give any inkling whatever as to the underlying organic laws of population growth in a particular community. It will simply give a rather exact empirical statement of the nature of the changes which have occurred in the past. No process of empirically graduating raw data with a curve can in and of itself demonstrate the fundamental law which causes the occurring change. In spite of the fact that such mathematical expressions of population growth are purely empirical, they have a distinct and considerable usefulness. This usefulness arises out of the fact that actual counts of population by census methods are made at only relatively infrequent intervals, usually 10 years and practically never oftener than 5 years. For many statistical purposes, it is necessary to have as accurate an estimate as possible of the population in inter-censal years. . . .

The usual method followed by census offices in determining the population in inter-censal years is of one or the other of two sorts, namely, by arithmetic progression or geometric progression. These methods assume that for any given short period of time the population is increasing either in arithmetic or geometric ratio. Neither of these assumptions is ever absolutely accurate even for short intervals of time, and both are grossly inaccurate for the United States, at least, for any considerable period of time. . . .

Obviously the best general method of estimating population in inter-censal years is that of fitting an appropriate curve to *all* the available data, and extrapolating for years beyond the last census, and reading off from the curve values for inter-censal years falling between earlier censuses. The methods of arithmetic or geometric progression use only two census counts at the most. Fitting a curve to all the known data regarding population by the method of least squares must obviously give a much sounder and more accurate result. In making this statement, one realizes perfectly, of course, the dangers of extrapolation. . . . In keeping sharply before our minds the dangers of extrapolation from a curve, we are apt to forget that the methods of extrapolation by arithmetic or geometric progression have much less general validity than from a curve, and the inaccuracies are found in practice, except by the rarest of accidents, to be actually greater.

The first one to attempt an adequate mathematical representation of the normal rate of growth of the population of the United States was Pritchett. Taking the census data from 1790 to 1880, inclusive, Pritchett fitted by the method of least squares the following equation:

$$P = A + Bt + Ct^2 + Dt^3 \qquad \text{(i)}$$

where P represents the population and t the time from some assumed epoch. As a matter of fact, Pritchett took the origin of the curve at 1840, practically the center of the series. With this third-order parabola Pritchett got a very accurate representation of the population between the dates covered. As will presently appear this curve did not give, even within the period covered, as accurate results as a more adequate curve would have done, and it overestimated the population after a very short interval beyond the last observed ordinate. . . .

Some 13 years ago one of the writers demonstrated the applicability of a logarithmic curve of the form

$$y = a + bx + cx^2 + d \log x \qquad \text{(ii)}$$

to the representation of growth changes, using the aquatic plant *Ceratophyllum* as material. Following the application of this curve to growth of this plant it was found equally useful in representing a wide range of other growth and related changes. . . .

While the increase in size of a population cannot on *a priori* grounds be regarded, except by rather loose analogy, as the same thing as the growth of an organism in size, nevertheless it is essentially a growth phenomenon. It, therefore, seems entirely reasonable that this type of curve should give a more adequate representation of population increase than a simple third-order parabola. The actual event justifies this assumption, as will presently appear. . . .

To the data of . . . [recorded population from 1790–1910] the following equation was fitted by the method of least squares, taking origin at 1780, and making due allowance in the abscissal intervals for the actual dates of the several censuses:

$$y = a + bx + cx^2 + d \log x$$

where y denotes population and x time. The actual equation deduced was

$$y = 9{,}064{,}900 - 6{,}281{,}430x + 842{,}377x^2 + 19{,}829{,}500 \log x. \qquad \text{(iii)}$$

The results [indicate] . . . that as a purely empirical representation of population growth in the United States equation (iii) gives results of a very high degree of accuracy. Indeed, interpolation on this curve for inter-censal years may obviously be relied upon with a greater probability that the estimated figures approximate the unknown true facts than is afforded by any other estimating expedient hitherto applied to the known data. . . .

It is quite clear on *a priori* grounds, as was first pointed out by Malthus in non-mathematical terms, that in any restricted area, such as the United States, a time must eventually come when population will press so closely upon subsistence that its rate of increase per unit of time must be reduced to the vanishing point. In other words, a population curve may start. . . with a convex face to the base, but presently it must develop a point of inflection, and from that point on present a concave face to the x axis, and finally become asymptotic, the asymptote representing the maximum number of people which can be supported on the given fixed area. Now, while an equation like (ii) can, and will in duc time, develop a point of inflection and become concave to the base it never can become asymptotic. It, therefore, cannot be regarded as a hopeful line of approach to a true law of population growth. . . .

It has seemed worth while to attempt to develop such a law, first by formulating a hypothesis which rigorously meets the logical requirements, and then by seeing whether in fact the hypothesis fits the known facts. The general biological hypothesis which we shall here test embodies as an essential feature the idea that the rate of population increase in a limited area at any instant of time is proportional (a) to the magnitude of the population existing at that instant (amount of increase already attained) and (b) to the still unutilized potentialities of population support existing in the limited area.

The following conditions should be fulfilled by any equation which is to describe adequately the growth of population in an area of fixed limits. (1). Asymptotic to a line $y = k$ when $x = +\infty$. (2). Asymptotic to a line $y = 0$ when $x = -\infty$. (3). A point of inflection at some point $x = \alpha$ and $y = \beta$. (4). Concave upwards to left of $x = \alpha$ and concave downward to right of $x = \alpha$. (5). No horizontal slope except at $x = \pm\infty$. (6). Values of y varying continuously from 0 to k as x varies from $-\infty$ to $+\infty$.

In these expressions y denotes population, and x denotes time. An equation which fulfils these requirements is

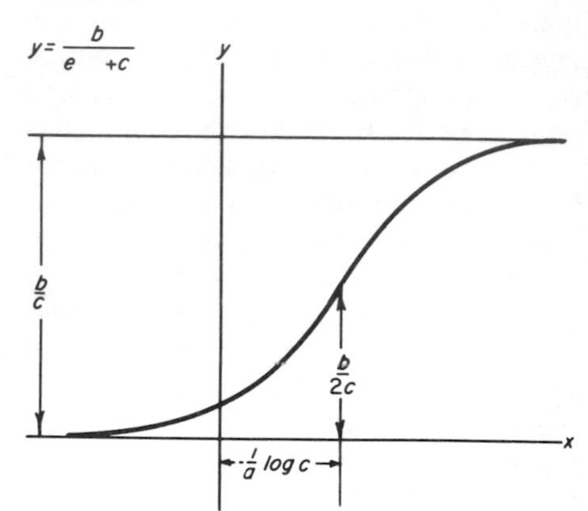

FIG. 2. *General form of curve given by equation (ix).*

$$y = \frac{be^{ax}}{1 + ce^{ax}} \qquad \text{(ix)}$$

when a, b and c have positive values.

In this equation the following relations hold:

$$x = +\infty \qquad y = \frac{b}{c} \qquad \text{(x)}$$

$$x = -\infty \qquad y = 0 \qquad \text{(xi)}$$

Relations (x) and (xi) define the asymptotes. The point of inflection is given by $1 - ce^{ax} = 0$, or

$$x = -\frac{1}{a}\log c \qquad y = \frac{b}{2c} \qquad \text{(xii)}$$

The slope at the point of inflection is $ab/4c$. Expressing the first derivative of (xi) in terms of y, we have

$$\frac{dy}{dx} = \frac{ay(b - cy)}{b} \qquad \text{(xiii)}$$

Putting the equation in this form shows at once that it is identical with that describing an autocatalyzed chemical reaction, a point to which we shall return later.

The general form of the curve is shown in figure 2.

The question now is how well does (ix) represent the known historical facts as to the growth in population of the United States, and to what legitimate deductions as to the future course of population in this country does it lead?. . . .

. . . The most that can be asserted is that equation (xviii) gives nearly or quite as good a fit to the observations as does the logarithmic parabola. If we properly graduated the data, by the method of moments, we should probably get a result measurably better than that from equation (iii).

The significance of the result lies in this consideration. A curve which on *a priori* grounds meets the conditions which must be satisfied by a true law of population growth, actually describes with a substantial degree of accuracy what is now known of the population history of this country. . . .

THE QUANTITATIVE ANALYSIS OF ENVIRONMENTAL FACTORS

Royal N. Chapman—1928

Reprinted by permission of the publisher from Ecology **9**:111 122, 1928.

The much used terms "biotic potential" and "environmental resistance" had their origin and empirical verification in this paper. But, perhaps Chapman's greater contribution to ecology was the direction he gave to laboratory population studies. In particular, his population research on the flour beetle was continued and very considerably expanded by Thomas Park and his students. Park reviewed much of this work in 1962 (Science **138**: *1369–1375).*

. . . It was once believed that mathematical expressions must be confined to the description of surfaces and solids just as we now have a feeling that they must be confined to phenomena in the field of physics. It was once considered that heat conduction was subject to too many factors to permit itself to be handled by mathematical calculations, just as we now have a feeling that ecological phenomena are subject to so many factors that they do not lend themselves to mathematical methods. Those of us who are engaged in the study of animal ecology may do well to pause and consider the future of our branch of science in the light of the work of Fourier, who more than a century ago, began to apply mathematical methods to the study of the transmission of heat through solids. In this day when it is possible for physicists and engineers to calculate so exactly the amount of heat required to warm a given space surrounded by walls with given coefficients of conduction and subject to known external conditions, it is hard to realize that there was once a day when it seemed to be impossible to apply quantitative calculations to the transmission of heat. All of the objections which now stand in the way of the use of these methods in ecology then stood in the way of the use of these methods in connection with thermodynamics. . . .

The animal ecologists find themselves handicapped in the use of quantitative methods because of the difficulty in obtaining quantitative samples, the lack of a method of expressing the abundance of organisms, and of expressing the effect of the environment in terms of the quantity of organisms. As a result of the consideration of some of these handicaps, it has seemed that it might be possible to find some characteristics, essentially biotic, which could be used as a measure of the organisms and the environment, and which might be subject to experimental verification.

It has long been known that the possibilities of reproduction of the various species of organisms are enormous, and that they far exceed the realization which the species ever has in numbers of individuals. The fact that eventually but two out of an enormous number of progeny would survive to replace the parents, was an essential part of Darwin's theory of the survival of the fittest and the action of natural selection. Many calculations have been made to show the possibilities of the various organisms to reproduce. . . .

. . . The variations in the abundance of insects, in so far as we have data to represent them, indicate a remarkable constance in numbers when compared with the potential number which might exist at any one time. Thus it seems that whatever the potential rate of development of an organism may be, its environment offers sufficient resistance to multiplication to cause its numbers to tend to remain constant. It is this fact, obvious though it may be, that will now be considered.

In drawing analogies from the works of Fourier and Ohm it is recognized that the cases may not be strictly comparable to animal abundance. Yet it seems evident that we have in nature a system in which the potential rate of reproduction of the animal is pitted against the resistance of the environment, and that the quantity of organisms which may be found is a result of the balance between the biotic potential, or the potential rate of reproduction, and the environmental resistance.

For this purpose, therefore, biotic potential may be defined as the mean maximum rate of reproduction in a given period of time under given conditions. The action of the environment, then, must necessarily be expressed in terms of resistance to this maximum rate of reproduction. An empirical formula similar to Ohm's formula, representing the concentration of organisms, or abundance of organisms, as equal to the biotic potential divided by the environmental resistance, may aid in making the complex factors of the organism and the environment appear as unity to us. At least, it is possible to conceive of everything as having a place in this formula. The environmental resistance will include the physical factors of the environment, temperature, humidity, etc. and also the biotic factors of the environment, parasites, competitors, etc. The advantage of the formula will be practically the same as those which Ohm realized. When concentration and biotic potential are known, a value may be ascribed to environmental resistance. A knowledge of any two of the three variables will make it possible to calculate the value of the third. . . .

The hypothesis needs the support of experimental data based upon controlled conditions. Such data have been obtained from a study of the confused flour beetle, *Tribolium confusum*. . . .

The conditions of the experiments were made as simple as possible. The object was to determine, first, whether a condition of equilibrium would be reached in which the population, as expressed in the number of individuals per gram of flour, would remain constant regardless of the size of the environment. Under such conditions the environmental resistance would be equal to the biotic potential and the conditions of the hypothetical formula would be satisfied. Secondly it was sought to determine whether the effective rate of reproduction of single pairs of beetles was inversely proportional to the environmental resistance, which, in this case, is a function of the total size of the environment.

To determine the first point, a series of environments was set up in which the depth of the pure whole wheat flour was constant at two centimeters, but the quantities of flour in the different environments formed a geometric series, containing 4, 8, 16, 32, 64 and 128 grams each. The populations of adult beetles which were introduced at the start also formed a geometric series such that there was one pair of bettles to each four grams of flour in each environment. The sexes of the beetles were determined but the ages were at random. The moisture was kept constant and the temperature was maintained at 27°C.

The eggs, larvae and pupae were counted and the flour renewed at each observation. The various stages of beetles were separated from the flour by means of standard silk bolting cloth. . . . there was a rapid increase in numbers, which was followed by a condition of relative stability with practically no larvae or pupae. The number of eggs present at each observation is an indication of the total biotic potential of the population. In spite of the large number of eggs which were always present, there were no appreciable changes in the number of adult beetles. When eggs were removed from the culture they hatched on schedule time, and an equal number of new eggs appeared in the original culture. This demonstrates the fertility of the eggs. The fact that the lack of increase in the population was due to the eggs being eaten by the adults was demonstrated by placing eggs in cultures which contained only male beetles. The per cent of eggs eaten varied directly with the population of adults per gram of flour. Pupae, and to some extent larvae, were also eaten in environments which contained high concentration of beetles. Thus we have an environmental resistance which is a function of the size of the environment. . . .

TABLE II. *Beetles* (*Tribolium confusum*) *per gram of flour*

Days	4 G.	8 G.	16 G.	32 G.	64 G.	128 G.
	.5	.5	.5	.5	.5	.5
15	15	17	20	17	21	19
30	30	25	26	22	24	23
50	35	33	32	35	32	34
64	39	39	34	39	40	37
78	35	41	39	36	37	39
101	40	46	38	44	49	39
114	48	45	36	43	40	40
134	37	50	41	41	48	45
156	38	49	46	44	45	47
171	46	49	46	43	42	40

The first point, therefore, seems well demonstrated. A condition of equilibrium is attained in which the biotic potential is equaled by the environmental resistance and the population remains relatively constant.

For the second point, namely the relation between the increase of a population and the size of the environment, attention is called to . . . [the] series of experiments [in which] a single pair of newly emerged adult beetles was placed in each of the environments which formed the same geometric series of sizes as in Table [II]. In this case, in the same period of time, one pair of beetles gave rise to 178 individuals in an environment of 4 grams and another gave rise to over 4,500 in 128 grams. The intermediate environments had populations of intermediate sizes. . . .

It is rather obvious that the formula $C = Bp/R$ must hold when C is the concentration of insects, Bp the biotic potential, and R the resistance. When we substitute the known values and solve for the value of resistance we get

$$43.97 = \frac{(43.97 \times 8.4)\ .25}{R}$$

or

$$R = \frac{(43.97 \times 8.4)\ .25}{43.97}.$$

The average number of eggs laid per female per day is 8.4 for these experiments, and 25 per cent of the population are females. The obvious solution is that $R = 2.1$. This is naturally the formula expressing the state of equilibrium and not the original increase of the population. Time does not enter into the formula in this case because population does not change with time.

The mere substantiation of the hypothesis would be of little consequence if it were not that by means of the method the quantitative analysis of environmental relationship is made possible. The valuation of each factor becomes subject to experimental verification. It is only necessary to vary one factor at a time and determine its effect upon the potential and actual populations. . . .

Thus, in the study of this particular species, the way seems open for the logical and methodical analysis of the environmental relationships. In the course of such an investigation certain fundamental principles are to be demonstrated which apply to animals in general, many of which do not lend themselves to such close analysis.

The next logical step is the consideration of the potential and resistance represented in each species of a natural community of organisms which are interdependent and self supporting. The analysis of such a system is complex but the analysis of the tensions and phases of a physical system is also complex but nevertheless possible. . . .

PERIODIC FLUCTUATIONS IN THE NUMBERS OF ANIMALS: THEIR CAUSES AND EFFECTS

Charles S. Elton—1924

Reprinted by permission of the author and publisher from Journal of Experimental Biology **2**:119–163, 1924.

Charles Elton's concern with conceptualizing ecology into basic principles was developed in his text (1927. Animal ecology, London, Sidgwick and Jackson) and gave new direction, impetus and stature to ecology. Among the many principles he developed was that of periodic fluctuations as characteristic of natural populations. The first scientific report on this phenomenon was the one that follows.

Professor Elton, Director of the Bureau of Animal Population, Oxford University since its founding in 1932, was honored as Eminent Ecologist by the Ecological Society of America in 1961. In our correspondence concerning the use of the following article he provided interesting commentary on the nature of scientific investigation and integrity. He wrote that the paper was the "honest effort of an enthusiastic 24-year old, working without a statistical environment. . . [*that*] *the correlation between Norwegian and Canadian lemming-fox cycles* may *actually exist . . . and* could *be synchronized through climate . . .* [*and*] *that the sunspot theory for the ten-year cycle was a dead duck even by 1930; but when I wrote the 1924 paper it was at any rate possible."*

The significance and reality of cycles is examined critically by L. C. Cole (1954. Some features of random population cycles. Journal of Wildlife Management **18**: *2–24).*

3. PERIODIC FLUCTUATIONS IN ANIMAL NUMBERS.

Lemmings. The lemmings are a group of rodents, resembling in appearance small guinea-pigs, which live in arctic and sub-arctic countries, where they occupy the ecological niche of the mice and rabbits of lower latitudes. Evidence is given below that the numbers of lemmings fluctuate periodically all over the arctic regions.

1. *Southern Norway.* The Norwegian Lemming (*Lemmus lemmus*) inhabits the arctic regions of Norway down to sea-level, and occurs further south in the mountains. It follows the zone of arctic-alpine tundra, above the tree limit, which in the mountains of South Norway is about 3000 to 4000 feet above sea-level. The data about the lemming are taken from Collett.

For many years the lemmings have periodically forced themselves upon public attention in Southern Norway by migrating down in swarms into the lowland in autumn, and in many cases marching with great speed and determination into the sea, in attempting to swim across which they perish. The details of the fate of the migrants do not concern us here and are fully described by Collett. The main point is that all these lemmings die, and none return to the mountains, the chief cause of death being an epidemic bacterial disease. It seems pretty certain that the immediate cause of the migration is overpopulation in the usual habitat. Lemming pairs usually have their own territory, nearly all the migrants are young animals of that year, and while large numbers are concerned in migrating, each individual still remains solitary and pursues its own independent course. These facts, taken with the stupendous numbers of migrants, and the fact that a certain number of lemmings stay behind and do not migrate, show that the phenomenon is analogous to infanticide among human beings as a method of preventing overpopulation. As a matter of fact the epidemic also attacks the stay-at-home animals, and thus the population is still further reduced. The lemming-years are such conspicuous phenomena that it is safe to assume that all which have occurred (since about 1860) have been recorded. Lemming-years in Norway have the status of great floods or terrible winters.

It should be remembered that lemming migration is only an indicator of overpopulation which passes a certain point, and therefore lemmings might have a small maximum which did not lead to migration. A study of the lemming-years of South Norway leads to the following results:

(*a*) Lemming overproduction occurs periodically every few years and culminates in an autumn migration. It is usually found either that some of the migrants of that year survive the first winter and carry on the invasion of the lowland in the next summer, or else overproduction in one district is followed in the next year by overproduction in a neighbouring one; so a lemming maximum may cover one or two years. For this reason, owing to the difficulty of knowing when the maximum has ended, in the following treatment, the first year of onset of migration is taken as the maximum, except in 1890 and 1894, when the migration was very small compared to that of the next year.

(*b*) The area of great over-increase varies in size and position, but often includes several distinct, and for lemmings isolated, mountain blocks.

(*c*) With one exception, a lemming maximum has occurred every three or four years (occasionally two or five). See diagram C, fig. 2.

(*d*) The exception noted above is the year 1898. It is probable, in view of the evidence to follow that there was a maximum of lemmings in the mountains, but not sufficient to cause a migration, especially as there was one in North Finland in 1897.

(*e*) If we assume a maximum in 1898, the mean period between maxima is 3.6 years (1862–1909).

I have not been able to obtain full information of lemming-years since 1910, but Dr. Grieg informs me that there was one in the Hardanger region in 1922–1923. It is highly probable that records will be found for 1914 and 1918.

The Wood Lemming (*Lemmus* (*Myopus*) *schisticolor*) which lives lower down on the mountains than its ally, is also subject to "good years" followed by migration. So far as the data go, over-increase is found to take place in the same years as the common lemming (1883, 1888, 1891–92, 1894–95, 1902, 1906). . . .

3. *Canada*. The Barren Grounds of Canada are inhabited by lemmings of several species, chiefly the Hudson Bay Lemming (*Lemmus* (*Dicrostonyx*) *richardsoni*), and the Tawny Lemming (*L. trimucronatus*). There is practically no direct evidence as to the periodicity of their fluctuations, or details about them. But they are well known to fluctuate, and according to Rae the North American species migrate in certain years after the manner of the Norwegian species. There was a big migration of Lemmus at Point Barrow, Alaska, in 1888. However, we can attack the question from another angle. The lemming is the main source of

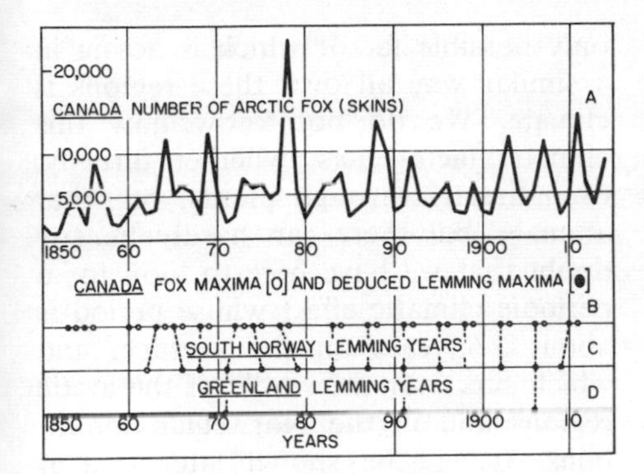

FIG. 2. *Years of lemming maxima in Canada, the mountains of South Norway, and Greenland. The years for Canada are deduced from the curve (A) of arctic fox skins taken annually by the Hudson Bay Company. (Data for Canada from Hewitt, 1921; for Norway from Collett, 1911; for Greenland from Winge, 1902, and Manniche, 1910).*

food of the arctic fox; there is not the smallest doubt that the latter depends very largely on the lemming, just as its allies further south depend on hares, rabbits, and mice. As will be shown later, the number of red foxes fluctuates with the number of rabbits (and probably mice), so we should expect the number of arctic fox to give a good indication of the number of lemmings. This is in fact so. The curve A in fig. 2 shows the variation from year to year of the number of arctic fox skins taken by the Hudson Bay Company. If we plot the year before each fox maximum as in diagram B, we obtain the years when there was presumably a maximum of lemmings. The agreement with lemming-years in Norway is seen to be remarkable. In three cases the maximum in Canada occurs a year before, and in three cases a year after that in South Norway, so that the variations cancel out and leave us with the same mean period: 3.6 years. The reason why the maximum of fox skins occurs in the year after that of the lemmings is clearly shown by Manniche's study of a lemming-year in Greenland. In the autumn of 1906 there were colossal numbers of lemmings, but these mostly disappeared before the winter was far advanced. He attributed this death to the cold early winter with little snow to protect the animals, but it is highly probable that disease was an important cause. The foxes swarmed in autumn, partly owing to immigration, but also presumably more young grew up successfully. They fed entirely on lemmings. But in the winter the lemmings had died or were inaccessible under the snow. Foxes make caches of lemmings for the winter, but by the spring these must have been used up, for Manniche was able to trap large numbers of foxes owing to their hunger. Now the Hudson Bay Company fur returns for any year include the catch of the winter before; in fact this is the main item, *i.e.* a maximum of skins in 1907 means many foxes caught in the winter 1906–1907, and in the spring. Such abundance will, of course, be the result of the year 1906, since arctic foxes mate in the spring and the young do not grow up until the autumn. So any abundance in fur returns for one year necessarily implies abundant food supply in the preceding year. . . .

Effect of lemming fluctuations. The lemming fluctuations have very powerful effects on the animals associated with them. This has already been shown for the arctic fox. In Norwegian lemming-years vast crowds of birds (owls, hawks, ravens, etc.), and mammals (stoats, foxes, etc.), are attracted to the mountains, and their numbers increase not only by their immigration but probably by their larger and more successful broods, due to the abundance of food. Similarly the arctic carnivores are profoundly affected. It is probable that many skuas and snowy owls only breed at all in lemming-years. There is not space here to follow out the readjustments of the food-cycle which result from the lemming-years. Two examples must suffice. The Short-eared Owl (*Asio flammeus*) collects in numbers and battens upon lemmings in South Norway lemming-years, and the Peregrine Falcon (*Falco peregrinus*), which hardly ever visits that country in normal years, comes and eats the owls. Again, in Greenland, an abundance of lemmings causes the arctic foxes to neglect other sources of food such as Ptarmigan and other birds. The latter accordingly increase. But in the next spring and summer, when there are few lemmings, these birds fare badly.

The causes of lemming fluctuations. It is clear that the causes of these fluctuations might lie either with the lemmings themselves or with their environment. It is possible to conceive that there might be some rough natural period in the increase of lemmings' numbers (in the sense of having an increase in their "bank balance" of numbers every year), which was terminated after a few years by migration and disease following upon overpopulation, and that the population was thus reduced and the process started all over again. A little consideration will show that such an explanation of lemming periodicity is quite untenable. It is inconceivable that such a process could cause synchronised maxima on the various mountain blocks of southern Norway, which as far as lemmings are concerned, are isolated from one another, or again in the different districts of Scandinavia. When we find further that the lemming maxima are practically synchronous all over the arctic regions and the mountains of southern Scandinavia, any such "natural rhythm" becomes out of the question. Of course the natural rate of increase is a very fundamental factor in determining the size of periodicity into which the fluctuations will fit. The cause of the periodicity must therefore lie with the environment, and here the only possible factor which is acting in a similar way all over these regions is climate. We do not know how this climatic factor acts, whether directly, or indirectly through plants, or other animals, but there can hardly be any doubt that we have here to look for a periodic climatic effect whose period is about 3.6 years on the average, and which acts over the whole of the arctic regions and in the Norwegian mountains. It will be shown later that it probably occurs in temperate regions also. . . .

I shall attempt to show that the 10- to 11-year period of the rabbit may be due primarily to the 11-year period in the sun. If this is so, the fox curve indicates that the solar period is having a slight effect in the arctic regions. This agrees with the conclusion reached from other evidence, that the effect of the solar variation is greatest in the tropics and gets fainter farther from the equator. It will be seen that there is no known cause for this well-marked 3 1/2-year period in the arctic climate. It might be caused by some short period in the sun, or by some unknown terrestrial factor, or the complicated interaction of several such factors.

Since the curve for the arctic fox shows a well-marked 3.6-year periodicity with a less distinct 10- or 11-year period underlying it, it might be thought probable that the curve for the numbers of the southern red fox, which shows a definite periodicity of about ten years, would have a concealed short period. This is found to be the case. . . . Now the southern fox feeds both on rabbits and mice. The rabbits cause the 10-year period in the fox, and it is shown later that there is a short period of $3\frac{1}{2}$ years in Norwegian mice. It is very probable that the short period in the red fox curve is caused by variations in the supply of mice in Canada. It might also be caused by climate acting directly; but the absence of any such period in the lynx curve goes against this idea, since the lynx eats rabbits only. In any case the ultimate cause must be climate.

It appears then that there are two periods in the numbers of foxes and their food, and that the effects of the shorter one are more marked in the arctic, while those of the longer one are more marked in the temperate regions. This difference must be to a large extent due to the difference in prey, *i.e.* lemmings in the one place and mice and rabbits in the other, but the climatic difference may also be of the same nature.

Finally, it should be noted that the lemming differs from most of the other fluctuating rodents in that it does not have more young in a brood in good years; it probably has more broods in a given time, and the young grow up more successfully under the good conditions. . . .

COOPERATION AND CONFLICT AMONG PRIMITIVE ORGANISMS

Paul R. Burkholder—1952

Reprinted by permission of the author and publisher from the American Scientist **40**:601–631, 1952.

The numerous potential interactions between species populations, and the wide diversity in which such relationships are expressed, can be meaningfully considered in terms of coaction theory. Although this is one of the salient concepts developed in this essay, two other major ideas are evident—that there is considerable cooperation among organisms, here evidenced at the microbial level, and that microbes have a little-explored ecology.

. . . In the complex struggle for survival, preservation of the individual and the perpetuation of its kind are of primary importance to all forms of life. In mixed natural populations of organisms, such main goals are attained by numerous kinds of coactions, both harmful and beneficial. Thus, organisms may be forced to compete for food and shelter, or they may have to devise special ways of protecting themselves against harm, while others come to depend upon associates for their own good or for mutual welfare. All organisms are dependent upon the varied activities of other organisms for the supplies of essential stuffs carrying elementary components which can be used and reused many times in the cycles of the elements which are part of the balance of nature. Countless hordes of microorganisms decompose the metabolic products formed by other organisms, processes which are continued in stepwise fashion until the complex organic compounds of worn out or dead protoplasm become disintegrated into simple molecules, once again available for the feeding habits of plant and animal life in forest, field, or fishery.

TYPES OF COACTION

. . . The relationships among various plant and animal organisms, including man and the causative agents of his diseases, can be analyzed profitably in terms of coaction theory. According to Edward Haskell, the physical and chemical activities of organisms involve two main categories of relationship which are associated with different degrees of power or influence upon the fundamental processes of growth, maintenance, reproduction, and other activities of individuals or classes. The power relationship has often been stated in terms of *the weak* and *the strong*, but any differences may be expressed simply as symbols a and α representing distinguishing characters in two systems. If 0 be taken to mean the rate of an activity, such as, for example, a process of metabolite utilization, carried on by each class in the absence of others, + for all accelerations of this activity in either class by some other, and — for decelerations, then the cross tabulation of +, 0, and — simply yields the possible main types of coactions as shown in Table I.

TABLE I. *The nine possible coactions between weak and strong organisms*

(a)	*weak*	−	0	+
(α)	+	− +	0 +	+ +
s		predation	allotrophy	symbiosis
t	0	− 0	0 0	+ 0
r		amensalism	neutrality	commensalism
o				
n	−	− −	0 −	+ −
g		synnecrosis	allolimy	parasitism

In regard to any metabolic activity then, a and α individuals or classes can exhibit nine qualitatively different relations toward each other. It can be shown that certain major properties of group relationships and social organization are regulated by numerous coactions of many types and with varying intensity of expression. The terms which Haskell applied to nutritional coactions were invented *de novo* or were taken from the literature of microbiology and ecology. In the table, the left-hand sign refers to the effect of coaction upon the weak and the right-hand sign signifies the effect upon the strong. In the case of neutrality (0 0), neither type is helped or hindered. Many saprophytic microbes appear to live together without appreciable influence on each other. In predation, the weak prey are damaged by the strong predators which benefit by the minus-plus relationship (— +). Parasitism, a plus-minus relationship (+ —) signifies that the weak parasite is benefited at the expense of the strong host. Commensalism generally connotes coactions in which the weak benefit and the strong are unaffected (+ 0). Some harmless bacteria living in the intestines of animals receive the benefits of shelter and food and are said to be commensals because, while bacteria profit greatly, the animal is supposed to lose or gain practically nothing from the relationship. A familiar example of commensalism in the bacteriological laboratory is found in the cultivation of facultative aerobic and obligate anaerobic bacteria near each other in nutrient media contained in sealed Petri dishes. The aerobe grows first and consumes the free oxygen with liberation of carbon dioxide; the anaerobe then is able to grow without accumulating hydrogen peroxide and other products of metabolism which would poison it. Thus the anaerobe is definitely benefited, whereas the aerobe is neither helped nor harmed. The opposite of commensalism is called amensalism (— 0). The relationship of allotrophy means feeding the other (0 +); and the opposite relationship, that is, starving the other, is termed allolimy (0 —). In the relationship of antibiosis, where one organism produces a substance which is harmful to another, the coaction might be of the parasitic, amensal or some other type, depending upon whether the organism producing the inhibitory substance derives benefit, harm, or nothing out of the relationship. Symbiosis signifies mutual aid (+ +); and finally, mutual depression or death together (— —) has been given the name synnecrosis. The broad nutritive relationships classified under the term metabiosis are concerned with the cycles of elements and are more general in effect than the specific relations between organisms as listed in the table of coactions.

The exploitation of various hosts by parasitic lower forms of life constitutes one of the most important types of coaction. . . . Most parasites occasion some damage to their host, and in this respect they are inept at their ungrateful mode of existence, for excessive injury to the host will result unfavorably to the parasite. Some main considerations in the parasite's struggle for existence are a good source of food, easy living, protection from enemies, and avoidance of competition. The wholly effective parasite must be adapted to live in or on its host without causing unfavorable reactions. The process of adaptation between parasite and host is probably mutual, and requires numerous generations of selection of the fittest individuals. Bacterial generations are a matter of thirty minutes, human generations thirty years. Assuming the same mutation frequency and similar adaptation rates, microbes have a fine chance to become adapted to human tissues before man becomes tolerant to parasites. Neophytic pathogens, like gonococcus and the whooping cough bacilli, cause violent reactions every time they multiply in a host. Other chronic pathogens and their host are better adapted; the host becomes accustomed to having the highly adapted etiological agents growing within its tissues. Syphilis, tuberculosis, and leprosy are important examples. In still other instances, the process of adaptation may progress to the level of commensalism, as is exemplified by harmless organisms of the human throat and intestine. In view of the extensive production of B vitamins by the intestinal microflora in animals and man, it may be that one stage in the evolution of parasitism to saprophytism is represented in true symbiosis. Plants apparently lack the ability to produce immune substances, and sometimes the plant host species succumbs to new parasites before adaptive mechanisms are given an opportunity to come into operation. Thus, the chestnut blight fungus *Endothia parasitica* all but wiped out the American chestnut tree two decades ago.

Coaction analysis has great significance for all who desire a broad understanding of life on the earth and who wish to do something constructive about it for mankind through the avenues of medicine and agriculture. In the field of human interests, undesirable activities of many parasites can be alleviated or avoided by the scientific application of chemical agents possessing selective and powerful inhibitory action against the causative agents of plant, animal, and human diseases. . . .

COOPERATION AND CONFLICT IN ECOLOGY

Metabiosis. . . . The production and exchange of water-soluble B vitamins among organisms living together or developing in sequence is of great significance in ecology. Beneficial exchange of growth factors among microbes, resulting in the formation of satellite colonies on agar plates, has become a familiar phenomenon to all bacteriologists. Microbes having deficient inheritance with regard to their ability to synthesize essential metabolites are enabled to grow near colonies of other microorganisms which produce enough vitamins and amino acids for themselves and also for their neighbors. . . . Thus, Robbins found that a fungus requiring thiamine could live in association with another mold which synthesizes this vitamin, and so flourish in an environment where otherwise it could not have survived owing to B_1 avitaminosis. Such exchanges may be nonspecific with regard to the kinds of organisms which are present, and it may be said that, in metabiosis, no constant biotic association is necessary as in the species-specific symbiotic relations which occur in lichens or legume nodules.

Symbiosis. Examples of cooperative association where two or more species live together in symbiosis with mutual benefit are abundantly present in nature. . . .

One of the finest examples of symbiosis in all of biology is found in the way of living shown by lichens. The lichen *Cladonia cristatella* is a beautiful green and red organism, composed of an alga and a fungus living together in a mutual welfare association. The alga reduces carbon dioxide to form carbohydrates for itself and for the fungus which cannot make such foodstuffs, and the fungus holds the partnership together while conserving moisture and making minerals available for both members of the household. When the two symbionts are divorced by suitable laboratory techniques, as Castle has recently done, then the alga and fungus cells may be grown separately on appropriate media. When attempts are made later to unite them by bringing the growing cultures of alga and fungus together, they fail to make a lichen, probably because of the imbalanced nutritive conditions in artificial media and unusual circumstances of the laboratory environment. So it must be admitted that the conditions necessary to make symbiosis function smoothly are not completely known. . . .

Antibiosis. . . . Frequently the struggle for "a place in the sun" is exhibited through negative coactions among primitive organisms, both in pure cultures as well as in mixed populations. Under crowded conditions lack of available food may limit growth and lead to selective elimination of weaker components. Bacteria, yeasts, molds, and protozoa may compete with each other for food and a place to live. Elaboration of waste products and formation of "staling" substances which are inimical to many organisms represent one aspect of microbial antagonism. Organic acids, alcohols, and specific toxic substances synthesized by some organisms often interfere with the metabolism of others so as to cause temporary cessation of growth or even to kill them outright. In other instances, metabolic products of one type of organism may be the essential basis of a food chain for many other types in series.

Antibiosis is a special case of antagonism in which an organism produces an injurious compound which may inhibit growth or destroy another organism. The word "antibiotic" was coined by Vuillemin in 1889, and ten years later extended by Ward to include the antagonistic relations among microbes. As long ago as 1889, the phenomenon of bacterial antibiosis in a Petri plate culture was demonstrated by Doehle and photographed by Hoppe-Seyler, so this kind of biotic relationship is not a new discovery of the 20th century. . . .

The interdependence of organisms for preservation of natural ecological equilibria is frequently not appreciated until some unusual event disturbs the balance. The main point is well illustrated by reference to the behavior of intestinal flora. For a long time the common bacteria harbored in the intestines of mammals were generally regarded as commensals with no great significance. Recent studies indicate the importance of the cellulose-decomposing bacteria in helping cattle to digest coarse feedstuffs in the rumen, and, in addition, demonstrate how very dependent the dairy industry is upon B vitamin synthesis by other members of the flora in the alimentary tract of *Bos*. Thus with the help of the intestinal flora, the cow supplies more vitamins in her milk than are contained in the feeds taken into her body. In a similar way, man also depends upon intestinal flora for help in the maintenance of normal conditions. Some individuals who lack the capacity to secrete a protein material called "intrinsic factor," in their stomachs become ill with pernicious anemia. It now appears as if bacteria in the stomach and intestines continually produce and absorb vitamin B_{12}, but in the absence of intrinsic factor the essential vitamin is not available for absorption into the human blood stream. . . .

Throughout the discussion of coactions among primitive organisms, the benefits derived out of cooperative relationships have been emphasized at the molecular, cellular, organismal, and societal levels of biological integration. A proper understanding of the ecology of microbes and man often provides means for improving the human welfare, as for example, when antibiotics are developed to relieve the ills of mankind or when harmful coactions are neutralized and converted into beneficial relationships.

During three thousand millions of years, progressive evolution from minerals to man has achieved for us an awareness of the cosmos and the imagination and ability to explore the universe with telescopes, test tubes and microscopes. Yet it is clear that we have much further to go than we have come, for we are only now at the beginning of understanding relationships among races and nations and our ultimate destiny. Those who believe that negative coactions must of necessity be expressed in the repeated uprising of weak against strong, leading to final synnecrosis, may do well to consider the possibility of embracing an ideology which seeks adequate knowledge and means for systematic conversion of negative relationships into positive coactions, so that human culture shall survive and man continue to expand his comprehension and enjoyment of the universe.

COMPETITION FOR COMMON FOOD IN PROTOZOA

G. F. Gause—1934

Reprinted by permission of the publisher from The struggle for existence. Baltimore, Williams and Wilkins Co., pp. 93–95, 98, 100–111, 1934.

Gause's Rule is essentially that two species cannot occupy the same niche at the same time. Although never formally stated by Gause, it is implicit in this discussion. The Gausian exclusion principle has been especially well studied by Peter Frank in Daphnia *(1957. Ecology* **38**: *510–519) and Thomas Park in* Tribolium *(1948. Ecological Monographs* **18**: *265–308). Slobodkin (1961. Growth and regulation of populations. New York, Holt, Rinehart and Winston) gives an excellent critique of Gause's studies and on the function of competition in population regulation. At the time of this study, Gause was associated with the Zoological Museum of the University of Moscow.*

Figure 18 represents the growth of the number of individuals in pure lines of *Paramecium caudatum* and *Stylonychia mytilus* cultivated separately and in a mixed population. These data are founded on two experiments which gave similar results. At the beginning of the experiment into each tube were placed five *Paramecium*, or five *Stylonychia*, or five *Paramecium* plus five *Stylonychia* in the case of a mixed population. *Stylonychia* for inoculation must be taken from young cultures to avoid an inoculation of degenerating individuals.

(5) The growth curves of the number of individuals in Figure 18 are S-shaped and resemble our well known yeast curves. After growth has ceased the level of the saturating population is maintained for a short time, and then begins the dying off of the population which is particularly distinct in *Stylonychia*. It is evident that this dying off is regulated by factors quite different from those which regulate growth, and that a new system of relations comes into play here. Therefore there is no reason to look for rational equations expressing both the growth and dying off of the populations.

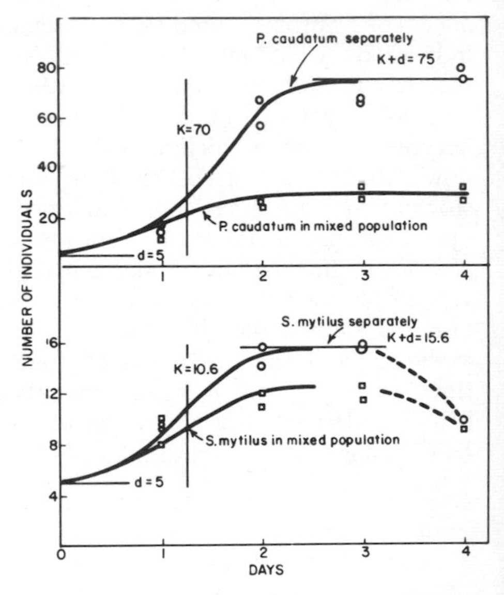

FIG. 18. *The growth in number of individuals of* Paramecium caudatum *and* Stylonychia mytilus *cultivated separately and in the mixed population.* d *denotes lower asymptote.*

Figure 18 shows that *Stylonychia*, and especially *Paramecium*, in a mixed culture attain lower levels than separately. The calculated coefficients of the struggle for existence have the following values: α (influence of *Stylonychia* on *Paramecium*) = 5.5 and

β (influence of *Paramecium* on *Stylonychia*) = 0.12. This means that *Stylonychia* influences *Paramecium* very strongly, and that every individual of the former occupics a place available for 5.5 Paramecia. With our technique of cultivation it is difficult to decide on what causes this depends. As a supposition only one can point to food consumption.

(6) We have but to change slightly the conditions of cultivation and we shall obtain entirely different results. [Let us consider]. . . the growth of populations of the same species on a dense "oaten medium with sediment" sown with various wild bacteria. Here owing to an increase in the density of food the absolute values of the maximal population in both species have considerably increased. The character of growth of the mixed population now essentially differs from the former one: *Paramecium* strongly influences *Stylonychia*, while *Stylonychia* has almost no influence upon *Paramecium*. . . .

(3) In an experiment of such a type all the properties of the medium are brought to a certain invariable "standard state" at the end of every 24 hours. Hence, we acquire the possibility of investigating the following problem: can two species exist together for a long time in such a microcosm, or will one species be displaced by the other entirely? This question has already been investigated theoretically by Haldane, Volterra and Lotka. It appears that the properties of the corresponding equation of the struggle for existence are such that if one species has any advantage over the other it will inevitably drive it out completely. It must be noted here that it is very difficult to verify these conclusions under natural conditions. For example, in the case of competition between two species of crayfish a complete supplanting of one species by another actually takes place. However, there is in nature a great diversity of "niches" with different conditions, and in one niche the first competitor possessing advantages over the second will displace him, but in another niche with different conditions the advantages will belong to the second species which will completely displace the first. Therefore side by side in one community, but occupying somewhat different niches, two or more nearly related species. . . will continue to live in a certain state of equilibrium. There being but a single niche in the conditions of the experiment it is very easy to investigate the course of the displacement of one species by another. . . .

. . . The curves of growth of pure populations of *P. caudatum* and *P. aurelia* with different concentrations of the bacterial food show that the lack of food is actually a factor limiting growth in these experiments. With the double concentration of food the volumes of the populations of the separately growing species also increase about twice (from 64 up to 137 in *P. caudatum;* $64 \times 2 = 128$; from 105 up to 195 in *P. aurelia*; $105 \times 2 = 210$). Under these conditions the differences in the growth of populations of *P. aurelia* and *P. caudatum* are quite distinctly pronounced: the growth of the biomass of the former species proceeds with *greater rapidity*, and it accumulates a *greater biomass than P. caudatum at the expense of the same level of food resources*. . . .

(3) We will now pass on to the growth of a mixed population of *P. caudatum* and *P. aurelia*. . . . For a detailed acquaintance with the properties of a mixed population we will consider the growth with a half-loop concentration of bacteria (Fig. 24). First of all we see that as in the case examined before the competition between our species can be divided into two separate stages: up to the fifth day there is a competition between

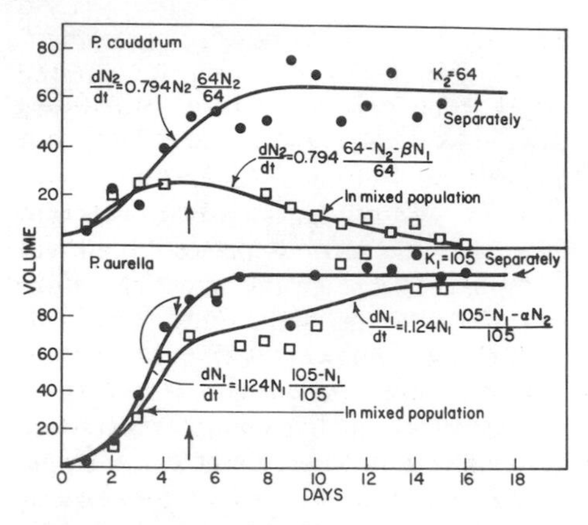

FIG. 24. *The growth of the "volume" in* Paramecium caudatum *and* Paramecium aurelia *cultivated separately and in the mixed population on the buffered medium with the "half-loop" concentration of bacteria.*

the species for seizing the so far unutilized food energy; then after the fifth day of growth begins the redistribution of the completely seized resources of energy between the two components, which leads to a complete displacement of one of them by another. The following simple calculations can convince one that on the fifth day all the energy is already seized upon. At the expense of a certain level of food resources which is a constant one in all "half-loop" experiments and may be taken as unity, *P. aurelia* growing separately produces a biomass equal to 105 volume units, and *P. caudatum* 64 such units. Therefore, one unit of volume of *P. caudatum* consumes $\frac{1}{64} = 0.01562$ of food, and one unit of volume of *P. aurelia* $\frac{1}{105} = 0.00952$. In other words, one unit of volume of *P. caudatum* consumes 1.64 times as much food as *P. aurelia*, and the food consumption of one unit of volume in the latter species constitutes but 0.61 of that of *P. caudatum*. These coefficients enable us to recalculate the volume of one species into an equivalent in respect to the food consumption volume of another species.

On the fifth day of growth of a mixed population the biomass of *P. caudatum* (in volume units) is equal to about 25, and of *P. aurelia* to about 65. If we calculate the total of these biomasses in equivalents of *P. aurelia*, we shall have: $(25 \times 1.64) + 65 = 106$ (maximal free growth of *P. aurelia* is equal to 105). The total of the biomasses expressed in equivalents of *P. caudatum* will be $(65 \times 0.61) + 25 = 65$ (with the free growth 64). This means that on the fifth day of growth of the mixed population the food resources of the microcosm are indeed completely taken hold of.

(4) The first period of competition up to the fifth day is not all so simple as we considered it in the theoretical discussion of the third chapter, or when examining the population of yeast cells. The nature of the influence of one species on the growth of another does not remain invariable in the course of the entire first stage of competition, and in its turn may be divided into two periods. At the very beginning *P. caudatum* grows even somewhat better in a mixed population than separately. . . apparently in connection with more nearly optimal relations between the density of Paramecia and that of the bacteria in accordance with the already mentioned data of Johnson. At the same time *P. aurelia* is but very slightly oppressed by *P. caudatum*. As the food resources are used up, the Johnson effect disappears, and the species begin to depress each other as a result of competition for common food.

It is easy to see that all this does not alter in the least the essence of the mathematical theory of the struggle for existence, but only introduces into it a certain natural complication: the coefficients of the struggle for existence, which characterize the influence of one species on the growth of another, do not remain constant but in their turn undergo regular alterations as the culture grows. . . .

(5) It remains to examine the second stage of the competition, i.e., the direct displacement of one species by another. An analysis of this phenomenon can no longer be reduced to the examination of the coefficients of multiplication and of the coefficients of the struggle for existence, and we have to do in the process of displacement with a quite new qualitative factor: the rate of the stream which is represented by population having completely seized the food resources. As we have already mentioned in Chapter III, after the cessation of growth a population does not remain motionless and in every unit of time a definite number of newly formed individuals fills the place of those which have disappeared during the same time. Among different animals this can take place in various ways, and a careful biological analysis of every separate case is here absolutely necessary. In our experiments the principal factor regulating the rapidity of this movement of the population that had ceased growing was the following technical measure: a sample equal to $\frac{1}{10}$ of the population was taken every day and then destroyed. In this way a regular decrease in the density of the population was produced and followed by the subsequent growth up to the saturating level to fill in the loss.

During these elementary movements of thinning the population and filling the loss, the displacement of one species by another took place. The biomass of every species was decreased by $\frac{1}{10}$ daily. Were the species similar in their properties, each one of them would again increase by $\frac{1}{10}$, and there would not be any alteration in the relative quantities of the two species. However, as one species grows quicker than another, it succeeds not only in regaining what it has lost but also in seizing part of the food resources of the other species. Therefore, every elementary movement of the population leads to a diminution in the biomass of the slowly growing species, and produces its entire disappearance after a certain time. . . .

In summing up we can say that in spite of the complexity of the process of competition between two species of infusoria, and as one may think a complete change of conditions in passing from one period of growth to another, a certain law of the struggle for existence which may be expressed by a system of differential equations of competition remains invariable all the time. The law is that the species possess definite potential coefficients of multiplication, which are realized at every moment of time according to the unutilized opportunity for growth. We have only had to change the interpretation of this unutilized opportunity. . . .

THE INFLUENCE OF INTERSPECIFIC COMPETITION AND OTHER FACTORS ON THE DISTRIBUTION OF THE BARNACLE *CHTHAMALUS STELLATUS*

Joseph H. Connell—1961

Reprinted by permission of the author and publisher from Ecology **42**:710–723, 1961.

Laboratory studies have the advantage of manipulating and controlling the environment in the analysis of population growth; such studies may lead to models restricted in application to the general situation, and thereby over- or underestimate the role of given phenomena. The lead paragraph of this article indicates such an instance. Fraught with the problem of vagaries of the environment and the resultant more difficult analysis of causative relationships, this study does demonstrate the need for and feasibility of studying population interactions under natural conditions. Connell's study was conducted at the Isle of Cumbrae, Scotland and received the 1963 Mercer Award of the Ecological Society of America as an outstanding contribution by a young ecologist during the preceding two years.

Most of the evidence for the occurrence of interspecific competition in animals has been gained from laboratory populations. Because of the small amount of direct evidence for its occurrence in nature, competition has sometimes been assigned a minor role in determining the composition of animal communities. . . .

In the course of an investigation of the animals of an intertidal rocky shore I noticed that the adults of 2 species of barnacles occupied 2 separate horizontal zones with a small area of overlap, whereas the young of the species from the upper zone were found in much of the lower zone. The upper species, *Chthamalus stellatus* (Poli) thus settled but did not survive in the lower zone. It seemed probable that this species was eliminated by the lower one, *Balanus balanoides* (L), in a struggle for a common requisite which was in short supply. In the rocky intertidal region, space for attachment and growth is often extremely limited. This paper is an account of some observations and experiments designed to test the hypothesis that the absence in the lower zone of adults of *Chthamalus* was due to interspecific competition with *Balanus* for space. . . .

METHODS

Intertidal barnacles are very nearly ideal for the study of survival under natural conditions. Their sessile habit allows direct observation of the survival of individuals in a group whose positions have been mapped. Their small size and dense concentrations on rocks exposed at intervals make experimentation feasible. In addition, they may be handled and transplanted without injury on pieces of rock, since their opercular plates remain closed when exposed to air. . . .

To measure the survival of *Chthamalus*, the positions of all individuals in a patch were mapped. Any barnacles which were empty or missing at the next examination of this patch must have died in the interval, since emigration is impossible. The mapping was done by placing thin glass plates (lantern slide cover glasses, 10.7 × 8.2

cm, area 87.7 cm^2) over a patch of barnacles and marking the position of each *Chthamalus* on it with glass-marking ink. The positions of the corners of the plate were marked by drilling small holes in the rock. Observations made in subsequent censuses were noted on a paper copy of the glass map. . . .

For censusing, the stones were removed during a low tide period, brought to the laboratory for examination, and returned before the tide rose again. . . .

The effect of competition for space on the survival of *Chthamalus* was studied in the following manner: After the settlement of *Balanus* had stopped in early June, having reached densities of 49/cm^2 on the experimental areas . . . a census of the surviving *Chthamalus* was made on each area. . . . Each map was then divided so that about half of the number of *Chthamalus* were in each portion. One portion was chosen (by flipping a coin), and those *Balanus* which were touching or immediately surrounding each *Chthamalus* were carefully removed with a needle; the other portion was left untouched. In this way it was possible to measure the effect on the survival of *Chthamalus* both of intraspecific competition alone and of competition with *Balanus*. . . .

RESULTS

The effects of physical factors. . . . In the absence of *Balanus* and *Thais*, and protected by the cages from damage by water-borne objects, the survival of *Chthamalus* was good at all levels. For those which had settled normally on the shore. . . . the poorest survival was on the lowest area. . . . On the transplanted stones. . . constant immersion in a tide pool resulted in the poorest survival. The reasons for the trend toward slightly greater mortality as the degree of immersion increased are unknown. . . .

Chthamalus is tolerant of a much greater degree of immersion than it normally encounters. This is shown by the survival for a year on area 12 in a tide pool, together with the findings of Fischer and Barnes, who found that *Chthamalus* withstood submersion for 12 and 22 months, respectively. Its absence below M.T.L. [mean tide level] can probably be ascribed either to a lack of initial settlement or to poor survival of newly settled larvae. . . .

At the upper shore margins of distribution *Chthamalus* evidently can exist higher than *Balanus* mainly as a result of its greater tolerance to heat and/or desiccation. . . . Records from a tide and wave guage operating. . . about one-half mile north of the study area showed that a period of neap tides had coincided with an unusual period of warm calm weather in April so that for several days no water, not even waves, reached the level of Area 1. In the period between the censuses of February and May, *Balanus* aged one year suffered a mortality of 92%, those 2 years and older, 51%. Over the same period the mortality of *Chthamalus* aged 7 months was 62%, those 1½ years and older, 2%. Records of the survival of *Balanus* at several levels below this showed that only those *Balanus* in the top quarter of the intertidal region suffered high mortality during this time.

Competition for space. . . . Intraspecific competition leading to mortality in *Chthamalus* was a rare event. For areas 2 to 7, on the portions from which *Balanus* had been removed, 167 deaths were recorded in a year. Of these, only 6 could be ascribed to crowding between individuals of *Chthamalus*. On the undisturbed portions no such crowding was observed. This accords with Hatton's observation that he never saw crowding between individuals of *Chthamalus* as contrasted to its frequent occurrence between individuals of *Balanus*.

Interspecific competition between *Balanus* and *Chthamalus* was, on the other hand, a most important cause of death of *Chthamalus*. This is shown both by the direct observations of the process of crowding at each census and by the differences between the survival curves of *Chthamalus* with and without *Balanus*. From the periodic observations it was noted that after the first month on the undisturbed portions of areas 3 to 7 about 10% of the *Chthamalus* were being covered as *Balanus* grew over them; about 3% were being undercut and lifted by growing *Balanus;* a few had died without crowding. By the end of the 2nd month about 20% of the *Chthamalus* were either wholly or partly covered by *Balanus;* about 4% had been undercut; others were surrounded by tall *Balanus*. These processes continued at a lower rate in the autumn and almost ceased during the later winter. In the spring *Balanus* resumed growth and more crowding was observed.... Above M.T.L., the *Balanus* tended to overgrow the *Chthamalus*, whereas at the lower levels, undercutting was more common. This same trend was evident within each group of areas, undercutting being more prevalent on area 7 than on area 3, for example. The faster growth of *Balanus* at lower levels (Hatton; Barnes and Powell) may have resulted in more undercutting. . . .

. . . *Chthamalus* kept free of *Balanus* survived better than those in the adjacent undisturbed areas on all but areas 2 and 14a. Area 2 was in the zone where adults of *Balanus* and *Chthamalus* were normally mixed; at this high level *Balanus* evidently has no influence on the survival of *Chthamalus*. On Stone 14a, the survival of *Chthamalus* without *Balanus* was much better until January when a starfish, *Asterias rubens* L., entered the cage and ate the barnacles. . . .

. . . crowding of newly settled *Chthamalus* by older *Balanus* in the autumn mainly takes the form of undercutting, rather than of smothering as was the case in the spring. The reason for this difference is probably that the *Chthamalus* are more firmly attached in the spring so that the fast growing young *Balanus* grow up over them when they make contact. In the autumn the reverse is the case, the *Balanus* being firmly attached, the *Chthamalus* weakly so.

Although the settlement of *Chthamalus* on Stone 15 in the autumn of 1954 was very dense, 32/cm^2, so that most of them were touching another, only 2 of the 41 deaths were caused by intraspecific crowding among the *Chthamalus*. This is in accord with the findings from the 1953 settlement of *Chthamalus*. . . .

. . . The mortality rates of *Balanus* were about the same as those of *Chthamalus* in similar situations except at the highest level, area 1, where *Balanus* suffered much greater mortality than *Chthamalus*. Much of this mortality was caused by intraspecific crowding at all levels below area 1. . . .

After a year of crowding the average population densities of *Balanus* and *Chthamalus* remained in the same relative proportion as they had been at the start, since the mortality rates were about the same. However, because of its faster growth, *Balanus* occupied a relatively greater area and, presumably, possessed a greater biomass relative to that of *Chthamalus* after a year.

The faster growth of *Balanus* probably accounts for the manner in which *Chthamalus* were crowded by *Balanus*. It also accounts for the sinuosity of the survival curves of *Chthamalus* growing in contact with *Balanus*.

The mortality rate of these *Chthamalus*... was greatest in summer, decreased in winter and increased again in spring. The survival curves of *Chthamalus* growing without contact with *Balanus* do not show these seasonal variations which, therefore, cannot be the result of the direct action of physical factors such as temperature, wave action or rain....

From all these observations it appears that the poor survival of *Chthamalus* below M.H.W.N. [mean high water, neap tide] is a result mainly of crowding by dense populations of faster growing *Balanus*.

At the end of the experiment in June, 1955, the surviving *Chthamalus* were collected from 5 of the areas... the average size was greater in the *Chthamalus* which had grown free of contact with *Balanus;* in every case the difference was significant ($P < .01$, Mann-Whitney U. test....)

These *Chthamalus* were examined for the presence of developing larvae in their mantle cavities.... in every area the proportion of the uncrowded *Chthamalus* with larvae was equal to or more often slightly greater than on the crowded areas. The reason for this may be related to the smaller size of the crowded *Chthamalus*. It is not due to separation, since *Chthamalus* can self-fertilize. Moore and Barnes have shown that the number of larvae in an individual of *Balanus balanoides* increases with increase in volume of the parent. Comparison of the cube of the diameter, which is proportional to the volume, of *Chthamalus* with and without *Balanus* shows that the volume may be decreased to $\frac{1}{4}$ normal size when crowding occurs. Assuming that the relation between larval numbers and volume in *Chthamalus* is similar to that of *Balanus*, a decrease in both frequency of occurrence and abundance of larvae in *Chthamalus* results from competition with *Balanus*. Thus the process described in this paper satisfies both aspects of interspecific competition as defined by Elton and Miller: "in which one species affects the population of another by a process of interference, i.e., by reducing the reproductive efficiency or increasing the mortality of its competitor...."

DISCUSSION

"Although animal communities appear qualitatively to be constructed as if competition were regulating their structure, even in the best studied cases there are nearly always difficulties and unexplored possibilities" (Hutchinson).

In the present study direct observations at intervals showed that competition was occurring under natural conditions. In addition, the evidence is strong that the observed competition with *Balanus* was the principal factor determining the local distribution of *Chthamalus*. *Chthamalus* thrived at lower levels when it was not growing in contact with *Balanus*....

The causes of zonation. The evidence presented in this paper indicates that the lower limit of the intertidal zone of *Chthamalus stellatus* at Millport was determined by interspecific competition for space with *Balanus balanoides*. *Balanus*, by virtue of its greater population density and faster growth, eliminated most of the *Chthamalus* by directing crowding.

At the upper limits of the zones of these species no interaction was observed. *Chthamalus* evidently can exist higher on the shore than *Balanus* mainly as a result of its greater tolerance to heat and/or desiccation.

The upper limits of most intertidal animals are probably determined by physical factors, such as these. Since growth rates usually decrease with increasing height on the shore, it would be less likely that a sessile species occupying a higher zone could, by competition for space, prevent a lower one from extending upwards. . . .

In regard to the lower limits of an animal's zone, it is evident that physical factors may act directly to determine this boundary. For example, some active amphipods from the upper levels of sandy beaches die if kept submerged. However, evidence is accumulating that the lower limits of distribution of intertidal animals are determined mainly by biotic factors. . .

TERRITORY IN BIRD LIFE

H. Eliot Howard—1920

Reprinted by permission of the publisher and of Collins Publishers from Territory in bird life. New York, E. P. Dutton and Co., Inc., 1920.

Territoriality is a means by which a population can regulate the limited physical and nutritive resources available to it. First described in a conceptual framework by Howard, the various modes of its expression and the range of vertebrate and invertebrate animals exhibiting such behavior has been increasingly recognized. The complexities of the phenomenon are discussed by C. R. Carpenter (1958. A. Roe and G. G. Simpson, eds. Territoriality: a review of concepts and problems. Behavior and evolution. New Haven, Yale University Press).

In his *Manual of Psychology* Dr. Stout reminds us that "Human language is especially constructed to describe the mental states of human beings, and this means that it is especially constructed so as to mislead us when we attempt to describe the working of minds that differ in a great degree from the human."

The use of the word "territory" in connection with the sexual life of birds is open to the danger which we are here asked to guard against, and I propose, therefore, before attempting to establish the theory on general grounds, to give some explanation of what the word is intended to represent and some account of the exact position that representation is supposed to occupy in the drama of bird life.

The word is capable of much expansion. There cannot be territories without boundaries of some description; there cannot well be boundaries without disputes arising as to those boundaries; nor, one would imagine, can there be disputes without consciousness as a factor entering into the situation; and so on, until by a simple mental process we conceive of a state in bird life analogous to that which we know to be customary amongst ourselves. Now, although the term "breeding territory," when applied to the sexual life of birds, is not altogether a happy one, it is difficult to know how otherwise to give expression to the facts observed. Let it then be clearly understood that the expression "securing a territory" is used to denote a process, or rather part of a process, which, in order to insure success to the individual in the attainment of reproduction, has been gradually evolved to meet the exigencies of diverse circumstances. Regarded thus, we avoid the risk of conceiving of the act of securing a territory as a detached event in the life of a bird, and avoid, I hope, the risk of a conception based upon the meaning of the word when used to describe human as opposed to animal procedure.

Success in the attainment of reproduction is rightly considered to be the goal towards which many processes in nature are tending. But what is meant by success? Is it determined by the actual discharge of the sexual function? So many and so wonderful are the contrivances which have slowly been evolved to insure this discharge, that it is scarcely surprising to find attention focused upon this one aspect of the problem. Yet a moment's reflection will show that so limited a definition of the term "success" can only be held to apply to certain forms of life; for where the young have to be cared for, fostered, and protected from molestation for periods of varying lengths, the actual discharge of the sexual function marks but one stage in a process which can only succeed if all the contributory factors adequately meet the essential conditions of the continuance of the species.

Securing a territory is then part of a process which has for its goal the successful rearing of offspring. In this process the functioning of the primary impulse, the acquirement of a place suitable for breeding purposes, the advent of a female, the discharge of the sexual function, the construction of the nest, and the rearing of offspring follow one another in orderly sequence. But since we know so little of the organic changes which determine sexual behaviour, and have no means of ascertaining the nature of the impulse which is first aroused, we can only deal with the situation from the point at which the internal organic changes reflect themselves in the behaviour to a degree which is visible to an external observer. That point is reached when large numbers of species, forsaking the normal routine of existence to which they have been accustomed for some months, suddenly adopt a radical change in their mode of behaviour. How is this change made known to us?. . . by all those movements. . . which the term migration, widely applied, is held to denote. Now the impulse which prompts these travelling hosts must be similar in kind whether the journey be long or short; and it were better, one would think, to regard such movements as a whole than to fix the attention on some one particular journey which fills us with amazement on account of the magnitude of the distance traversed or the nature of the difficulties overcome. For, after all, what does each individual seek? the majority seek neither continent nor country, neither district nor locality is their aim, but a place wherein the rearing of offspring can be safely accomplished; and the search for this place is the earliest visible manifestation in many species of the reawakening of the sexual instinct.

The movements of each individual are then directed towards a similar goal, namely, the occupation of a definite station; and this involves for many species a distinct change in the routine of behaviour to which previously they had been accustomed. Observe, for example, one of the numerous flocks of Finches that roam about the fields throughout the winter. Though it may be composed of large numbers of individuals of different kinds, yet the various units form an amicable society actuated by one motive—the procuring of food. And since it is to the advantage of all that the individual should be subordinated to the welfare of the community as a whole there is no dissension, apart from an occasional quarrel here and there.

In response, however, to some internal organic change, which occurs early in the season, individuality emerges as a factor in the developing situation, and one by one the males betake themselves to secluded positions, where each one, occupying a limited area, isolates itself from companions. Thereafter we no longer find that certain fields are tenanted by flocks of greater or less dimensions, while acres of land are uninhabited, but we observe that the hedgerows and thickets are divided up into so many territories, each one of which contains its owner. This procedure, with of course varying detail, is typical of that of many species that breed in Western Europe. . . . Whilst for the purpose of the theory I shall give expression to this behaviour in terms of that theory, and speak of it as a disposition to secure a territory, using the word disposition, which has been rendered current in recent discussion, for that part of the inherited nature which has been organised to subserve a specific biological purpose—strict compliance with the rules of psychological analysis requires a simpler definition; let us therefore say "disposition to remain in a particular place in a particular environment."

But even granting that this disposition forms part of the hereditary equipment of the bird, how is the process of reproduction furthered? The mere fact of remaining in or about a particular spot cannot render the attainment of reproduction any less arduous, and may indeed add to the difficulties, for any number of individuals might congregate together and mutually affect one another's interests. A second disposition comes, however, into functional activity at much the same stage of sexual development, and manifests itself in the male's intolerance of other individuals. And the two combined open up an avenue through which the individual can approach the goal of reproduction. In terms of the theory I shall refer to this second disposition as the one which is concerned with the defence of the territory. . . .

Now the male inherits a disposition which leads it to remain in a restricted area, but the disposition cannot determine the extent of that area. How then are the boundaries fixed? That they are sometimes adhered to with remarkable precision, that they can only be encroached upon at the risk of a conflict—all of this can be observed with little difficulty. But if we regard them as so many lines definitely delimiting an area of which the bird is cognisant, we place the whole behaviour on a different level of mental development, and incidentally alter the complexion of the whole process. It would be a mistake, I think, to do this. Though conscious intention as a factor may enter the situation, there is no necessity for it to do so; there is no necessity, that is to say, for the bird to form a mental image of the area to be occupied and shape its course accordingly. The same result can be obtained without our having recourse to so complex a principle of explanation, and that by the law of habit formation. In common with other animals, birds are subject to this law in a marked degree. An acquired mode of activity becomes by repetition ingrained in the life of the individual, so that an action performed to-day is liable to be repeated to-morrow so long as it does not prejudice the existence or annul the fertility of the individual. . . .

The intolerance that the male displays towards other individuals, usually of the same sex, leads to a vast amount of strife. Nowhere in the animal world are conflicts more frequent, more prolonged, and more determined than in the sexual life of birds; and though they are acknowledged to be an important factor in the life of the individual, yet there is much difference of opinion as to the exact position they occupy in the drama of bird life. Partly because they frequently happen to be in evidence, partly because they are numerically inferior, and partly, I suppose, because the competition thus created would be a means of maintaining efficiency, the females, by common consent, are supposed to supply the condition under which the pugnacious nature of the male is rendered susceptible to appropriate stimulation. And so long as the evidence seemed to show that battles were confined to the male sex, so long were there grounds for hoping that their origin might be traced to such competition. But female fights with female, pair with pair, and, which is still more remarkable, a pair will attack a single male or a single female; moreover, males that reach their destination in advance of their prospective mates engage in serious warfare. How then is it possible to look upon the individuals of one sex as directly responsible for the strife amongst those of the other, or how can the female supply the necessary condition? As long as an attempt is made to explain it in terms of the female, the fighting will appear to be of a confused order; regard it, however, as part of a larger process which demands, amongst other essential conditions of the breeding situation, the occupation of a definite territory, and order will reign in place of confusion.

But even supposing that the male inherits a disposition to acquire a suitable area, even supposing that it inherits a disposition which results indirectly in the defence of that area, how does it obtain a mate?. . .

. . . Here the song, or the mechanically produced sound, comes into play, and assists in the attainment of this end. Nevertheless if every male were to make use of its powers whether it were in occupation of a territory or not, if the wandering individual had an equal chance of attracting a mate, then it would be idle to attempt to establish any relation between "song" on the one hand, and "territory" on the other, and impossible to regard the voice as the medium through which an effectual union of the sexes is procured. But there is reason to believe that the males utilise their powers of producing sound only under certain well-defined conditions. For instance, when they are on their way to the breeding grounds, or moving from locality to locality in search of isolation, or when they desert their territories temporarily, as certain of the residents often do, they are generally silent; but when they are in occupation of their territories they become vociferous—and this is notoriously the case during the early hours of the day, which is the period of maximum activity so far as sexual behaviour is concerned. So that just at the moment when the sexual impulse of the female is most susceptible to stimulation, the males are betraying their positions and are thus a guide to her movements. Nevertheless, even though she may have discovered a male ready to breed, success is not necessarily assured to her; for with multitudes of individuals striving to procreate their kind, it would be surprising if there were no clashing of interests, if no two females were ever to meet in the same occupied territory. Competition of this kind is not uncommon, and the final appeal is to the law of battle, just as an appeal to physical strength sometimes decides the question of the initial ownership of a territory. . . .

A STUDY OF SOME ANT LARVAE WITH A CONSIDERATION OF THE ORIGIN AND MEANING OF THE SOCIAL HABIT AMONG INSECTS

William Morton Wheeler—1918

Reprinted by permission of the publisher from Proceedings of the American Philosophical Society **57**:293–343, 1918.

Communication among organisms assumes many diverse behavioral expressions and utilizes various physical and chemical media. In this selection, Wheeler introduces the term trophallaxis and discusses its significance in the establishment and maintenance of ant societies. Wheeler's work on the behavior of social insects, notably ants, not only stimulated considerable work but also considerable discussion of his analogy of the insect society and the individual organism. (*See also Allee, p. 98.*)

The facts collated in the foregoing paragraphs relate to the exudate organs, but we had previously seen that the salivary glands of larval ants probably subserve a similar function in the life of the colony in addition to digesting proteid foods extraintestinally and producing silk at the time of pupation. The question arises as to whether there is any evidence that in other groups of social insects the salivary glands of the larva produce substances which are consumed by the worker nurses. Fortunately there are some very pertinent observations at hand in the French literature which is so rich in splendidly original works on the habits and taxonomy of insects. The observations to which I refer relate to the social wasps. Du Buysson observed that the larvæ of *Vespa* "secrete from the mouth an abundant liquid. When they are touched the liquid is seen to trickle out. The queen, the workers and the males are very eager for this secretion. They know how to excite the offspring in such a way as to make them furnish the beverage." And Janet was able to prove that the secretion is a product of the salivary, or spinning glands and that it flows from an opening at the base of the labium. "This product," he says, "is often imbibed by the imagines, especially by the just emerged workers and by the males, which in order to obtain it, gently bite the head of the larva."

The most illuminating study of this matter, however, is found in a fine paper by Roubaud on the wasps of Africa. His account of the primitive wasps of the genus *Belonogaster* presents a striking picture of one of the earliest stages in the social life of wasps. . . .

Roubaud summarizes the general bearing of his observations in the following paragraph:

> The reciprocal exchange of nutriment between the adult females and the larvæ, the direct exploitation of the larval secretion without alimentary compensation by the males and just emerged females are trophobiotic phenomena the elucidation of which is of great importance to an understanding of the origin of the social tendencies in the Vespidæ, as we shall show in the sequel. The retention of the young females in the nest, the associations between isolated females, and the coöperative rearing of a great number of larvae are all rationally explained, in our opinion, by the attachment of the wasps to the larval secretion. The name *œcotro-*

phobiosis (from οἶκος, family) may be given to this peculiar family symbiosis which is characterized by reciprocal exchanges of nutriment between larvæ and parents, and is the *raison d'être* of the colonies of the social wasps. The associations of the higher Vespids has, in our opinion, as its first cause the trophic exploitation of the larvæ by the adults. This is, however, merely a particular case of the *trophobiosis* of which the social insects, particularly the ants that cultivate aphids and coccids, furnish so many examples.

It does not seem to me that the term "œcotrophobiosis" is aptly chosen. Apart from its length, it implies, as Roubaud states, a relationship between adult and larval members of the same colony or family, comparable with that existing between ants on the one hand and Aphids, Coccids, Membracids and Lycænid larvæ on the other. This relationship, however, is, so far as nutrition is concerned, one-sided since the ants exploit the aphids, etc., and may defend or even transport them, but do not feed them. Moreover, even in *Belonogaster* the feeding of adults and larvæ is reciprocal, and the latter could not be reared if they were actually exploited to such an extent as to interfere with their growth. As the relationship is clearly coöperative or mutualistic, I suggest the term *trophallaxis* (from τροφή, nourishment and ἀλλάττειν, to exchange) as less awkward and more appropriate than "œcotrophobiosis."...

Although considerable evidence thus points to trophallaxis as the source of the social habit in wasps, ants and termites, it must be admitted that the phenomenon has not been observed in the social bees. That the latter may have passed through a phylogenetic stage like that of *Synagris* seems to be indicated by the solitary bees of the genus *Allodape* to which I have already referred. Brauns' observations, though meager, show nevertheless that *Allodape* has reached Roubaud's fourth stage, that of direct feeding of the larvæ from day to day, and if I am right in supposing that the peculiar appendages of the larvæ are exudate organs, there would be grounds for assuming that trophallaxis occurs in this case. On the other hand, it has often been suggested (*e. g.*, by von Buttel-Reepen) that the three social subfamilies, the stingless bees (Meliponinæ), bumble-bees (Bombinæ) and honey bees (Apinæ) have developed from the solitary bees by another and more direct path, for the Meliponinæ, though living in populous societies, still bring up their brood in essentially the same way as the solitary bees, *i, e.*, by sealing up the eggs in cells provisioned with honey-soaked pollen. The Bombinæ, however, keep opening the cells from time to time and giving the larvæ a little food at a time, and in the honey bee the cells are left open till pupation and the larvæ fed more coninuously. Numerous facts indicate that the Bombinæ are the most primitive, the Apinæ the most specialized of existing social bees, and that the Meliponinæ, though closely resembling the solitary bees in the care of the young, are nevertheless in other respects very highly specialized (vestigial sting, elaborate nest architecture, etc.). It is therefore not improbable that these bees, after passing through a stage more like that of the Bombinæ, have reverted secondarily to a more ancient method of caring for their brood....

Another objection that may be urged against the view that trophallaxis is so fundamental as I contend, is the behavior of the ants towards their inert pupæ, which though transported and defended as assiduously as the larvæ, yield neither liquid exudates nor secretions. This does not seem to me to be a serious objection, because the pupæ evidently have an attractive odor and may therefore be said to produce volatile exudates like certain myrmecophiles. Both the larvæ and pupæ, moreover, evidently represent so much potential or stored nutriment available for the adult ants when the food-supply in the environment of the colony runs very low or ceases entirely. Infanticide and cannibalism then set in with the result that the devouring of the young of all stages may keep the adult personnel of the colony alive till the trophic conditions of the environment improve. Certain predatory tropical species (Dorylinæ, Cerapachyini) regularly raid the colonies of other ants and carry home and devour their brood. . . .

If we confine our attention largely to the ants, I believe it can be shown that trophallaxis, originally developed as a mutual trophic relation between the mother insect and her larval brood, has expanded with the growth of the colony like an ever-widening vortex till it involves, first, all the adults as well as the brood and therefore the entire colony; second, a great number of species of alien insects that have managed to get a foothold in the nest as scavengers, prædators or parasites (symphily); third, alien social insects, *i.e.*, other species of ants (social parasitism); fourth, alien insects that live outside the nest and are "milked" by the ants (trophobiosis), and, fifth, certain plants which are visited or sometimes partly inhabited by the ants (phytophily). In other words the ants, have drawn their living environment, so far as this was possible, into a trophic relationship, which, though imperfect or one-sided in the cases of trophobiosis and photophily, has nevertheless some of the peculiarities of trophallaxis. A brief sketch of each of these five expansions, indicated as annular areas in the accompanying diagram (Fig. 12), may not be out of place.

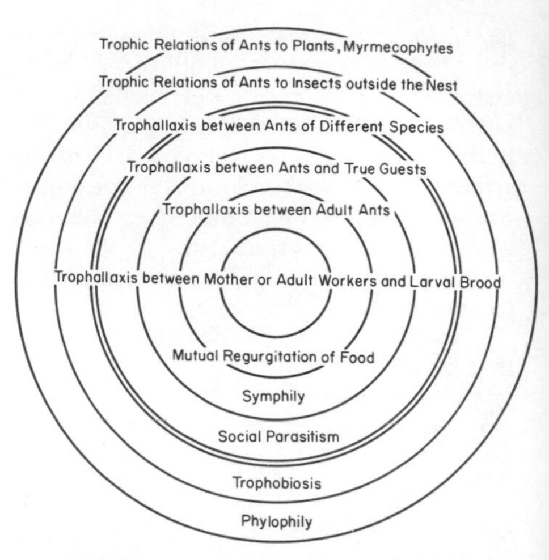

FIG. 12. *Diagram to illustrate the expansions of the trophallactic and trophic relationships within and outside the ant colony. The confines of the next are indicated by the double line.*

1. There is a very close resemblance between the behavior of adult ants towards one another and their behavior towards their young. The adults feed one another with regurgitated food or even with secretions as is the case with *Crematogaster* (*Physocrema*) *inflata*, an Indomalayan species, the workers of which have great sugar-glands in the back of the thorax. Many ants transport each other, and the transported ant assumes a quiescent, larval or pupal attitude. This is best seen in certain Ponerinæ, *e.g.*, in the species of *Lobopelta*, which carry their males under the body as if they were larvæ or pupæ. On such occasions the males keep their legs and antennæ in the pupal position. Moreover, when the food-supply of the colony is cut off ants often devour other ants of the colony as if they were larvæ or pupæ. The largest workers (soldiers) are eliminated first, either because they represent more stored food or because their continued life in the colony constitutes a greater drain on the food resources, or for both reasons. . . .

2. Among myrmecophiles and termitophiles Wasmann has shown that there are certain species (symphiles) that have trophallactic relations

with their hosts. Among ants especially these relations are so intimate that the symphiles may be regarded as integral members of the colony. The adult Lomeschusine beetles, *e.g.*, are not only fed and licked, but their young are treated as if they were ant larvæ, owing to the presence of trichome glands ("external exudate organs" of Wasmann) in the former and fatty, or internal exudatoria in the latter.

3. The various parasitic ants, of which a number of species have come to light within recent years and have been described by Wasmann, Donisthorpe, Emery, myself and others, can be shown to have established trophallactic relations with their host species. One of the most instructive is *Leptothorax emersoni* which lives with *Myrmica canadensis*. I have described its habits and those of one of its subspecies in three of my former papers.

4. The relations of ants to plant-lice and other Homoptera and to the larvæ of Lepidoptera outside the nest are, as I have said, incompletely trophallactic, since these insects are not fed, though they may be defended by the ants. The Homoptera are not fed probably for the simple reason that their mouth-parts are so peculiarly specialized for piercing plant-tissues and sucking their juices, and the Lepidopteron larvæ have, as a rule, no occasion to abandon their leaf diet. There are, however, several cases in which both caterpillars and Homoptera have entered into more intimate association with the ants. Many of the root aphids and coccids and their eggs are collected and kept by the ants in their nests, at least during certain seasons of the year. . . .

5. The fifth expansion of trophallaxis, namely the acquisition of trophic relations with the myrmecophytes, or plants possessing extra-floral nectaries or food-bodies, is also imperfect like ordinary trophobiosis, since the ants merely obtain nutriment from the plants and possibly afford them some protection. The nectar and other plant-foods are for the purposes of the ants merely so many exudates like the excrement of the Homoptera (honey-dew) and the sweet secretions of the Lycænid caterpillars which feed on the foliage. . .

STUDIES IN ANIMAL AGGREGATIONS: CAUSES AND EFFECTS OF BUNCHING IN LAND ISOPODS

W. C. Allee—1926

Reprinted by permission of the publisher from Journal of Experimental Zoology **45**:255–277, 1926.

The phenomenon of animal aggregations received its major exploitation by Allee at the University of Chicago and Wheeler (see p. 94) at Harvard University, the two foremost students of animal sociology during the first half of the twentieth century. This is Allee's first paper dealing with the topic; it indicates the analytic, interpretive and conceptual framework in which his subsequent research was conducted.

STATEMENT OF THE GENERAL PROBLEM

Many animals ordinarily living without physical contact with their fellows in nature at times come together to form more or less dense clusters or aggregations. Classic examples of this are furnished by the swarms of the honey-bee and of Eciton, the army ant, or by the hibernating aggregations of the coccinellid beetles. Deegener has devoted an extensive monograph to cataloging and naming the different types of such aggregations as well as others in which physical contact is not necessarily established.

Other species that are not known to form such aggregations in nature do so readily enough when brought into artificial conditions in the laboratory. The formation of such bunches by controlled stimulation, the effects of various environmental conditions upon their formation, and particularly the analysis of movements which result in aggregations were a favorite study some years ago during the height of the 'tropism' and 'trial and error' controversy. . . .

In addition to the large literature dealing with the formation of aggregations under laboratory conditions, there are many descriptions of aggregations more or less incidentally discovered in nature. Such groupings have excited particular attention when they have shown some signs of integration in behavior.

There is, however, a lack of information of the physiological effect of such congregations upon the animals forming them. The present report is largely concerned with this aspect of the general aggregations problem, although attention must necessarily be paid to the conditions under which aggregations occur. . . .

FACTORS CONTROLLING BUNCHING IN LAND ISOPODS

1. Moisture. These isopods may be found aggregated in damp places during dry periods or at least in situations where they are protected from the evaporating power of the air. This suggested the possibility that their bunching reaction might be controlled in part by controlling the moisture present. . . . When land isopods (Cylisticus convexus DeG., Porcellio scaber Latr., Oniscus asellus L., Tracheoniscus rathkei Brandt, or Armadillidium vulgare Latr.) are placed on air-dry filter-paper they tend to collect in bunches within a few minutes unless the paper and the atmosphere are too dry, in which case they remain scattered and frantically active until death. . . .

2. Temperature. In experiments on the effect of temperature on bunching, fifteen isopods of either Porcellio or Cylisticus or both were placed in crystallization dishes on slightly moistened filterpaper making conditions favorable for bunching. . . .

These observations indicate that while temperature affects the bunching reaction of land isopods, it does not control the reaction so markedly or completely as does the moisture content of the substratum.

3. Light. When these isopods were exposed to light there was a differential effect depending on the amount of moisture present in the substratum. The isopods are strongly photonegative, and bunching occurred even on a moist background when the animals were illuminated, but these bunches broke up when the light was removed. On the other hand, the bunches on a dry substratum were more dense in the darkness than in the light, since the latter stimulated those on the upper layer to move about while in darkness they heaped into one large compact bunch. In all cases there was more bunching on the dry substratum than on the moist. . . .

4. Contact. Land isopods are strongly positive in their thigmotropic reaction; this combined with their reactions to moisture and to light sends them under boards and in crevices. When such places are not available, there is a tendency to form aggregations with each other which will satisfy the same tactile reaction. Bunches are more likely to be found near the angle or corner of a container than out in the open and all possible use is made of available surfaces. As in the other elements making for aggregation, reaction to contact is less strong than the effect of moisture. . . .

METHOD OF FORMING AGGREGATIONS

The aggregations so far described were formed by what has been called the 'selection of random movement' type of reaction. Usually the animals wandered over the surface of their container, preferably around the margin, and came to rest in the position in which they were apparently least stimulated. In order to find how the aggregations were formed when the conditions were as nearly uniform in all parts of the container as they could be made, Mr. Vernon S. Downs conducted a long series of observations. Under uniform conditions, the isopods usually wandered about until one came to rest for some reason or other. Sometimes inequalities developed in an environment at first uniform and at other times the isopod apparently stopped for internal reasons. After one stopped there was a distinct tendency for the others to come to rest near by. They might or might not be in physical contact with the first, although they had frequently just crawled over it before stopping. In their incipient stages these bunches were frequently rather loose. The isopods would then alternate periods of rest and of motion. During some of the latter many or even all might start up again. Often a nucleus remained consisting of the original isopod and one or more others. Around such a nucleus the isopods would again gather. The bunch would become consolidated by slight movements toward the more stationary individuals on the part of those on the periphery. Partially successful attempts were made to control the place of bunch formation on a uniform field by gluing a recently killed isopod to the substratum.

When a drop of water was introduced on a dry background the isopods tended to occupy all of that favorable location regardless of whether or not they were in contact. The bunching in physical contact came later and might take place as a thigmotropic reaction, perhaps modified by chemical stimuli. . . .

PHYSIOLOGICAL EFFECT OF AGGREGATING

1. On water content. Experiments were run on Oniscus asellus and Cylisticus convexus to determine the effect upon body weight of exposure to increased or to decreased water content in their environment. . . .

Summary of experiment

1. Six bunched O. asellus, average weight 82.3 mg.; one isolated isopod, weight 85.5 mg. After eighteen hours on moist filter-paper, showed a gain of 12 and 21 per cent, respectively.
2. Ten bunched O. asellus, average weight 115 mg.; two isolated isopods weighed 138 and 124, respectively. After eighteen hours under less moist conditions, showed gains of 0.3, 0.9, and 1 per cent, respectively.
3. Ten bunched C. convexus, average weight 36.7 mg., gained 2.3 per cent in twenty-four hours, while five isolated animals weighing from 30 to 32 mg. gained 9, 12.6, 11, 12.2, and 10 per cent respectively.

These three bunches gained an average of 3.8 per cent under conditions which caused eight similar isolated animals to gain 9.7 per cent. The rate of gain was two to four times as fast when the isopods were isolated as when they were bunched.

Similar experiments when bunches and single individuals were allowed to dry showed that the aggregated isopods lose water less rapidly than isolated ones and that the lag is at about the same ratio as in the preceding case. . . .

These observations show that the formation of aggregations tends to render the isopods less easily affected by the water content of their environment and markedly decreases the rapidity of change of body moisture when this is not in equilibrium with the surroundings.

2. Effect of bunching on respiration. . . .Large Armadillidium vulgare. . . isolated for one hour had a respiratory rate equivalent to a movement of mercury 85.5 mm. per second and kilogram in one set and 79.6 in another as compared with 61.1 and 54, respectively, for those bunched the same length of time. The difference is about of the same order as for Tracheoniscus. In exact ratios, the rate of oxygen consumption with bunched and isolated Armadillidium was 1:1.486 and 1:1.368, while with the Tracheoniscus this ratio was 1:1.214 and 1:1.344.

The Armadillidium tests allow other comparisons. Since groups of isolated or bunched individuals were set away in the dark for approximately twenty-four hours, one can compare their physiological condition near the beginning of this period with that at the end and also make cross comparisons.

In general, the determinations show that, under the conditions of the experiment, there is a very marked decrease in oxygen consumption after twenty-four hours' isolation (and starvation); 70 and 65 per cent, respectively, in two sets of experiments. There is a similar, but less pronounced, reduction when the animals are bunched (and starved); 31 and 29 per cent, respectively. At the end of twenty-four hours, the bunched isopods were uniformly using more oxygen per unit weight than were the isolated individuals. The observed ratios were: 1:1.64 and 1:1.48. All the differences mentioned are statistically significant, since the least difference in means is still over 11.5 times their combined probable error. . . .

SIGNIFICANCE OF THE BUNCHING HABIT IN LAND ISOPODS

...Under ordinary conditions, aggregations of these land isopods are formed as a result of individual reactions and occur as follows: There is first a period of random movement which is more rapid at high temperatures and is slowed down by cold. During this period movement is stimulated by light and by evaporation. There is a tendency for individuals to stop in conditions that least stimulate them, such as a more moist place on the paper, a region satisfying thigmotropic reactions, or in least illumination. When a number of isopods stop in the same general region there is a tendency for them to move together even if not quite touching—a reaction probably caused by chemical stimulation and later by responses to both tactile and chemical stimuli.

During their wandering the isopods may stop near a quiet individual apparently as they would stop near any other object which gave them the same tactile satisfaction.

Considering all the evidence at hand, it seems that these isopods aggregate primarily through a tolerance of other individuals in a restricted favorable region which may lead to a use of other individuals in satisfying thigmotropic tendencies or in avoiding light. There is, however, an element of mutual attraction which Deegener calls 'social instinct' and Wallin regards as 'prototaxis' shown by the fact that the isopods will occupy less than the whole available and apparently equally desirable space. The question not settled is whether to the isopod the vacated space is as near isopod optimum as the space taken, regardless of the presence of other isopods.

One hesitates to ascribe a positive primitive social impulse to the reactions of these animals so long as it is possible to explain the observed phenomena on other grounds. We know that what were formerly regarded as 'social instincts' in the breeding season have been further analyzed in large part into chemotropism, thigmotropism, etc. Wallin's 'prototaxis' seems to belong to the same type of reactions as those usually described as social instincts so far as it applies to the relations between animals, since it is admittedly built of other recognizable components, such as chemotropism. Certainly, only the elements of a reaction that cannot be explained otherwise should be ascribed to 'prototaxis.' ...

If the foregoing analysis be sound, as it appears to be, then the first step toward social life in lower animals is the appearance of tolerance for other animals in a limited space where they have collected as a result of tropistic reactions to environmental stimuli. Such collections frequently occur in connection with some phase of breeding activity or of reproduction, but in the land isopods it is well exhibited without sexual significance.

A first advance in social life is made when these groupings serve to promote the welfare of the individuals forming them. This is accomplished in the land isopods by keeping the animals more quiet and so preserving their vitality, by conserving their water content and probably by lessening the rate of change of temperature. Robertson's infusoria and most of the animals tested by Drzewina and Bohn appear to so react on their environment as to render it more favorable.

The land isopods have gone little beyond such a stage in their social development. There is some slight evidence of mutual attraction, but the experiments to date do not reveal how much of this would be exhibited toward similar inanimate objects. There is also evidence of integrated group behavior in that the bunch shows occasional periods of activity apparently originating in one individual and passed mechanically through the group. Such activity may be the beginning of disintegration of the bunch, but it frequently results in a closer aggregation because the animals tend to move together as a result of their brief period of mild activity. Such group behavior is much more simple than that which Newman and Allee observed for aggregated phalangids, or Blair, Hess, and others have found in fireflies, and is far removed from the complex group behavior of the social insects or mammals.

NATURAL SELECTION AND FAMILY SIZE IN THE STARLING

David Lack—1948

Reprinted by permission of the author and publisher from Evolution **2**:95–110, 1948.

Lack's major premise of population regulation is that it is determined by natural selection acting through various processes. In the case in point, clutch-size in birds is determined by natural selection acting through survival of the young. The comprehensive statement of his viewpoint was elaborated in Natural regulation of animal numbers (1954. Oxford, Clarendon Press). Professor Lack has been Director of the Edward Gray Institute of Field Ornithology at Oxford University for many years.

. . . the limitation of clutch-size to a comparatively small number of eggs cannot be adequately explained on purely physiological grounds. The view that it is adjusted to the mortality of the species is also untenable. The alternative hypothesis was put forward that it is ultimately selected by the number of young which the parents can raise, the latter being determined by the available food supply. This view, so acceptable *a priori* to the population-geneticist and so difficult, apparently, for the traditional ecologist, was supported by much circumstantial evidence, chiefly relating to seasonal and regional trends of variation in clutch-size.

In the present paper, an attempt is made to provide direct evidence, to test whether, in fact, the young from broods of large size are at a disadvantage compared with those from broods of small size. It might be expected that, for broods above the average size, proportionate mortality among the young would rise as brood-size increased. When this is so, a point is quickly reached where an increase in the number of eggs is offset by the increased mortality, so that there is no increase in the number of young raised. One might reasonably hope to find evidence for this turning point in nature. . . .

CLUTCH-SIZE

In Britain, Holland and Switzerland, the Starling lays its first clutch in April or early May. A smaller number of layings occur in late May and in June, these being due partly to one-year-old birds breeding for the first time, partly to older birds whose first layings were destroyed, and partly to older birds which have already raised one brood in the season. In this paper, all clutches laid in April, and all broods with young old enough to band in May, have been classified as "early" broods, and they have been separated from later layings, which are on the average somewhat smaller in size.... In general, 5 is the commonest size of an early laying, and 4 of a late clutch.

The Starling also shows a regional variation in clutch-size. As in many other passerine species, average clutch-size is somewhat smaller in England than in central Europe at the same latitude....

PARENTAL FEEDING RATE

The hypothesis of this paper rests on the assumption that the parent Starlings bring less food to each nestling in a large than a small brood. This was found by Kluijver to hold in the Starling, ... but further data on this point are desirable. However, a similar result was obtained for most other species in which this problem has been investigated by Moreau. To summarise these data: with a brood of larger size, the parents increase the number of their feeding visits, but the increase is not sufficient to offset the larger number of young, so that each nestling is fed less often in a large than in a small brood.

MORTALITY IN THE NEST

Owing to the above fact, it was expected that the young would show, on the average, a proportionately higher mortality in large than small broods. The nesting data for the Starling in Britain did not suggest this, but were too few for analysis. Fortunately, extensive nest records are available from Holland since 1922, in the form of the number of eggs laid and the number of young alive on the observer's last visit. These... show decisively that the above expectation is not realized.

...in early layings, the proportion of eggs which give rise to fledged young is approximately the same for clutches of 3, 4, 5, 6, 7 and 8 eggs. For late layings, the answer is similar; (except for an apparent lower success for clutches of 6, which is attributable merely to random sampling, as a similar drop is not found for clutches of 7). When the losses of entire broods are included in the analysis...the results for early layings again show no variation with clutch-size, and the apparent variation in late layings is doubtless due to random sampling, the losses of entire broods being very erratic in their incidence from place to place and year to year. Nestling mortality was found to be independent of brood-size in the four other small passerine species in which this point has been studied....

NESTLING WEIGHT

The fact that nestling mortality is similar for broods of different sizes was first discovered for the Robin (*Erithacus rubecula*). To investigate the problem further, nestling Robins were weighed daily from hatching to flying. This unexpectedly revealed that there were extremely marked individual variations in the weight of the nestlings.... Lees has found similar large variations in the other small passerine species which he has weighed. In such species, the nestling can remain alive, and develop its feathers normally, although badly under weight, and the chief effect of undernourishment on a nestling is not death in the nest, but a reduced weight when it leaves the nest. The only comparative data so far available on the weights of nestling Starlings in broods of different sizes were obtained in 1947 by R. Carrick for three broods of different sizes, all raised by fully adult parents, all in the same locality, and all starting incubation on the same date. The results... fit the view that the average nestling weight decreases as brood-size increases, but many more data are needed before this point can be considered established.

POST-FLEDGING SURVIVAL IN SWITZERLAND

Those young which are below normal weight on leaving the nest might well have a reduced chance of subsequent survival. Moreover, any differences in their fledging weight associated with size of brood would tend to be intensified in the period immediately after leaving the nest, when the young are still dependent on their parents for a time; hence the greater the number of young, the less often each will tend to be fed. This means that the possible adverse effects of a large brood-size on survival can be revealed only if the data are extended to cover the period after leaving the nest. . . .

Should there be, in the period shortly after leaving the nest, a heavier mortality among the young from large than from small broods, then proportionately more individuals from small than large broods should survive to maturity. . . .

The results... are highly suggestive. In early broods, 5 is the commonest size of family. The recovery-rate for birds more than three months out of the nest is about the same for those coming from broods of 3, 4 or 5 young, in each case being around 2%. On the other hand, as soon as the brood-size exceeds 5, the recovery-rate falls. For individuals from broods of 6 it is only 1.7%, and for those from broods of 7–8 it is only 1.4%. If, now, the proportion of individuals recovered is multiplied by the original number of young in the brood (as in the right-hand column of table 6) [deleted], it is seen that, on the average, a brood of 5, 6 or 7 young gives rise to the same number of recoveries, about 0.1 per brood. If these recoveries are representative of the population, this must mean that an increase in brood-size between 5 and 7 young is approximately counterbalanced by an increase in proportionate mortality among the young, taking place in the period shortly after they leave the nest. . . .

The above data fit the hypothesis advanced earlier, viz. that when brood-size rises above the average, mortality also rises, so that productivity is not increased. Unfortunately, the proportion of birds recovered is so small that, despite the large numbers banded, the totals recovered are too small for the apparent differences in recovery-rate to be statistically significant. One could not expect bigger differences in the recovery-rates than those actually obtained, since, according to theory, the productivity per brood should be about equal for a brood of 5, 6 or 7 young, as in fact it is. (Had the young from broods of 6 or 7 survived less well, broods of 6 and 7 would have been less productive than broods of 5, and so would presumably have been extremely scarce.) Hence the lack of a significant result is due to the small number of recoveries, and not to the size of the difference found. For a significant result, about twice the present number of recoveries is needed, on the assumption that they are recovered in the same proportions. . . .

. . . in late broods 4 is the commonest size of family, and the recovery-rate falls from 2.2% in broods of 4, to 1.8% in broods of 5, and to about 1.4% in broods of 6. Once again, if the proportion of individuals recovered is multiplied by the number of young in the brood, it is seen that broods of 4, 5 and 6 young are about equally productive. Hence the results from late broods corroborate those from early broods. Unfortunately, the data are again too few for the result to be statistically significant. . . .

THE REGIONAL DIFFERENCE

It will be noted that in early broods the commonest number of young is 5 in Switzerland but only 4 in Britain, while in late broods it is 4 in Switzerland but only 3 in Britain. Lack showed that there was a widespread tendency for the average clutch-size of passerine birds to be larger in Central Europe than in Britain at the same latitude, and argued that a general trend suggests an adaptation. The data. . .fit in with this suggestion, since, in early broods, the survival-rate begins to decrease with a brood of more than 5 young in Switzerland, but with a brood of more than 4 young in Britain, while in late broods the decrease commences with a brood of more than 4 young in Switzerland but with a brood of more than 3 young in Britain. This presumably means that more food is available for young Starlings in Switzerland than in Britain, but there are as yet no data on this point. In the parallel case of the Swift (*Apus apus*) in the two regions, there is suggestive evidence that not only average clutch-size but also food supply is greater in Switzerland than in Britain.

Lack also showed a general tendency in passerine birds for average clutch-size to be higher in the north than the south of the European range. There are not yet sufficient data on this point for the Starling. . . .

POPULATION TURN-OVER

. . .the Starling has a lower reproductive rate in Britain than in Switzerland. While in both countries the Starling has been increasing in numbers in the last fifty years, the increase has probably been sufficiently slow to mean that the average number of young born each year is very nearly equal to the average annual mortality. The higher reproductive rate of Swiss than of British Starlings should therefore mean that the Swiss birds have a higher annual mortality than the British. This point can be tested by analysing the age at death of each banded bird later recovered. . . . This indicates that the mortality in the first year is 73% for Swiss but only 66% for British Starlings, while in later years it is 62% for Swiss and only 55% for British birds. These differences are statistically significant, and therefore support the above hypothesis. However, it is possible that the small percentage of recovered Starlings is slightly biassed as to age, as discussed in greater detail by Lack and Schifferli. It is scarcely necessary to add that, in a balanced population, a higher mortality-rate is an inevitable result of a higher reproductive rate. The types of danger to which Swiss and British Starlings are respectively subjected are a purely secondary consideration.

CONCLUSION

The data in this paper suggest that, as brood-size increases, the mortality among the young also increases, in such a way that the commonest brood-size found in nature is also the size with optimum productivity. This result appears to hold under the differing seasonal conditions of first and late broods, and the differing regional conditions of Switzerland, Holland and Britain. The facts therefore support the view that clutch-size is determined by natural selection acting through the survival of the young. . . .

THE ROLE OF WEATHER IN DETERMINING THE DISTRIBUTION AND ABUNDANCE OF ANIMALS

L. C. Birch—1957

Reprinted by permission of the author and publisher from Cold Spring Harbor Symposium on Quantitative Biology, **22**:203–215, 1957.

L. C. Birch is representative of those who consider populations to be regulated by factors largely external to the population and independent of the size of the population. Climate is an example of such a factor. H. G. Andrewartha and Birch, both of the University of Sydney, Australia, develop these concepts of population regulation in The distribution and abundance of animals (1954. Chicago, University of Chicago Press).

The thesis of this paper is that weather is a component of the environment of animals which effectively determines the limits to distribution and the abundance of some species. Short term and long term changes in weather determine short term and long term changes in distribution and abundance. That weather can be effective in determining the limits of abundance within the distribution of an animal has been doubted by some ecologists who believed that only "density-dependent" factors can "determine" the density of populations. Density dependent factors or as they have more recently been called "density-governing" factors are defined as those factors which "permit populations to grow when at relatively low densities, and oppose growth when the densities become relatively high" (see Nicholson). Weather is not classed as a "density governing" factor because it is claimed that it does not react to a change in density of animals. The upholders of this point of view maintain that in the absence of "density governing" factors populations would either grow without check or alternatively they would tend towards extinction.

We shall examine a partly hypothetical model, and illustrate it with examples, of how short term and long term changes in weather may influence the chance to survive and multiply in such a way as to prevent unlimited increase in numbers even in the absence of "density governing" factors. It will be shown in the same model that weather can operate in such a way that there will be little chance of extinction provided the fluctuations of weather are kept within limits which would need to be defined for each species. As these limits are approached the chance of extinction increases. Over a long period of time the chances of these limits being exceeded is greater than for a short period of time.

It is not contended that the numbers of all animals are determined primarily by weather nor that weather is more important than other components of environment. All components have a part to play. But in studying any one species it is usual to find that one component plays a primary role in determining numbers. Sometimes this is weather.

Weather is also a component of natural selection and so may play a part in determining the qualitative composition of a population. Selection through components of weather may change an animal's chance to survive and multiply and this will be reflected in changes in its distribution and abundance.

SHORT TERM CHANGES IN WEATHER

The grasshopper *Austroicetes cruciata* has a well defined distribution in south eastern Australia in a belt of country running roughly east to west. There is another grasshopper belt in western Australia which is separated from the eastern one by the Nullarbor desert. There the belt runs diagonally across the south western corner of the continent. . . . isopleths for moisture based on rainfall and evaporation. . . delineate quite nicely the distribution of the species. North of the distribution the country is too dry for the grasshopper to survive, south of the distribution it is too wet. . . . The contraction and expansion of the grasshopper belt in a north-south direction is associated with fluctuations of weather. Both these changes and the changes in abundance within the belt were studied by Andrewartha and Birch over a number of years. . . . From our understanding of these changes we built up a generalised diagram which summarises the situation [and] represents a section of the grasshopper belt from north to south. A central strip of country is inhabited permanently. Numbers there are likely to be higher than elsewhere. To the north and south the country is inhabited temporarily in sequences of favourable years. If we now select three localities within the grasshopper belt, one in the center, one in the north and one in the south, we might represent the change in abundance in time as in Figure 3. Locality A is a place where numbers are often high, locality B is a place which is unfavourably wet and numbers never so high. Locality C is a place which is so dry that grasshoppers become extinct in some years. Their presence in subsequent years is dependent upon dispersal from the south. . . . These changes are largely due to seasonal change in weather. Knowing the effect of weather on the survival of grasshoppers, Andrewartha and Birch were able to make an estimate of the chance, in each of these localities, of obtaining a sequence of years that would permit multiplication to plague numbers. At C the chance is extremely small. At A it is much greater. Conversely it would be true to say that the chance for survival and multiplication is small at B and C but high at A. This is a probabilistic way of looking at distribution and abundance. By introducing the idea of chance we have removed the necessity to consider whether temperature, rainfall and other components are "density-dependent" or "density-independent" factors. We do not deny the existence of density-dependent factors but we deny the assertion that populations can only be regulated by "density-dependent" factors. From the probabilistic point of view any component of environment might assume this role.

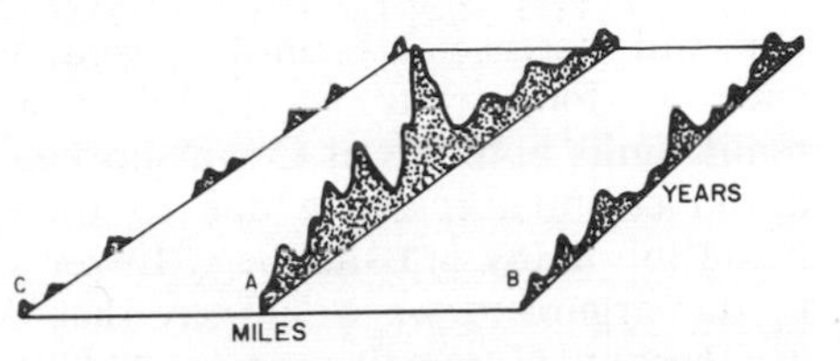

FIG. 3. *Hypothetical diagram, showing the change in mass of grasshoppers during many years in the localities marked A, B, and C, in Figure 2* [*deleted*]. (*After Andrewartha and Birch, 1954*).

Let us now look more closely at how weather determines numbers at A, B and C so that grasshoppers are never so common at B and C as at A. Those who do not think that weather can regulate numbers argue that at a place such as C the weather is tolerable, otherwise the animals would not be there at all. If tolerable, then numbers will increase at C until a resource such as food runs short. So what really limits numbers at C is a shortage of an essential resource due to there being too many grasshoppers. In reply to this argument we would say that if weather at C remained tolerable all the time, then to be sure, numbers would increase until food or some other resource became limiting. But the situation at C is much more complex and this complexity alters the argument. Two characteristics of natural environments which have not been considered in this argument have to be taken into account. These are (a) fluctuations in the favourableness of weather and in other components of environment which affect survival and multiplication and (b) spatial patchiness of the environment. In other words we have to consider the heterogeneity of the environment in time and in space.

Consider the situation at C (Fig.3) which is within the distribution of the grasshopper but near the northern boundary. . . . There is only one generation of grasshoppers each year; they lay their eggs late in spring. During the summer and winter only the egg stage is present. The curve shows how the mass of grasshoppers might vary over a five year period. Each year without exception there is a crash in numbers after increase in bio-mass in the spring. But the increase in bio-mass is not the cause of the crash. The cause of the crash is the hot dry summer which inevitably follows the favourable season of spring. The earliness and extent of the crash in numbers will be determined by the earliness and severity of the unfavourable period. Likewise the upper limit to numbers each year is determined by the length and favourableness of the spring and the severity of the previous season. In the second year the unfavourable season was so severe that the grasshoppers were completely wiped out before they laid any eggs. The chance of this happening is high in the northern extremity of the distribution though it must be quite small in the more central localities. It is to be noted that in the third year grasshoppers were again present. We shall suppose that they arrived by dispersal from a locality, some ten miles or so south, which was more hospitable to grasshoppers in the previous season. . . .

The first point our model illustrates is that in an area of extreme unfavourableness in which the weather is sometimes intolerable for grasshoppers, it is still possible for grasshoppers to be found there. This is by virture of the patchiness of the environment.

Let us next consider what prevented grasshoppers from increasing indefinitely in both the locality in the north . . . and in a locality further south. . . . When the nymphs first hatch they are not likely to be short of food because this is the season of the year when the grass is growing most strongly. When swarms were present, the later stages sometimes experienced a shortage of food, not because there was insufficient grass in the area, but because it dried up before the grasshoppers could complete their development. It will be necessary to consider the nature of the food shortage at this stage in a moment. There is good evidence that grasshoppers do not suffer from food shortage while the grass is mostly green. Sheep share the pastures with grasshoppers and it is the aim of farmers to have enough dry grass standing in their paddocks to carry their flocks through summer. During the plague years 1935 to 1939 the number of sheep living in the pastures almost doubled. If there had been a shortage of dry food the farmers would most certainly have removed them. In other words the grasshoppers always left enough grass to provide large stocks of dry grass in the summer.

The small amount of green food that is left at the end of the spring is related not to the number of grasshoppers but to the onset of the hot dry summer. It might be argued that the grasshoppers would then suffer from competition for the little food that was left. The green food that remained then consisted of short blades at the base of dried up tufts of grass. These green blades were sparsely scattered over many plants. The last grasshopper died of starvation before all the green food had disappeared. What was left it could not find at a rate fast enough to keep it alive. It is true that more grasshoppers will eat more food. But our observations convinced us that the total amount they ate was small in relation to what was available, even at the end of the season. Because grasshoppers find so little of the food that remains with the approach of summer the chance of a grasshopper finding food is independent of the number searching for it. This is the principle of the relative shortage of food described by Andrewartha and Birch. . . .

THE SELF-ADJUSTMENT OF POPULATIONS TO CHANGE

A. J. Nicholson—1957

Reprinted by permission of the author and publisher from Cold Spring Harbor Symposium on Quantitative Biology **22**: 153–172, 1957.

According to Nicholson, the density of a population is governed not by biotic and abiotic factors per se but by attributes of these elements (availability, accessibility, intensity, etc.). More important, however, is his contention that "the ability to adjust themselves to great changes in their environments" is inherent in all populations. The essence of this hypothesis and part of the empirical basis for it are found in this selection. The author is associated with the Commonwealth Scientific and Industrial Organization, Canberra, Australia.

For some years my method of approach to an understanding of population problems has been to use laboratory colonies of the Australian sheep-blowfly, *Lucilia cuprina* Wied., under precisely defined laboratory conditions. The method consists of introducing a small number of *L. cuprina* into a cage and, from then on, maintaining predetermined conditions constant, including the supply of such depletable requisites as food and water at a constant rate. The population is left entirely to its own devices and, apart from maintaining the predetermined conditions, the only action taken is to keep a careful day-to-day record of the numbers of individuals of some, at least, of the various developmental stages—supplementing this at times with other observations. . . .

L. cuprina is representative of the large group of animals which "scramble" for their food, the rate of supply of which is determined by factors other than the activity of the animals. With gross crowding such scrambling leads to much wastage of the governing requisite so that, with excessive numbers of animals, there is either excessive mortality or the fertility may be temporarily reduced below the replacement rate. This tends to produce violent oscillations in the size of the populations which are not caused by environmental fluctuations, and it generally limits the average density of the animals far below that which the supply of governing requisites could maintain if there were no wastage.

In contrast to this is the category of animals which "contest" for their limiting requisite. That is to say, each successful individual lays claim to a supply of requisites sufficient to maintain it, and to enable it to produce offspring. The unsuccessful individuals are denied access to critical requisites by their successful competitors. This kind of competition eliminates, or greatly reduces, the wastage of requisites, so permitting a relatively high density of animals to be maintained and, in addition, preventing such intraspecific oscillation as occurs in *L. cuprina*. There is room for only a certain limited number of individuals; consequently those which are unsuccessful in obtaining room "overflow" into less favourable parts of the environment from which critically important requisites are absent, or present in inadequate amounts. . . .

In the two categories of population regulation just discussed the amount and rate of production of the governing requisite, which is critical to the animals, is independent of their activities. There is another large and important category in which the activities of the animals not only influence the degree of depletion of their governing requisites, but also determine the amount produced. These are such phytophagous animals and predators as limit their own population densities by limiting the production of their host-plants or prey, thereby reducing these to the threshold levels, at which the enemies can find barely sufficient food to maintain their own numbers. . . . Note that "parasites" of the insect type are really predators, as their larvae eat their "hosts".

This category of population regulation is of exceptional interest because of the unexpected and varied results of interaction between animals and the organisms upon which they feed. The considerations which first caused me to consider population problems seriously conveniently illustrate the situation represented by this category.

Many years ago I was puzzled by the fact that the degree of infestation of citrus trees by scale insects appeared to be quite independent of the number of citrus trees in any particular area; for this indicated that the population of scale insects was directly influenced by the number of citrus trees—in spite of the fact that there was evidently space for far more scales on the foliage and branches, and that, as the citrus trees remained healthy, the food supply was presumably capable of supporting far more scale insects than it did. It occurred to me that the puzzling phenomenon could be due to the action of natural enemies, for the citrus trees not only provided food for the scale insects, but also constituted the area over which the enemies had to search. Simple considerations indicated that, if the number of scale insects was very high, large numbers of parasites would breed from them, and that these parasites, operating in the next generation, would collectively search the greater part of the foliage of the trees, so attacking most of the scale insects and causing their numbers to fall to a low level in the following generation. Continuing this kind of argument it became clear that the numbers of scale insects and of their natural enemies should produce effects upon one another which would always tend to reduce over-large populations, and to allow very small populations to increase.

The mechanism visualized was that, if few enemies searched a large area, each would spend most of its time exploring previously unsearched areas; whereas if the searching enemies were numerous, each would spend most of its time searching previously explored areas within which most of the scale insects would presumably have been attacked already. Assuming that the enemies were fairly evenly or randomly distributed over the foliage, it was easy to construct a curve which represented quantitatively the reduction in the success of the searching individuals in exploring previously unexplored areas, in which the unattacked scales would presumably lie. This I called the "competition curve." . . . Using this curve it was possible to examine a number of hypothetical arithmetical examples by assigning arbitrary "powers of increase" to the hosts and "areas of discovery" (which represent the searching abilities of the parasites) to the parasites.

To my astonishment, no matter how I varied the two basic properties, the arithmetical examples indicated that the reactions between the two kinds of insects, although always of the right kind to oppose, and to change the direction of the current displacements, gave rise to oscillations in the numbers of both hosts and parasites, and these grew in amplitude with time! In other words, this simple system of corrective reaction was over-violent and proved to be intrinsically unstable. Subsequently Bailey confirmed and extended these conclusions by the use of mathematics.

Thus, in this situation, density-induced reactions were produced in populations of both kinds of interacting animals which were of the right sign to counteract departures from the equilibrium position but they were over-violent, so causing successively greater and greater over- and undershooting of the equilibrium position. The growth in amplitude of the oscillations is probably related to the fact that two systems of oscillation are involved. The well known predator-prey oscillations of Volterra lead to systems of sustained oscillations which may be referred to as "coupled oscillations". . . as they are due to a linkage between the two changing populations. Each as it passes its equilibrium density alters the direction of change of the other population; but Volterra's populations consisted of hypothetical animals with the curious property that they interacted from the moment they were born, which means that they were born fully mature. In contrast to this, insect hosts and their parasites require a considerable time to develop, and changes in density induced by interaction produce their effects only after the lapse of a generation. This tends to give rise to "lag-oscillations", such as were observed in the *Lucilia cuprina* cultures. The superimposition of these lag-oscillations upon the coupled oscillations seems to be the likely cause of growth in amplitude of successive oscillations, and of the consequent instability of this system of interaction.

Two arithmetically calculated examples are given in Figure 9 of this type of system, each example representing the interaction of a specific host and a specific parasite. That is to say, increase in the host density is limited solely by the action of one particular species of parasite, and the parasite attacks hosts of this species only, and so limits its own density by restricting that of its host. It will be seen that the violence of reaction is greater in B than in A, which illustrates the general conclusion

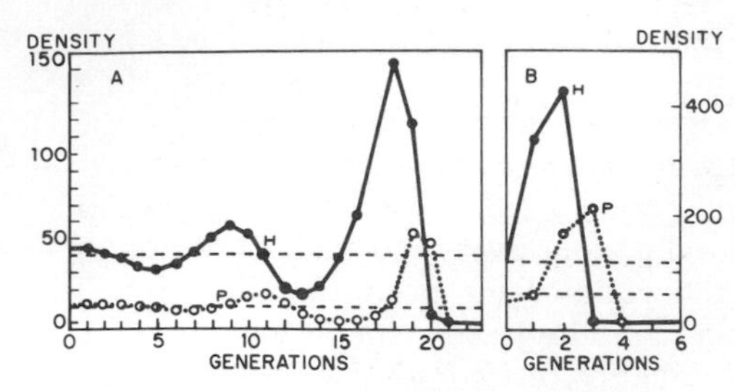

FIG. 9. *Calculated interspecific oscillations produced by interaction between a specific host and a specific parasite. Power of increase in A is 2, and in B it is 10 times per generation; all other properties and conditions are the same in the two systems illustrated. Heavy lines, host populations; dotted lines, parasite populations (shown at half the scale used for hosts); broken lines, steady densities.*

that the violence of oscillation mounts with increase in the "power of increase" of the host. . . . The magnitude of the "area of discovery" of the parasite does not influence the character of the oscillation. In both the examples given, it is assumed that initially one of the interacting species is at its equilibrium density whereas the other is displaced slightly from its equilibrium density. Only by making this assumption is it possible to show several successive oscillations for, otherwise, the violence of reaction is so great that one of the populations is quickly reduced to fractional numbers, and the other population follows—as is indicated in Figure 9 B. The graphs shown in Figure 9, and similar ones published elsewhere. . . are not intended to show what may be expected to happen to interacting hosts and parasites in nature, but simply to illustrate the probable underlying mechanism which leads to certain interesting events which are sometimes observed in nature. . . .

There is not sufficient time to discuss other categories of population regulation. . . I can only state that in all of these, just as in the three categories already discussed, it has been found that automatic compensatory mechanisms exist which permit the populations to adapt themselves to widely different circumstances by density-induced reactions. Because of much misunderstanding upon the point, I would like to stress that my investigations and theoretical considerations based upon them, do not imply that density governing reaction should operate upon a population at all times. At times populations may multiply without check, or their numbers may be progressively reduced over a period by adverse external factors, without there being any compensatory reaction during that period. In spite of this, it is necessary, and inevitable, that density-induced reaction should limit populations in relation to the prevailing environmental conditions from time to time at least, so determining the general levels of abundance from which the uncontrolled variations just spoken of may take place.

The foregoing considerations have shown that some kinds of animals, at least, induce reactions in their environments, and within their own populations, which bring about an automatic self-adjustment of their population densities at levels which are determined both by their own properties and by those of their environments. Theoretical considerations go farther than this . . . and indicate that no population can be persistent unless it has a mechanism of density-induced compensatory reaction to maintain it in being. . . .

COMMUNITY STRUCTURE, POPULATION CONTROL, AND COMPETITION

Nelson G. Hairston, Frederick E. Smith, and Lawrence B. Slobodkin 1960

Reprinted by permission of the authors and publisher from the American Naturalist **94**:421–425, 1960.

In spite of acknowledging limited application, proponents of given population models tend to discuss them as all inclusive. It is at that point that the model encounters difficulty. Part of this difficulty arises from the heterogeneity of organisms in contrast to the homogeneity of the populations which provide the empirical basis for most of the models. The general pattern of population control which is developed in this brief, persuasive argument is an attempt by these three University of Michigan ecologists to reconcile diverse points of view.

The methods whereby natural populations are limited in size have been debated with vigor during three decades, particularly during the last few years (see papers by Nicholson, Birch, Andrewartha, Milne, Reynoldson, and Hutchinson, and ensuing discussions in the Cold Spring Harbor Symposium, 1957). Few ecologists will deny the importance of the subject, since the method of regulation of populations must be known before we can understand nature and predict its behavior. Although discussion of the subject has usually been confined to single species populations, it is equally important in situations where two or more species are involved.

The purpose of this note is to demonstrate a pattern of population control in many communities which derives easily from a series of general, widely accepted observations. The logic used is not easily refuted. Furthermore, the pattern reconciles conflicting interpretations by showing that populations in different trophic levels are expected to differ in their methods of control.

Our first observation is that the accumulation of fossil fuels occurs at a rate that is negligible when compared with the rate of energy fixation through photosynthesis in the biosphere. Apparent exceptions to this observation, such as bogs and ponds, are successional stages, in which the failure of decomposition hastens the termination of the stage. The rate of accumulation when compared with that of photosynthesis has also been shown to be negligible over geologic time. . . .

If virtually all of the energy fixed in photosynthesis does indeed flow through the biosphere, it must follow that all organisms taken together are limited by the amount of energy fixed. In particular, the decomposers as a group must be food-limited, since by definition they comprise the trophic level which degrades organic debris. There is no a priori reason why predators, behavior, physiological changes induced by high densities, etc., could not limit decomposer populations. In fact, some decomposer populations may be limited in such ways. If so, however, others must consume the "left-over" food, so that the group as a whole remains food limited; otherwise fossil fuel would accumulate rapidly.

Any population which is not resource-limited must, of course, be limited to a level *below* that set by its resources.

Our next three observations are interrelated. They apply primarily to terrestrial communities. The first of these is that cases of obvious depletion of green plants by herbivores are exceptions to the general picture, in which the plants are abundant and largely intact. Moreover, cases of obvious mass destruction by meteorological catastrophes are exceptional in most areas. Taken together, these two observations mean that producers are neither herbivore-limited nor catastrophe-limited, and must therefore be limited by their own exhaustion of a resource. In many areas, the limiting resource is obviously light, but in arid regions water may be the critical factor, and there are spectacular cases of limitation through the exhaustion of a critical mineral. The final observation in this group is that there are temporary exceptions to the general lack of depletion of green plants by herbivores. This occurs when herbivores are protected either by man or natural events, and it indicates that the herbivores are able to deplete the vegetation whenever they become numerous enough, as in the cases of the Kaibab deer herd, rodent plagues, and many insect outbreaks. It therefore follows that the usual condition is for populations of herbivores *not* to be limited by their food supply.

The vagaries of weather have been suggested as an adequate method of control for herbivore populations. The best factual clues related to this argument are to be found in the analysis of the exceptional cases where terrestrial herbivores have become numerous enough to deplete the vegetation. This often occurs with introduced rather than native species. It is most difficult to suppose that a species had been unable to adapt so as to escape control by the weather to which it was exposed, and at the same time by sheer chance to be able to escape this control from weather to which it had not been previously exposed. This assumption is especially difficult when mutual invasions by different herbivores between two countries may in both cases result in pests. Even more difficult to accept, however, is the implication regarding the native herbivores. The assumption that the hundreds or thousands of species native to a forest have failed to escape from control by the weather despite long exposure and much selection, when an invader is able to defoliate without this past history, implies that "pre-adaptation" is more likely than ordinary adaptation. This we cannot accept.

The remaining general method of herbivore control is predation (in its broadest sense, including parasitism, etc.). It is important to note that this hypothesis is not denied by the presence of introduced pests, since it is necessary only to suppose that either their natural predators have been left behind, or that while the herbivore is able to exist in the new climate, its enemies are not. There are, furthermore, numerous examples of the direct effect of predator removal. The history of the Kaibab deer is the best known example, although deer across the northern portions of the country are in repeated danger of winter starvation as a result of protection and predator removal. Several rodent plagues have been attributed to the local destruction of predators. More recently, the extensive spraying of forests to kill caterpillars has resulted in outbreaks of scale insects. The latter are protected from the spray, while their beetle predators and other insect enemies are not.

Thus, although rigorous proof that herbivores are generally controlled by predation is lacking, supporting evidence is available, and the alternate hypothesis of control by weather leads to false or untenable implications.

The foregoing conclusion has an important implication in the mechanism of control of the predator populations. The predators and parasites, in controlling the populations of herbivores, must thereby limit their own resources, and as a group they must be food-limited. Although the populations of some carnivores are obviously limited by territoriality, this kind of internal check cannot operate for all carnivores taken together. If it did, the herbivores would normally expand to the point of depletion of the vegetation, as they do in the absence of their normal predators and parasites.

There thus exists either direct proof or a great preponderance of factual evidence that in terrestrial communities decomposers, producers, and predators, as whole trophic levels, are resource-limited in the classical density-dependent fashion. Each of these three can and does expand toward the limit of the appropriate resource. We may now examine the reasons why this is a frequent situation in nature.

Whatever the resource for which a set of terrestrial plant species compete, the competition ultimately expresses itself as competition for space. A community in which this space is frequently emptied through depletion by herbivores would run the continual risk of replacement by another assemblage of species in which the herbivores are held down in numbers by predation below the level at which they damage the vegetation. That space once held by a group of terrestrial plant species is not readily given up is shown by the cases where relict stands exist under climates no longer suitable for their return following deliberate or accidental destruction. Hence, the community in which herbivores are held down in numbers, and in which the producers are resource-limited will be the most persistent. The development of this pattern is less likely where high producer mortalities are inevitable. In lakes, for example, algal populations are prone to crash whether grazed or not. In the same environment, grazing depletion is much more common than in communities where the major producers are rooted plants.

A second general conclusion follows from the resource limitation of the species of three trophic levels. This conclusion is that if more than one species exists in one of these levels, they may avoid competition only if each species is limited by factors completely unutilized by any of the other species. It is a fact, of course, that many species occupy each level in most communities. It is also a fact that they are not sufficiently segregated in their needs to escape competition. Although isolated cases of non-overlap have been described, this has never been observed for an entire assemblage. Therefore, interspecific competition for resources exists among producers, among carnivores, and among decomposers.

It is satisfying to note the number of observations that fall into line with the foregoing deductions. Interspecific competition is a powerful selective force, and we should expect to find evidence of its operation. Moreover, the evidence should be most conclusive in trophic levels where it is necessarily present. Among decomposers we find the most obvious specific mechanisms for reducing populations of competitors. The abundance of antibiotic substances attests to the frequency with which these mechanisms have been developed in the trophic level in which interspecific competition is inevitable. The producer species are the next most likely to reveal evidence of competition, and here we find such phenomena as crowding, shading, and vegetational zonation.

Among the carnivores, however, obvious adaptations for interspecific competition are less common. Active competition in the form of mutual habitat-exclusion has been noted in the cases of flatworms and salamanders. The commonest situation takes the form of niche diversification as the result of interspecific competition. This has been noted in birds, salamanders and other groups of carnivores. Quite likely, host specificity in parasites and parasitoid insects is at least partly due to the influence of interspecific competition.

Of equal significance is the frequent occurrence among herbivores of apparent exceptions to the influence of density-dependent factors. The grasshoppers described by Birch and the thrips described by Davidson and Andrewartha are well known examples. Moreover, it is among herbivores that we find cited examples of coexistence without evidence of competition for resources, such as the leafhoppers reported by Ross and the psocids described by Broadhead. It should be pointed out that in these latter cases coexistence applies primarily to an identity of food and place, and other aspects of the niches of these organisms are not known to be identical.

THE STUDY OF COMMUNITIES

At least as early as the time of Theophrastus it was recognized that different species show particular spatial relationships in groupings of one sort or another. The existence of assemblages and a seeming appearance of pattern in their composition and distribution have provided a considerable arena for ecological investigation.

Stimulated and oriented largely by the Danish botanist Eugene Warming at the turn of the century, the study of communities has been directed primarily towards plants. Considerable effort has been expended in the analysis of vegetational units (composition, physiognomy, stratification, distribution, etc.) and the investigation of such dynamic events as phenological and successional change. These studies on the general nature and composition of the plant community with respect to time and space were involved in reciprocal stimulation from concurrent theoretical developments and philosophical discussions.

Animal community studies were given major thrust by the English ecologist Charles Elton in the 1920's. Elton's concept of key industry animals functioning in integrating the community through a food chain focused attention on the relations of numbers of organisms and the nature of food chains and ecological niches. These aspects of community study are covered in the section on ecosystems.

REPORT ON THE MOLLUSCA AND RADIATA OF THE AEGEAN SEA, AND ON THEIR DISTRIBUTION CONSIDERED AS BEARING ON GEOLOGY

Edward Forbes—1844

Reprinted by permission of the publisher from Report of the British Association for the Advancement of Science for 1843, pp. 130–193, 1844.

One of the earliest clear recognitions of the existence of particular assemblages of different species was in this report by Forbes, who was Professor of Botany at Kings College, London. This study is quite remarkable in its description of spatially distributed communities, or what Forbes called "provinces of depth," and the realization of the dynamic interaction of abiotic and biotic forces in yielding the observed distribution.

The distribution of marine animals is determined by three great primary influences, and modified by several secondary or local ones. The primary influences are climate, sea-composition and depth, corresponding to the three great primary influences which determine the distribution of land animals, namely climate, mineral structure and elevation. The first of these primary marine influences is uniform in the eastern Mediterranean. From Candia to Lycia, from Thessaly to Egypt, we find the same species of Mollusca and Radiata assembled together under similar circumstances. The uniformity of distribution throughout the Mediterranean is very surprising to a British naturalist, accustomed as we are to find distinct species of the same genera, *climatally representative* of each other, in the Irish and North seas, and on the shores of Devon and Zetland. The absence of certain species in the Aegean which are characteristic of the western Mediterranean, is rather to be attributed to sea-composition than to climate. The pouring in of the waters of the Black Sea must influence the fauna of the Aegean and modify the constitution of its waters. To such cause we must attribute the remarkable fact that with few exceptions individuals of the same species are dwarfish compared with their analogues in the western Mediterranean. This is seen most remarkably in some of the more abundant species, such as *Pecten opercularis*, *Venerupis irus*, *Venus fasciata*, *Cardita trapezia*, *Modiola barbata*, and the various kinds of *Bulla*, *Rissoa*, *Fusus*, and *Pleurotoma*, all of which seemed as if they were but miniature representatives of their more western brethren.

To the same cause may probably be attributed the paucity of *Medusae* and of corals and corallines. Sponges only seem to gain by it. The influence of depth is very evident in the general character of the Aegean fauna, in which the aborigines of the deeper recesses of the sea play an important part numerically, both as to amount of species and individuals.

The secondary influences which modify the distribution of animals in the Aegean are many. First in importance ranks the character of the sea-bottom, which, though uniform in the lowest explored region, is very variable in all the others. According as rock, sand, mud, weedy or gravelly ground prevails, so will the numbers of the several genera and species vary. The presence of the sponges of commerce often depends on the rising up of peaks of rock in the deep water near the coast. As mud forms by much the most extensive portion of the bottom of the sea, bivalve Mollusca abound more individually though not specifically than univalves. As the deepest sea-bottom is of fine mud, the delicate shells of Pteropoda and Nucleobranchiata are for the most part only preserved there. Where the bottom is weedy we find the naked Mollusca more numerous than elsewhere; where rocky, the strong-shelled Gasteropoda and active Cephalopoda. Few species either of Mollusca or Radiata inhabit all bottoms indifferently.

The nature of the sea-bottom is mainly determined by the geological structure of the neighbouring land. The general character of the fauna of the Aegean is in a great measure dependent on the great tracts of scaglia which border it, and of which so many of its islands are formed. The degradation of this cretaceous limestone fills the sea with a white chalky sediment, especially favourable to the development of Mollusca. Where the coast is formed of scaglia numerous marine animals abound which are scarce on other rocks. The genera *Lithodomus* and *Clavagella* among Mollusca, the *Cladocora caespitosa* among Zoophytes, are abundant in such localities only.

In a report on the distribution of British terrestrial and fluviatile Mollusca, which I had the honour of presenting to the Association at Birmingham, I asserted that a remarkable negative influence was exercised by serpentine on the distribution of pulmoniferous Mollusca. This I have had peculiarly favourable opportunities of confirming in the Aegean, where whole islands being formed of serpentine, the almost total absence of those animals which are abundant on the islands of other mineral structure is most striking. But I found further, that not only does serpentine exercise a negative influence on air-breathing Mollusca, but also on marine species. An extensive tract on the coast of Lycia and Caria, indented with deep and land-locked bays, is formed of that rock. In such bays, with the exception of a few littoral species which live on all rocks, we find an almost total absence of Testacea; whilst in correspondent bays in the neighbouring districts, formed of scaglia, of saccharine marble, and even of slate, we find an abundance of Testacea, so that it can hardly be doubted that the absence or scarcity of shelled Mollusca in such case is owing to negative influence exercised by the serpentine. *The outline of the coast* is evidently an important element in such influences, or in modifying it.

Tides and currents in most seas are important modifying influences. In the Aegean the former are so slight as scarcely to affect the fauna; the latter, in places, must be powerful agents in the transportation of species and of the spawn of marine animals. Their action, however, like that of storms, appears materially to affect the upper regions only; the transportation of the species of one region into another seldom extending further than that of the regions immediately bounding that in which it is indigenous. Certain species, such as the *Rissoae*, which live on sea-weed, may occasionally fall to the bottom region, of which they are not true natives, and may live for a time there, but such cases appear to be rare, and the sources of fallacy from *natural transportation* are fewer than might be imagined at first thought, and in most cases have arisen rather from the form of the coast than from currents. Thus where the coast-line is very steep, the sea suddenly deepening to 60 or 70 fathoms close to the rocks, limpets, littoral *Trochi* and other shells, when they die, fall to the bottom, and are found along with the exuviae of the natural inhabitants of those depths.

Several instances of this occurred during dredging.

The *influx of fresh water*, whether continual, as where a river empties itself into the sea, or temporary, as on the coast of Asia Minor during the rainy season, when every little ravine becomes suddenly filled with a raging torrent, bearing down trees and great masses of rock, and charged with thick mud, frequently modifies the marine fauna of certain districts very considerably. The first generates great muddy tracts, which present a fauna peculiar to themselves: the second, though of short duration, deposits detached patches of conglomerate, and by the sudden settling of the fluviatile mud forms thin strata at the bottom of the sea, often containing the remains of terrestrial and fluviatile animals, soon to be covered over by marine deposits with very different contents. From the influx of a great river we may have tropical or subtropical, terrestrial or fluviatile forms mingled with temperate marine . . . .

PROVINCES OF DEPTH

There are eight well-marked regions of depth in the eastern Mediterranean, each characterised by its peculiar fauna, and when there are plants, by its flora. These regions are distinguished from each other by the associations of the species they severally include. Certain species in each are found in no other, several are found in one region which do not range into the next above, whilst they extend to that below, or *vice versa*. Certain species have their maximum of development in each zone, being most prolific in individuals in that zone in which is their maximum, and of which they may be regarded as especially characteristic. Mingled with the true natives of every zone are stragglers, owing their presence to the action of the secondary influences which modify distribution. Every zone has also a more or less general mineral character, the sea-bottom not being equally variable in each, and becoming more and more uniform as we descend. The deeper zones are greatest in extent; so that whilst the first or most superficial is but 12, the eighth, or lowest, is above 700 feet in perpendicular range. Each zone is capable of subdivision in smaller belts, but these are distinguished for the most part by negative characters derived from the cessation of species, the range of which is completed, and from local changes in the nature of the sea-bottom . . . .

The eight regions in depth are the scene of incessant change. The death of the individuals of the several species inhabiting them, the continual accession, deposition and sometimes washing away of sediment and coarser deposits, the action of the secondary influences and the changes of elevation which appear to be periodically taking place in the eastern Mediterranean, are ever modifying their character. As each region shallows or deepens, its animal inhabitants must vary in specific associations, for the depression which may cause one species to dwindle away and die will cause another to multiply. The animals themselves, too, by their over-multiplication, appear to be the cause of their own specific destruction. As the influence of the nature of sea-bottom determines in a great measure the species present on that bottom, the multiplication of individuals dependent on the rapid reproduction of successive generations of Mollusca, &c. will of itself change the ground and render it unfit for the continuation of life in that locality until a new layer of sedimentary matter, uncharged with living organic contents, deposited on the bed formed by the exuviae of the exhausted species, forms a fresh soil for similar or other animals to thrive, attain their maximum, and from the same cause die off. This, I have reason to believe, is the case, from my observations in the British as well as the Mediterranean seas. The geologist will see in it an explanation of the phænomenon of interstratification of fossiliferous and non-fossiliferous beds.

AN OYSTER-BANK IS A BIOCÖNOSE, OR A SOCIAL COMMUNITY

Karl Möbius—1877

Reprinted from Die Auster und die Austerwirthschaft. Berlin, Wiegundt, Hempel, and Parey, 1877. In Report of the U.S. Commission of Fisheries, translated by H. J. Rice, pp. 683–751, 1880.

By proposing the term biocönosis to describe a "community of living beings," Möbius clearly recognized that the species involved had something in common. Möbius' discussion is decidedly modern in its conception of interaction and regulation within the community as well as between the living community and its nonliving environment; this latter aspect is less well identified, however.

. . . The territory of an oyster-bed is not inhabited by oysters alone but also by other animals. Over the Schleswig-Holstein sea-flats, and also along the mouths of English rivers, I have observed that the oyster-beds are richer in all kinds of animal life than any other portion of the sea-bottom. As soon as the oystermen have emptied out a full dredge upon the deck of their vessel, one can see nimble pocket-crabs (*Carcinus mænas*) and slow horn-crabs (*Hyas aranea*) begin to work their way out of the heap of shells and living oysters, and try to get to the water once more. Old abandoned snail-shells begin to move about, caused by the hermit-crabs (*Pagarus bernhardus*), which have taken up their residence in them, trying to creep out of the heap with their dwelling. Spiral-shelled snails (*Buccinum undatum*) stretch their bodies as far out of the shell as they can, and twist from side to side, trying, with all their power, to roll themselves once more into the water. Red starfish (*Asteracanthion rubens*), with five broad arms, lie flat upon the deck, not moving from the place, although their hundreds of bottle-shaped feet are in constant motion. Sea-urchins (*Echinus miliaris*), of the size of a small apple, bristling with greenish spines, lie motionless in the heap. Here and there a ring-worm (*Nereis pelagica*), of a changeable bluish color, slips out of the mass of partially dead, partially living, animals. Black edible mussels (*Mytilus edulis*) and white cockles (*Cardium edule*) lie there with shells as firmly closed as are those of the oysters. Even the shells of the living oysters are inhabited. Barnacles (*Balanus crenatus*), with tent-shaped, calcareous shells and tendril-shaped feet, often cover the entire surface of one of the valves. Frequently the shells are bedecked with yellowish tassels a span or more in length, each of which is a community of thousands of small gelatinous bryozoa (*Alcyonidium gelatinosum*), or they are overgrown by a yellowish sponge (*Halichondria panicea*), whose soft tissue contains fine silicious spicules. Upon many beds the oysters are covered with thick clumps of sand which are composed of the tubes of small worms (*Sabellaria anglica*). These tubes, called "sand-rolls," resemble organ-pipes, and are formed from grains of sand cemented into shape by means of slime from the skin of the worm. The shell forms a firm support upon which the worms can thus live close together in a social community. Upon certain beds near the south point of the island of Sylt, where the finest-flavored oysters of our sea-flats are to be found, there lives upon the oyster-shells a species of tube-worm (*Pomatoceros triqueter*) whose white, calcareous, three-sided tube is very often twisted about like a great italic *S*. The shells of many oysters upon these beds also carry what are called "sea-hands" (*Alcyonium digitatum*), which are white or yellow communities of polyps of the size and shape of a clumsy glove. Often the oyster-shells are also covered over with a brownish, clod-like mass, which consists of branched polyps (*Eudendrium rameum* and *Sertularia pumila*), or they may be covered with tassels of yellow stems which are nearly a finger long and have at their distal ends reddish polyp-heads (*Tubularia indivisa*). Among these polyps, and extending out beyond them, are longer stems, which bear light yellow or brown polyp-cups (*Sertularia argentea*). Within the substance of the shell itself animals are also found. Very often the shells are penetrated from the outside to the innermost layer, upon which the mantle of the living oyster lies, by a boring sponge (*Clione celata*), and in the spaces between the layers of the shell in old oysters is found a greenish-brown worm (*Dodecaceræa concharum*), armed with bristles, and bearing twelve large tentacles upon its neck. I once took off and counted, one by one, all the animals living upon two oysters. Upon one I found 104 and upon the other 221 animals of three different species. The dredge also at times brings up fish, although it is not very well adapted for catching them. Soles (*Platessa vulgaris*), which seek by jumping to get out of the vessel and once more into the water, stone-picks (*Aspidophorus cataphractus*), and sting-rays (*Raja clavata*), which strike about with their tails, are abundant upon the oyster-banks. Besides those already mentioned, there are many other larger animals which are taken less frequently in the dredge. There are also a host of smaller animals covered up by the larger ones, and which can be seen only with a magnifying glass. Very few plants grow upon the banks. Upon only a single one of the oyster-beds of the sea-flats has eel-grass (*Zostera marina*) taken root. Upon other beds reddish-brown algæ (*Floridiæ*) are found, and, floating in the water which flows over the beds, occur microscopic algæ (*Desmidiæ* and *Diatomaceæ*), which serve as nourishment to the oysters. If the dredge is thrown out and dragged over the sea-flats between the oyster-beds, fewer and also different animals will be found upon this muddy bottom than upon the sand. Every oyster-bed is thus, to a certain degree, a community of living beings, a collection of species, and a massing of individuals, which find here everything necessary for their growth and continuance, such as suitable soil, sufficient food, the requisite percentage of salt, and a temperature favorable to their development. Each species which lives here is represented by the greatest number of individuals which can grow to maturity subject to the conditions which surround them, for among all species the number of individuals which arrive at maturity at each breeding period is much smaller than the number of germs produced at that time. The total number of mature individuals of all the species living together in any region is the sum of the survivors of all the germs which have been produced at all past breeding or brood periods; and this sum of matured germs represents a certain quantum of life which enters into a certain number of individuals, and which, as does all life, gains permanence by means of transmission. Science possesses, as yet, no word by which such a community of living beings may be designated; no word for a community where the sum of species and individuals, being mutually limited and selected under the average external conditions of life, have, by means of transmission, continued in possession of a certain definite territory. I propose the word *Biocœnosis** for such a community. Any change in any of the relative factors of a biocönose produces changes in other factors of the same. If, at any time, one of the external conditions of life should deviate for a long time from its ordinary mean, the entire biocönose, or community, would be transformed. It would also be transformed, if the number of individuals of a particular species increased or diminished through the instrumentality of man, or if one species entirely disappeared from, or a new species entered into, the community. When the rich beds of Cancale, Rochefort, Marennes, and Oléron were deprived of great masses of oysters, the young broods of the cockles and edible mussels which lived there had more space upon which to settle, and there was more food at their disposal than before, hence a greater number were enabled to arrive at maturity than in former times. The biocönose of those French oyster-banks was thus entirely changed by means of over fishing, and oysters cannot again cover the ground of these beds with such vast numbers as formerly until the cockles and edible mussels are again reduced in number to their former restricted limits, because the ground is already occupied and the food all appropriated. The biocönose allows itself to be transformed in favor of the oyster, by taking away the mussels mentioned above, and at the same time protecting the oysters so that the young may become securely established in the place thus made free for them. Space and food are necessary as the first requisites of every social community, even in the great seas. Oyster-beds are formed only upon firm ground which is free from mud, and if upon such ground the young swarming oysters become attached in great numbers close together, as happened upon the artificial receptacles in the Bay of Saint-Brieux, their growth is very much impeded, since the shell of one soon comes in contact with that of another, and they are thus unable to grow with perfect freedom. Not only are they impeded in growth in this manner, but each oyster can obtain less nourishment when placed close together than when lying far apart. . . .

In our seas, with their equitable temperature, a mild winter, followed by a spring and summer with the temperature much higher than usual during spawning time, is especially favorable to the production of a vast number of embryos. All living-members of a social community hold the balance with their organization to the physical conditions of their biocönose, for they live and propagate notwithstanding the influence of all external attractions, and notwithstanding all assaults upon the continuance of their individuality. Although every species is differently organized, in each the different forces act together for the growth and maintenance of the individual, and although each species has from this fact its own

*From *βίος*, life, and *κοινόειν*, to have something in common.

organic equivalent, yet they all possess the same (balancing) power for the totality of the external conditions of life of their biocönose. Hence all species must respond to a deviation in the conditions of life from the ordinary mean by a corresponding action of their forces, so that their efficacy may increase or diminish uniformly. If favorable temperature makes one species more fruitful, it will, at the same time, increase the fertility of all the others. If more young oysters exist upon an oyster-bed because the old ones receive more warmth and food than during ordinary years, then the snails, crabs, sea-urchins, and star-fish, and all other species living together upon the bank, will also produce more young, as repeated observations have shown to be the case. But since there is neither room nor food enough in such a place for the maturing of all of the excessively large number of germs, the sum of individuals in the community soon returns to its former mean. The surplus which nature has produced by the augmentation of one of the biocönotic forces is thus destroyed by a combination of all the forces, and the biocönotic equilibrium is by this means soon restored again. Where it is possible for one to furnish suitable ground and food for an excessive number of young germs, a greater proportion of them can arrive at maturity than in an entirely natural biocönose . . . .

. . . Every biocönotic territory has, during each period of generation, the highest measure of life which can be produced and maintained there. All the organic material which is there ready to be assimilated will be entirely used up by the beings which are procreated in each such territory. Hence at no place which is capable of maintaining life is there still left any organizable material for spontaneous generation. If, in a biocönose the number of individuals which arrive at maturity would be maintained at the highest point, even though the number of breeding individuals is being artificially lessened, the natural causes which act towards the destruction of the embryos must be diminished at the same time. . . .

OECOLOGY OF PLANTS, AN INTRODUCTION TO THE STUDY OF PLANT COMMUNITIES

Eugene Warming—1909

Reprinted by permission of the publisher from the translation by Percy Groom and Isaac Balfour. Oxford, Clarendon Press, pp. 1–3, 5–6, 12–13, 131–133, 1909.

In spite of the earlier results and suggestions of community studies on animals, the impetus to and direction of community ecology came primarily through the Danish botanist Warming. In his discussion of "Oecological plant-geography" Warming formulated the several basic questions to which community ecology has given much of its attention since the turn of the century.

CHAPTER I. FLORISTIC AND OECOLOGICAL PLANT-GEOGRAPHY

Plant-geography deals with the distribution of plants upon the earth, and with the principles determining this. We may regard this distribution from two different standpoints, and accordingly may divide the subject into two branches, *floristic plant geography* and *oecological plant-geography;* but these are merely different aspects of the same science, touching at many points and occasionally merging into one another.

Floristic plant-geography is concerned with—

1. The compilation of a 'Flora', that is, a list of species growing within a larger or smaller area. . . .
2. The division of the earth's surface into natural floristic tracts . . . according to their affinities . . . .
3. The sub-division of the larger natural floristic tracts . . . and the precise definition of these.
4. The discussion of the limits of distribution of species, genera, and families. . . .

The thoughtful investigator will not remain content with the mere recognition of facts; he will seek after their *causes.* These are, in part, *modern* (geognostic, topographical, and climatic), and, in part, *historical.* . . .

Oecological plant-geography has entirely different objects in view:—

It teaches us how plants or plant-communities adjust their forms and modes of behaviour to actually operating factors, such as the amounts of available water, heat, light, nutriment, and so forth.

A casual glance shows that species by no means dispose their individuals uniformly over the whole area in which they occur, but group them into communities of very varied physiognomy. Oecology seeks—

1. To find out which species are commonly associated together upon similar habitats (stations). . . .
2. To sketch the physiognomy of the vegetation and the landscape. . . .
3. To answer the questions—
   Why each species has its own special habit and habitat,
   Why the species congregate to form definite communities,
   Why these have a characteristic physiognomy. . . .
4. To investigate the problems concerning the economy of plants, the demands that they make on their environment, and the means that they employ to utilize the surrounding conditions and to adapt their external and internal structure and general form for that purpose. We thus come to the

consideration of the *growth-forms* of plants.

CHAPTER II. GROWTH-FORMS

Every species must be in harmony, as regards both its external and internal construction, with the natural conditions under which it lives; and when these undergo a change to which it cannot adapt itself, it will be expelled by other species or exterminated. Consequently one of the most weighty matters of oecological plant-geography is to gain an understanding of the *epharmony* of species. This may be termed its *growth-form* in contradistinction to its *systematic form*. It reveals itself especially in the habit, and in the form and duration, of the nutritive organs (in the structure of the foliage-leaf and of the whole vegetative shoot, in the duration of life of the individual, and so forth), but shows to a less extent in the reproductive organs. This subject leads us into deep morphological, anatomical, and physiological investigations; it is very difficult, yet very alluring; but only in few cases can its problems be satisfactorily solved at the present time. Thus we impinge upon the problem of the origin of different species.

But difficulty is imparted to the question under discussion by the circumstance that, not only is a species changed in form by external factors and capable of adapting itself to these, but each species is also endowed with certain hereditary tendencies, which, for inherent but unknown causes, evoke morphological characters that cannot be correlated with the present environment and are consequently inexplicable. These inherent tendencies, differing as they do according to systematic affinity, render it possible for different species, in their evolution under the influence of identical factors, *to achieve the same object by the most diverse methods*. While one species may adapt itself to a dry habitat by means of a dense coating of hairs, another may in the same circumstances produce not a single hair, but may elect to clothe itself with a sheet of wax, or to reduce its foliage and assume a succulent stem, or it may become ephemeral in its life-history. . . .

Just as species are the units in systematic botany, so are growth-forms the units in oecological botany. It is therefore of some practical importance to test the possibility of founding and naming a limited number of growth-forms upon true oecological principles. It cannot be sufficiently insisted that the greatest advance, not only in biology in its wider sense, but also in oecological phyto-geography, will be the oecological interpretation of the various growth-forms: from this ultimate goal we are yet far distant. . . .

Growth-forms may be arranged in the following six main classes, namely:

1. Heterotrophic.
2. Aquatic.
3. Muscoid.
4. Lichenoid.
5. Lianoid.
6. All other autonomous land-plants.

Heterotrophic growth-forms are shown by all holosaprophytes and holoparasites, which are undoubtedly derived from autophytes and are degenerate in form and structure. Hemi-saprophytes and hemi-parasites, on the contrary, are under the dominance of chlorophyll and exhibit the same rich diversity of form as other green plants.

Aquatic growth-forms differ from those shown by land-plants so widely as regards their morphology, anatomy, and physiology, that they must be regarded as constituting a separate class.

The muscoid and lichenoid growth-forms are seen, almost only, in mosses and lichens. Their powers of enduring extreme loss of water and of rapidly replacing this by means of absorption over the whole free surface, are oecologically very important. Associated with these characters are a number of others. The distinction between the muscoid and lichenoid types lies in the method of nutrition, as autotrophic and symbiotic respectively.

The lianoid growth-form is mainly determined by social conditions, and shows peculiar oecological and physiological characters. . . .Epiphytes, on the contrary, form an edaphic community of autotrophic land-plants including many different types.

The sixth class includes the growth-forms adopted by all the remaining autotrophic land-plants that contain chlorophyll and, as regards nutrition, are independent of other plants, and are thus *autonomous*. The growth-forms of Pteridophyta are included here, although these differ so widely from those of Spermophyta as regards their reproductive organs. . . .

Oecological botany has further to investigate the natural plant-communities, which usually include many species of extremely varied growth-form.

Certain species group themselves into natural associations, that is to say, into communities which we meet with more or less frequently, and which exhibit the same combination of growth-forms and the same facies. As examples in Northern Europe may be cited a meadow with its grasses and perennial herbs, or a beech-forest with its beech-trees and all the species usually accompanying these. Species that form a community must either practise the same economy, making approximately the same demands on its environment (as regards nourishment, light, moisture, and so forth), or one species present must be dependent for its existence upon another species, sometimes to such an extent that the latter provides it with what is necessary or even best suited to it (Oxalis Acetosella and saprophytes which profit from the shade of the beech and from its humus soil); a kind of symbiosis seems to prevail between such species. In fact, one often finds, as in beech-forests, that the plants growing under the shade and protection of other species, and belonging to the most diverse families, assume growth-forms that are very similar to one another, but essentially different from those of the forest-trees, which, in their turn, often agree with one another.

Oecological plant-geography has also to inquire into the kinds of natural communities in existence, their special methods of utilizing their resources, and the frequent intimate association together of species differing in growth-form and economy. The physical and other characters of the habitat play a fundamental part in these matters. . . .

The oecological analysis of a plant-community leads to the recognition of the growth-forms composing it as its ultimate units. From what has just been said in regard to growth-forms it follows that species of very diverse physiognomy can very easily occur together in the same natural community. But beyond this, as already indicated, species differing widely, not only in physiognomy but also in their whole economy, may be associated. We may therefore expect to find both great variety of form and complexity of inter-relations among the species composing a natural community; as an example we may cite the richest of all types of communities—the tropical rain-forest. It may also be noted that the physiognomy of a community is not necessarily the same at all times of the year, the distinction sometimes being caused by a rotation of species. . . .

The different communities, it need hardly be stated, are scarcely ever sharply marked off from one another. Just as soil, moisture, and other external conditions are connected by the most gradual transitions, so likewise are the plant-communities, especially in cultivated lands. In addition, the same species often occur in several widely different communities; for example, Linnaea borealis grows not only in coniferous forests, but also in birch-woods, and even high above the tree-limit on the mountains of Norway and on the fell-fields of Greenland. It appears that different combinations of external factors can replace one another and bring into existence approximately the same community, or at least can satisfy equally well one and the same species, and that, for instance, a moist climate often completely replaces the forest-shade of dry climates.

It is evident that all these circumstances render very difficult the correct scientific interpretation, delimitation, diagnosis, and systematic classification of plant communities, especially when we consider the condition of our present knowledge—for we have only just commenced to investigate growth-forms and communities, and what we do not know seems infinite. Another difficulty, to which allusion has already been made, is to assign suitable names to the more or less comprehensive, principal or subordinate, plant-communities occurring on the Earth and imparting to the landscapes entirely different physiognomies. Nor is it easy to estimate the true significance of floristic distinctions. . . .

OECOLOGICAL CLASSIFICATION

The foregoing chapters have made it clear that the distinctions between water-plants and land-plants are deep-seated, and concern the external form as well as the internal structure. Plant-communities must therefore be grouped in the first place into aquatic and terrestrial; but between these there is no sharp boundary, for there is a group of plants, marsh-plants (*helophytes*), which, like water-plants, develop their lower parts (roots, rhizomes, and, to some extent, leaves) in water or at least in soaking soil, but have their assimilatory organs mainly adapted to existence in air, as is the case with land-plants to which they are closely allied. Helophytes give rise to special forms of communities. Yet we must include among water-plants all those plants that, like Nymphaeaceae, approximate to land-plants in so far as they have floating-leaves, which are more or less adapted to existence in air, but are nevertheless mainly designed for existence upon water.

It has already been shown that land-plants exhibit many grades of adaptation to their mode of life in contact with air, and that those which encounter the greatest difficulties in regard to securing water are termed *xerophytes;* while others are described as *mesophytes* because in some respects they stand midway between the two extremes, hydrophytes and xerophytes. The differentiation of the land-plant in one or the other direction is decided by the oecological factors, edaphic and climatic, that prevail in the *station* or *habitat*. But edaphic and climatic factors cannot be regarded separately: the plant-community is always the product of both together. The nature of a soil is also influenced by climate, and it is incontestible that climate (rainfall) calls forth the wide differences between, say, desert and tropical rain-forest. But it is far from being true that climate alone calls into existence the different communities of plants which will hereafter be defined as *formations*. Characters of the soil are of supreme importance in determining the production of formations, and they must therefore be the foundation of oecological classification. Clements, with reason, has objected to Schimper's scheme of distinguishing between climatic and edaphic formations, if indeed it was Schimper's meaning that a sharp distinction is throughout possible, and that both groups of factors are of equal potency....

When endeavouring to arrange all land-plants, omitting marsh-plants, into comprehensive groups, we meet with, first, some communities that are evidently influenced in the main by the physical and chemical characters of soil which determine the amount of water therein; secondly, other communities in which extreme climatic conditions and fluctuations, seasonal distribution of rain, and the like, decide the amount of water in soil and character of vegetation. In accordance with these facts, land-plants may be ranged into groups, though in a very uncertain manner. The prevailing vagueness in this grouping *is* due to the fact *that oecology* is *only in its infancy,* and that *very few* detailed investigations of plant-communities have been conducted, the published descriptions of vegetation being nearly always one-sided and floristic, as well as very incomplete and unsatisfactory from an oecological standpoint. . . .

THE ECOLOGICAL RELATIONS OF THE VEGETATION ON THE SAND DUNES OF LAKE MICHIGAN

Henry C. Cowles—1899

Reprinted from the Botanical Gazette **27**: 95–117, 167–175, 1899.

Of the several characteristics of communities, the phenomenon of succession has had considerable study and has provided the basis for much theoretical speculation. Cowles' paper is one of the classic early ones dealing with the topic. He recognized succession to be a dynamic process and in this descriptively analytical report he attempts to translate the static scene into an ongoing phenomenon. Cowles, along with C. B. Davenport, C. A. Whitman, and C. M. Child and such graduate students as C. C. Adams and V. E. Shelford, constituted a vigorous "school" of ecology at the University of Chicago at the turn of the century, the influence of which continues in various guises today.

. . . The ecologist employs the methods of physiography, regarding the flora of a pond or swamp or hillside not as a changeless landscape feature, but rather as a panorama, never twice alike. The ecologist, then, must study the order of succession of the plant societies in the development of a region, and he must endeavor to discover the laws which govern the panoramic changes. Ecology, therefore, is a study in dynamics. For its most ready application, plants should be found whose tissues and organs are actually changing at the present time in response to varying conditions. Plant formations should be found which are rapidly passing into other types by reason of a changing environment.

These requirements are met *par excellence* in a region of sand dunes. Perhaps no topographic form is more unstable than a dune. Because of this instability plant societies, plant organs, and plant tissues are obliged to adapt themselves to a new mode of life within years rather than centuries, the penalty for lack of adaptation being certain death. The sand dunes furnish a favorable region for the pursuit of ecological investigations because of the comparative absence of the perplexing problems arising from previous vegetation. Any plant society is the joint product of present and past environmental conditions, and perhaps the latter are much more potent than most ecologists have thought. As will be shown in another place, even the sand dune floras are often highly modified by preexisting conditions, but on the whole the physical forces of the present shape the floras as we find them. The advancing dune buries the old plant societies of a region, and with their death there pass away the influences which contributed so largely to their making. In place of the rich soil which had been accumulating by centuries of plant and animal decay, and in place of the complex reciprocal relations between the plants, as worked out by a struggle of centuries, the advance of a dune makes all things new. By burying the past, the dune offers to plant life a world for conquest, subject almost entirely to existing physical conditions...

A plant society is defined as a group of plants living together in a common habitat and subjected to similar life conditions. The term is taken to be the English equivalent of Warming's *Plantesamfund*, translated into the German as *Pflanzenverein.* The term formation, as used by Drude and others, is more comprehensive, in so far as it is not synonymous. It may be well to consider the individual habitat groups in a given locality as plant societies, while all of these groups taken together comprise a formation of that type, thus giving to the word formation a value similar to its familiar geological application. For example, one might refer to particular sedge swamp societies near Chicago, or, on the other hand, to the sedge swamp formation as a whole; by this application formation becomes a term of generic value, plant society of specific value. . . .

In the following pages an attempt is made to arrange the plant societies in the order of development, the author's belief being that this order more faithfully expresses genetic relationships than any other. In the historical development of a region the primitive plant societies pass rapidly or slowly into others; at first the changes are likely to be rapid, but as the plant assemblage more and more approaches the climax type of the region, the changes become more slow. In the dune region of Lake Michigan the normal primitive formation is the beach; then, in order, the stationary beach dunes, the active or wandering dunes, the arrested or transitional dunes, and the passive or established dunes. The established dunes pass through several stages, finally culminating in a deciduous mesophytic forest, the normal climax type in the lake region. Speaking broadly, the conditions for plant life become less and less severe through all these stages, until there is reached the most genial of all conditions in our climate, that which results in the production of a diversified deciduous forest. On the beach there are to be found the most extreme of all xerophytic adaptations in this latitude, and, as one passes through the above dune series in the order of genetic succession, these xerophytic structures become less and less pronounced, finally culminating in the typical mesophytic structures of a deciduous forest.

A. THE BEACH

As the author hopes to show in a subsequent paper, the beach formations of Lake Michigan are of two distinct types. One may be called the xerophytic beach, the other the hydrophytic beach. . . .

The xerophytic beach is essentially a product of wave action and comprises the zone which is or has been worked over by the waves. Hence the beach may be defined as the zone between the water level and the topographic form produced by other agents; in the region under study the upper limit of the beach is commonly a fringe of sand dunes or a bluff of clay or gravel. The xerophytic beach in its typical expression is very naturally subdivided into three zones, which may be called the lower beach, middle beach, and upper beach. . . .

1. *The lower beach.* The lower beach has been defined as the zone of land washed by the waves of summer storms. It might almost be defined as that portion of the beach which is devoid of vegetation. Perhaps there is no flora in the temperate zone quite so sparse as that of the lower beach, unless we except bare rocks and alkaline deserts. A survey of the life conditions in this zone reveals at once the reason for the scanty vegetation. Land life is excluded because of the frequency and violence of storms; the waves tear away the sand in one spot only to deposit it in another. Even though a seed had the temerity to germinate, the young plant would soon be destroyed by the breakers. Nor is there great likelihood that seeds will find a lodgment in this unstable location. As will be seen later the seeds ripened by tenants of the middle beach are almost entirely scattered away from the lake instead of toward it. The action of both wind and wave tends to carry seeds away from the lower beach. Again, few seeds could endure the alternate extremes of cold and heat, wetting and drying so characteristic of this zone.

Water life is excluded because of the extreme xerophytic conditions which commonly prevail on the lower beach. While algæ may propagate themselves in the shallow pools or even in the wet sand during a prolonged season of wet weather, a cessation of activity if not death itself soon follows the advent of dry weather. . . .

Thus the lower beach is a barren zone between two zones of life. Below it there exist algæ and other hydrophytic forms which flourish in the fury of the breakers; above it there exists the flora of the middle beach, a flora adapted to the most intense xerophytic conditions. At no particular time, perhaps, are the conditions too severe for some type of life; vegetation is excluded because of the alternation of opposite extremes.

2. *The middle beach.* The middle beach is situated between the upper limits of the summer and winter waves, comparatively dry in summer but washed by the high storms of winter. It may also be defined as the zone of succulent annuals. The upper limit of this beach is commonly marked by a line of driftwood and débris. The instability of the beach conditions is often shown by the presence of a number of such lines, marking wave limits for different seasons. A very heavy storm will carry the débris line far up on the upper beach, to all intents and purposes carrying the middle beach just so much farther inland, as the flora of the next season testifies. Another season may be without the visitation of heavy storms and the middle beach will encroach upon the territory of the lower beach. The limits of the middle beach are altered more permanently by changes in the lower beach. In many places the lower beach is growing outwards, reclaiming land from the lake, while at other points the lake encroaches upon the land. Speaking broadly, the middle beach advances or recedes *pari passu* with the advance or recession of the lower beach. To some extent the débris lines register these changes, as their notable departure from persistent parallelism may indicate; however, there is

a considerable lack of parallelism in the débris lines of a single season, owing to variations in the direction of the wind and other factors.

The life conditions in this zone are exceedingly severe, and result in a flora of the most pronounced xerophytic characters. The fury of the winter storms as they wash over the middle beach, tearing up here and depositing there, excludes almost entirely the possibility of survival through that period. In other words, biennials and perennials are practically excluded from maturing flowers and fruits, although their vegetative structures may flourish for a single season. In the summer the xerophilous conditions are extreme. Nowhere in the dune region are the winds more severe than here; the middle beach is close enough to the lake to feel all the force of its winds and yet far enough away for the wind to pick up sand from the lower beach and bring to bear upon the flora the intense severity of the sand-blast. No flora is more exposed to the extreme desiccating influences of the summer sun than that which grows upon the bare and open beach. Even though the roots can readily penetrate to the water level, the great exposure of the aerial organs to wind and sun results in the working out of that most perfect of all xerophytic organs, the succulent leaf. Just as succulent plants inhabit deserts where no other high grade plants can grow, so, too, they are able to withstand the severe conditions of the beach. . . .

3. *The upper beach.* In the strictest sense the upper beach is not a portion of the beach at all, since it is beyond the reach of the waves; it might perhaps be called a fossil beach, but the fact that it is continuous with the beach proper seems to exclude that term, as does the recency of its fossilization. The expression fossil beach will be reserved for a formation of greater geological age and separated from the present beach by other topographic forms. Where dunes are superposed upon the beach, the upper limits of this third beach zone are quite vague, though the theoretical line of demarcation is where the sand is first accumulated by the wind. Where clay bluffs are present at the water's edge, the beach is quite narrow and the upper limit fairly well defined, though at times obscured by alluvial fans. Occasionally the upper beach approaches very close to the water's edge; this is the case where the lower and middle beaches are very narrow because of a high gradient. Sometimes the lower or middle beach zone is replaced by a tiny cliff; in such a case the upper beach may approach to the edge of this cliff. The limits of the upper beach, as of other beach zones, are constantly shifting. The lower limits are carried lakeward or landward by the waves of winter storms, but on the whole the lower limits are pushed out more and more lakeward, keeping pace with the advance of the lower beach. The shifting of the wind causes variations in the upper limits, but on the whole the dunes likewise are commonly formed more and more lakeward, as will be shown further on. The three beaches, then, shift from year to year with apparent irregularity, but there appears to be as a resultant a general progressive movement of them all out into the lake. As a whole the three beach zones slope gradually and somewhat evenly upward, toward the dunes or bluffs beyond; depressions, however, are not at all uncommon, and at times they reach down to the water level, so that a beach pool results.

The life conditions are much less severe than on the middle beach, and chiefly because of the freedom from the wave action of the winter storms. The exposure to the sun is almost as great as on the lower zones, but there is more protection from the wind because of the abundance of driftwood. . . The decay of the driftwood may also add no inconsiderable portion to the food materials of the beach plants.

The flora of the upper beach is much richer than that of the middle beach, both in species and in individuals, but here as there the vegetation is so sparse that the tone to the landscape is given by the soil. . . .

At this point it will be well to emphasize one of the fundamental principles of ecological plant groupings. It is comparatively seldom that any single species can be regarded as perfectly characteristic of a formation, while a group of five or ten species can be so selected as to enable one to detect that formation almost anywhere within a large area. No one of the above six species can be regarded as perfectly typical of the upper beach, although Lathyrus approaches such a type, but together they form an assemblage that cannot be found in any other formation, except perhaps locally on the closely related beach dunes. Even on these beach dunes which grade into the upper beach, the relative proportions existing between the above species are very different from those found on the beach, and, as will be shown later, plant species occur on these dunes which are absent from the beach altogether. . . .

THE ROLE OF ECOTYPIC VARIATION IN THE DISTRIBUTION OF THE CENTRAL GRASSLAND OF NORTH AMERICA

Calvin McMillan—1959

Reprinted by permission of the author and publisher from Ecological Monographs **29**: 285–308, 1959.

Although this study is concerned with the nature of the grassland community with focus on the variation from community to community based on analysis of populations, the implications for other communities are patent. By experimental procedure and field observation the relationship of genetic and habitat gradients is assessed. McMillan's discussion should be compared with those of Clements (p. 140), Cain (p. 157), and Whittaker (p. 159). McMillan received the 1960 George Mercer Award of the Ecological Society of America for this paper, recognizing it as the outstanding contribution published by a young ecologist in the preceding two years.

Significant clues to understanding grassland distribution are provided by plant behavior. The interpretation of behavior lies in the separation of the two variables primarily affecting it: (1) the site variable, involving both differences from point to point, microhabitat, and from year to year, annual fluctuation, and (2) the genetic variable, that is, differences in responses to the same habitat due to the different genetic potentials of the individuals involved. Axiomatically, the genetic potential of an individual controls its expression in a particular site, and therefore, an individual may be potentially an early-flowering plant, but whether it flowers or not will depend upon the conditions of its environment. The transplant garden, as employed by Clausen, Keck & Hiesey and others, has been useful in providing a habitat in which the site variable is near the minimum. It has allowed the expression of genetic potentials, particularly of differences in maturity. The greenhouse, representing a minimum in site variable, has been useful in studying the effect of light period on maturity. Observations in the natural habitats have indicated the combined influence of the site variable and the genetic variable in plant behavior. . . .

The goal of the present study is to further understanding of the nature of grassland vegetation, particularly the causes of its continuity over a broad geographic area. The role of ecotypic variation in the distribution of the North American grasslands will be analyzed as the possible mechanism which has allowed an apparently uniform vegetation (i.e., the geographic repetition of combinations of certain species and genera) to be elaborated over an obviously non-uniform habitat. . . .

Studies of ecotypic variation within grassland vegetation indicate that climatic selection has yielded northern communities with individuals that can grow and mature under long daylengths and short frost-free periods. Progressively southward are communities containing individuals that mature under shorter daylengths and longer frost-free periods. Certain of these studies also have indicated that western sites have selected individuals which can mature under a shorter frost-free period than those of eastern sites. . . .

The present transplant garden and light period studies strongly indicate a genetic basis for differences in flowering time of several species of grasses. These studies support Goodwin in his suggestion that the rate of flower bud development is determined "more by heredity than by habitat conditions." This is not intended to suggest that habitat conditions are totally ineffective, but within the broad limits of the conditions in a number of habitats, the genetic pattern which governs the relative rate of flower bud development is affected but little. . . .

The variable climatic values, different yearly dates of last killing frost in spring, yearly deviations in the precipitation pattern, and fluctuations in the yearly temperature patterns play a vital role in the selection of grassland vegatation. These deviations and fluctuations express the environmental amplitude which an individual must tolerate for continued existence, not necessarily involving reproductive processes, within a grassland community. The marked degree of variability within a species-population in grassland vegetation is a visible response to the highly variable nature of the habitat. . . .

The role of climate in vegetational selection is nowhere more evident than in grassland studies. The community behavior in a northern community (e.g. Devils Lake, N. D.) is obviously attuned to a shorter frost-free period than are communities to the south. The recurrence of a variable frost-free period, shorter in duration than those to the south, has resulted in the selection of populations able to reproduce under these shortened conditions. The climatic variability of late spring frost or early fall frost will result some years in failure to flower or a failure to produce mature seed in a number of populations. This yearly variability will seldom present an extreme that the population cannot tolerate, in part or as a whole. The selection of individuals with characteristics of early maturity in a number of different species and the selection of opportunist species showing early maturity (such as Stipa) allows survival in a habitat where there is a variable but short frost-free period.

The length of the light period has played a role in the latitudinal distribution of the grassland vegetation. Olmsted's work on Bouteloua and Larsen's work on Andropogon have suggested the selective influence of the light period. From their studies, longer day requirements by clones from northern communities and shorter day requirements in southern communities are suggested. The light period studies presented above on a limited number of experimental communities provide further evidence of the selective influence of day length. . . .

The yearly moisture deviations undoubtedly have played a vital role in selection. An extremely variable moisture pattern during the warmer part of the year would favor later flowering among species of characteristic late maturity. This type of selective pressure is more common in southern and eastern communities. The unreliability of a moisture pattern makes the higher average precipitation of these communities deceiving. The northern and western communities with a lower annual precipitation tend to have greater reliability in moisture pattern. The greatest precipitation during the early part of the growing season has aided in the selection of individuals with early maturity.

Less variation in time of flowering is noted both within populations and between populations in areas with a greater likelihood of annual recurrence of similar habitat conditions. The magnitude of the variation is intensified under the extended and erratic moisture patterns of southern communities.

The taller growth form of many species occurs in the southern and eastern communities. For survival in these areas of higher rainfall, the later maturity types have been selected for the advantage of greater vegetative height as well as greater height of flowering culms. . . .

The temperature sequences during the warmest part of the growing season have a remarkable similarity across much of the grassland area. Higher day temperatures may occur in the western sites along with somewhat cooler night temperatures. During July, in the normally hottest week, much of the eastern grassland area has a normal daily range of temperature from 12° to 17°C. Slightly greater temperature variation is shown to the west and slightly less in the southeastern sites.

The communities of the north and west are subjected to cooler night temperatures than are found in the transplant garden. The warmer nights of the garden may have resulted in more rapid development than would have occurred in the native habitat. However, much of the flowering within material transplanted from northern and western communities occurred during June, when the temperature sequence at Lincoln would greatly resemble the July sequence of the northern communities. There is a further possibility that slower activity by southern types resulted from the somewhat cooler temperature sequence of the Lincoln garden.

The selective role of soil is significant within the overall action of climatic influence. Certain local modifications in behavior gradients are undoubtedly affected by soil. While the date of growth resumption in an area may be highly variable from one year to the next, differences in soil may modify time of growth resumption locally in any one year. Although not clearly demonstrated, local soil differences may result in the selection of earlier or later maturing types. The recurrence of edaphically-controlled habitat conditions might be expected to result in genetic adjustments within populations. . . .

These studies of ecotypic variation clarify certain aspects of the nature and distribution of grassland vegetation, for they indicate that a certain combination of species in two areas may result from different phenomena. Through natural selection in different areas, groupings of individuals referable to the same species represent fundamentally different communities. The present studies indicate that the uniformity within a type of grassland community is apparent only as it reflects the geographic repetition of certain species combinations and the continuity of a physiognomic type.

The grassland climax as proposed by Clements, rather than being rendered untenable by studies of ecotypic variation, becomes more easily understood in its application to the present distribution of grasses. The mechanism for the broad distribution of the grassland climax involves the intimate relationship between the genetic gradients within vegetation and the habitat gradients, of which the selective influence of climate is paramount. The recognition of site climax communities as proposed by Whittaker receives additional support through an evaluation of ecotypic variation. The result of selection within the grassland climax has been the creation of geographic continua made up of site climax communities which are self-maintaining and have reached a partial stability and high productivity under the existing habitat pressures.

The origin of grasslands becomes more complex and intriguing in the light of ecotypic studies. Problems of origin are not easily reduced to simple considerations of grassland versus forests. These grassland communities are surviving in North America because grasses, admirably suited to the highly variable nature of the habitat, have received selective preference. The complex nature of grassland vegetation and the selective forces which have produced it indicate a closer affinity than is possible by a relatively simple one factor explanation, such as the creation and maintenance through burning. Although fire has undoubtedly played a significant role in grassland history, the action of fire is not basically directed toward the vital populational processes which have molded grassland vegetation. The patterns of variation within the grassland and presumably within forests have resulted from complex selective processes.

Genetic diversity among members of a species was probably characteristic of pre-glacial grasslands in North America. Toward the north, natural selection had probably favored early-maturing types with an ability to grow and reproduce under long day conditions. With the advance of glaciation, it is likely that these forms did not migrate southward because of the light period conditions and because of the narrow limits of population variation within northern types. It is likely that variants within communities toward the south continued to survive due to their adjustment to southern light period conditions and to their breadth of behavioral variation.

Following the retreat of glaciation, the northward advance of grassland vegetation could be greatly facilitated by conceiving three primary distribution points, a western semi-montane area such as that now found near Colorado Springs, Colo., a southern area such as that in southern Oklahoma and northern Texas, and an area in southeastern United States. The expansion of grasslands into South Dakota, North Dakota, and adjacent Canada would have been greatly facilitated by the availability of western forms with their pre-adaptation to a short growing period. The mid-latitude, semi-montane types, such as those near Colorado

Springs, are able to reproduce under longer light periods and many of these forms could be successfully used to re-populate northern areas with a minimum of selection. From southern communities, adapted to growth under shorter day conditions, but broad in their range of intra-populational variation, could have come material for moving rapidly across Kansas and into eastern Nebraska. From southeastern communities could have come the potential for moving into eastern sites. . . .

The problem of getting a particular aggregation of species together is largely a speculative matter. Often suggestions that a relict community was "left behind" implies that it remains unchanged. To this point the results of this study should be directed. The distribution of grassland vegetation in the past was undoubtedly based on the same fundamental principles which govern its present distribution. The key to its distribution, widespread or in relicts, is undoubtedly due to the variants which make each stand of grassland at a given time fundamentally different from any other stand. . . .

This demonstration of grassland potential is an introductory example of the nature of variation that produces harmony between vegetation and its habitat. It further suggests that as a natural resource, the preservation of grassland potential calls for more than the protection of one large grassland area or even two. It demands the intelligent management of grassland potential by the protection of grassland remnants throughout central North America.

STUDIES ON CONNECTICUT LAKE SEDIMENTS. I. A POSTGLACIAL CLIMATIC CHRONOLOGY FOR SOUTHERN NEW ENGLAND

Edward S. Deevey, Jr.—1939

Reprinted by permission of the author and publisher from American Journal of Science **237**: 691–724, 1939.

The study of the succession of communities in geological time provides still another dimension to ecology. Analysis of pollen provides the basis for interpretation based on a uniformitarian principle of comparable climatic conditions being correlated with comparable plant assemblages in the past and present. Some of the perplexing problems of this aspect of paleoecology are evident in this paper.

The many factors which contribute to uncontrolled variation in single pollen spectra, such as sampling error, local variation in flora, peculiarities in composition of sediment, preservation of pollen, and over-representation of certain species, have been frequently discussed, particularly by Voss, Erdtmann, and Wodehouse, and need not be elaborated here. Most investigators, however, have confined their attention to the retention of pollen by peat, and although Groschopf has considered flotation and lacustrine sedimentation of pollen, differences in permeability to water and sinking speed among various types of pollen have not been adequately studied. It is obvious that conditions in the epilimnia and hypolimnia of lakes are not equally favorable for the preservation of pollen, and it is quite conceivable that the chestnut pollen owes its fossilization in the hypolimnion of Linsley Pond to the low redox potential prevailing in that region. . . .

The over-representation of pine in pollen-spectra, due to excessive production or transportation from afar or both, creates a difficulty which is comparatively easy to circumvent when recognized. Although it has hitherto proved impossible to obtain a quantitative estimate of this disparity, its order of magnitude is indicated by some figures given by Wodehouse, who found that a forest containing 0.2 per cent pine was represented in modern lake sediments by a pine pollen percentage of 25 per cent.

But in spite of all the factors which prevent complete reliance on pollen-spectra as accurate indices of the composition of the surrounding forest, the major postglacial changes in vegetation can be inferred, provided that a sufficiently large number of profiles is available for a region. Since not all changes in vegetation are due to climatic variation, the chronologist must distinguish those events of climatic importance, which may be expected to occur over wide areas, from those of local or edaphic significance. Complete fulfillment of this task is impossible in the present state of North American pollen-analytical research. . . .

HISTORY OF THE CONNECTICUT VEGETATION

In its broad outlines the vegetational history of the New Haven region has already been treated, and the more precise details may be referred to students of plant ecology for elaboration. The need for more exact knowledge of the botanical corollaries of a decaying ice-sheet has been indicated; the relative extent and duration of the late-glacial tundra must be discovered, as well as the center of refuge and speed of migration of the coniferous trees which were the first certainly known invaders of southern Connecticut. With the acquisition of this information ecologists will be in a position to answer the interesting question raised by Flint —whether forests did not grow upon thin stagnant ice near the margin of the waning glacier, as they do today on the Malaspina glacier in Alaska, thus prolonging the period of melting.

Since deglaciation Connecticut has passed through a vegetational stage climatically equivalent to eastern Canada (northern coniferous forest), and through a stage edaphically, if not climatically similar to certain areas in the Lake States (pine climax). Evidence of both periods exists today in relict areas, the most notable examples being spruce-bogs and sandy pine plains or "edaphic deserts." With the onset of favorable climatic conditions the forest gradually acquired its characteristic mesophytism. The subsequent fluctuations in moisture régime, though perceptible in the pollen profiles and evidently general throughout eastern North America, have been of subordinate importance, and quite probably have found floristic expression only in critical localities, where physiography has permitted.

The sequence observed in southern Connecticut, unimpressive though it may be in comparison to the temperature changes attendant upon deglaciation, gains considerable interest from the discussion of the composition of the "original forest type." Bromley and Raup have presented evidence that the New England forest in colonial days was somewhat less mesophytic than studies of virgin forest remnants suggest. Bromley concluded from a search of the historic records that the precolonial type in southern New England was an open oak-hickory forest, and attributed the maintenance of this condition to the frequent fires set by the Indians. Raup, while criticizing Bromley's sources on the basis of unfamiliarity with the interior, and questioning the importance of the aboriginal pyromania, reached the same conclusion after study of the accounts of more adventurous and presumably more reliable observers. He therefore supposed the "xerothermic period of about 3000 years ago" to have been responsible for the inferred xerophytism, and considered that the persistence of the forest until such recent times was due to an inherent stubbornness in the face of a moister climate. Proceeding to a stimulating review of the evidence for a postglacial climatic optimum accompanied by widespread dry conditions, Raup was able to find reasonable arguments for assigning to this period such diverse phenomena as the "Virginian element" in the New England-Acadian marine fauna and the diffusion of Old Algonquian cultures into New York and New England from the mound-builder area.

The concept of widespread and long-continued persistence of forests not adjusted to the prevailing climate logically leads to a negation of ecological theory, and Raup's hypothesis must be construed to include only local areas of relict vegetation. The possibility that such areas were encountered by early American travellers cannot be questioned, whether or not the delay in succession be attributed to fire. That climatic elements propitious for the development of oak-hickory forest obtained in southern Connecticut at the time of the climatic optimum can be determined by reference to the pollen-diagrams. . . .

PLANT SUCCESSION, AN ANALYSIS OF THE DEVELOPMENT OF VEGETATION

Frederic E. Clements—1916

Reprinted by permission of the publisher from Carnegie Institution of Washington Publication 242, pp. 1–512 (pp. 3–4, 6–7, 98–99, 105–107), 1916.

Besides containing an account of the various forces and characteristics in succession, this monograph presents a philosophic viewpoint about the nature of the community which has prompted considerable discussion. In Clements' view, the plant community is an organic entity having attributes describable in terms of an individual (see also Braun-Blanquet, p. 147). Further controversy has arisen over his concept that all succession leads to one climax type in a given area owing to the pervading influence of climate. The major opposing viewpoint to Clements' organismic concept is expressed by Gleason (see p. 153) and Ramensky (see p. 151); Whittaker (p. 159), among others, suggests an alternate theory on the nature of the climax. Professor Clements was one of the most influential early American ecologists both as a faculty member at the Universities of Nebraska and Minnesota and as a research associate of the Carnegie Institution.

CONCEPT AND CAUSES OF SUCCESSION

The formation an organism. The developmental study of vegetation necessarily rests upon the assumption that the unit or climax formation is an organic entity. As an organism the formation arises, grows, matures, and dies. Its response to the habitat is shown in processes or functions and in structures which are the record as well as the result of these functions. Furthermore, each climax formation is able to reproduce itself, repeating with essential fidelity the stages of its development. The life-history of a formation is a complex but definite process, comparable in its chief features with the life-history of an individual plant.

Universal occurrence of succession. Succession is the universal process of formation development. It has occurred again and again in the history of every climax formation, and must recur whenever proper conditions arise. No climax area lacks frequent evidence of succession, and the greater number present it in bewildering abundance. The evidence is most obvious in active physiographic areas, dunes, strands, lakes, flood-plains, bad lands, etc., and in areas disturbed by man. But the most stable association is never in complete equilibrium, nor is it free from disturbed areas in which secondary succession is evident. An outcrop of rock, a projecting boulder, a change in soil or in exposure, an increase or decrease in the water-content or the light intensity, a rabbit-burrow, an ant-heap, the furrow of a plow, or the tracks worn by wheels, all these and many others initiate successions, often short and minute, but always significant. Even where the final community seems most homogeneous and its factors uniform, quantitative study by quadrat and instrument reveals a swing of population and a variation in the controlling factors. Invisible as these are to the ordinary observer, they are often very considerable, and in all cases are essentially materials for the study of succession. In consequence, a floristic or physiognomic study of an association, especially in a restricted area, can furnish no trustworthy conclusions as to the prevalence of succession. The latter can be determined only by investigation which is intensive in method and extensive in scope.

Viewpoints of succession. A complete understanding of succession is possible only from the consideration of various viewpoints. Its most striking feature lies in the movement of populations, the waves of invasion, which rise and fall through the habitat from initiation to climax. These are marked by a corresponding progression of vegetation forms or phyads, from lichens and mosses to the final trees. On the physical side, the fundamental view is that which deals with the forces which initiate succession and the reactions which maintain it. This leads to the consideration of the responsive processes or functions which characterize the development, and the resulting structures, communities, zones, alternes, and layers. Finally, all of these viewpoints are summed up in that which regards succession as the growth or development and the reproduction of a complex organism. In this larger aspect succession includes both the ontogeny and the phylogeny of climax formations. . . .

Processes in succession. The development of a climax formation consists of several essential processes or functions. Every sere must be initiated, and its life-forms and species selected. It must progress from one stage to another, and finally must terminate in the highest stage possible under the climatic conditions present. Thus, succession is readily analyzed into initiation, selection, continuation, and termination. A complete analysis, however, resolves these into the basic processes of which all but the first are functions of vegetation, namely, (1) nudation, (2) migration, (3) ecesis, (4) competition, (5) reaction, (6) stabilization. These may be successive or interacting. They are successive in initial stages, and they interact in most complex fashion in all later ones. In addition, there are certain cardinal points to be considered in every case. Such are the direction of movement, the stages involved, the vegetation forms or materials, the climax, and the structural units which result. . . .

Developmental aspect. The essential nature of succession is indicated by its name. It is a series of invasions, a sequence of plant communities marked by the change from lower to higher life-forms. The essence of succession lies in the interaction of three factors, namely, habitat, life-forms, and species, in the progressive development of a formation. In this development, habitat and population act and react upon each other, alternating as cause and effect until a state of equilibrium is reached. The factors of the habitat are the causes of the responses or functions of the community, and these are the causes of growth and development, and hence of structure, essentially as in the individual. Succession must then be regarded as the development or life-history of the climax formation. It is the basic organic process of vegetation, which results in the adult or final form of this complex organism. All the stages which precede the climax are stages of growth. They have the same essential relation to the final stable structure of the organism that seedling and growing plant have to the adult individual. Moreover, just as the adult plant repeats its development, *i. e.*, reproduces itself, whenever conditions permit, so also does the climax formation. The parallel may be extended much further. The flowering plant may repeat itself completely, may undergo primary reproduction from an initial embryonic cell, or the reproduction may be secondary or partial from a shoot. In like fashion, a climax formation may repeat every one of its essential stages of growth in a primary area, or it may reproduce itself only in its later stages, as in secondary areas. In short, the process of organic development is essentially alike for the individual and the community. The correspondence is obvious when the necessary difference in the complexity of the two organisms is recognized.

Functional aspect. The motive force in succession, *i. e.*, in the development of the formation as an organism, is to be found in the responses or functions of the group of individuals, just as the power of growth in the individual lies in the responses or functions of various organs. In both individual and community the clue to development is function, as the record of development is structure. Thus, succession is preeminently a process the progress of which is expressed in certain initial and intermediate structures or stages, but is finally recorded in the structure of the climax formation. The process is complex and often obscure, and its component functions yield only to persistent investigation and experiment. In consequence, the student of succession must recognize clearly that developmental stages, like the climax, are only a record of what has already happened. Each stage is, temporarily at least, a stable structure, and the actual processes can be revealed only by following the development of one stage into the succeeding one. In short, succession can be studied properly only by tracing the rise and fall of each stage, and not by a floristic picture of the population at the crest of each invasion. . . .

Stabilization. The progressive invasion typical of succession everywhere produces stabilization. The latter is the outcome of greater occupation due to aggregation and migration and of the resulting control of the habitat by the population. In other words, stabilization is increase of dominance, culminating in a stable climax. It is the mutual and progressive interaction of habitat and community, by which extreme conditions yield to a climatic optimum and life-forms with the least requirements are replaced by those which make the greatest demands, at least in the aggregate. So universal and characteristic is stabilization that it might well be regarded as a synonym of succession. It has the advantage of suggesting the final adult stage of the development, while succession emphasizes the more striking movement of the stages themselves.

Causes of stabilization. The essential cause of stabilization is dominance. The latter is partly due to the increasing occupation of a bare area, but is chiefly the result of the life-form. The occupation of annuals in an initial or early stage of a secondary sere is often complete, but the dominance is usually transient. Effective dominance can occur only when the prevailing life-form exerts a significant reaction, which holds the population in a certain stage until the reaction becomes distinctly unfavorable to it, or until the invasion in force of a superior life-form. Dominance is then the ability of the characteristic life-form to produce a reaction sufficient to control the community for a period. Dominance may mean the control of soil factors alone, primarily water-content, of air factors, especially light, or of both water and light. Initial life-forms such as algæ, lichens, and mosses are characteristic but not dominant, since the reaction they produce prevents control rather than gives it. This is the essential difference between the initial and the final stages of succession. While both react upon the habitat, the reaction of the one favors invaders, that of the other precludes them. The reactions of the intermediate stages tend to show both effects. At first the reaction is slight and favors the aggregation of occupants; then it becomes more marked and produces conditions more and more favorable to invasion. On the other hand, when the reaction is distinctly unfavorable to the occupants, the next stage develops with greater rapidity. Each stage is itself a minor process of stabilization, a miniature of the increasing stabilization of the sere itself. Reaction is thus the cause of dominance, as of the loss of dominance. It makes clear the reason why one community develops and dominates for a time, only to be replaced by another, and why a stage able to maintain itself as a climax or subclimax finally appears. Thus, reaction furnishes the explanation of stabilization, as it does of the successive invasions inherent in succession.

Relation to the climax. The end of the process of stabilization is a climax. Each stage of succession plays some part in reducing the extreme condition in which the sere began. It reacts to produce increasingly better growing conditions, or at least conditions favorable to the growth of a wider range of species. This is equivalent to reducing an excess of water-content or remedying a lack of it. The consequence is that the effect of stabilization on the habitat is to bring it constantly nearer medium or mesophytic conditions. Exceptions to this occur chiefly in desert regions, though they may occur also in water areas, where processes of deposit and erosion alternate. The effect upon the plant population is corresponding. The vast majority of species are not pioneers, *i. e.*, xerophytes and hydrophytes, but mesophytes with comparatively high but balanced requirements for ecesis. For this reason the number of species and individuals grows larger in each succeeding stage, until the final dominance of light, for example, becomes restrictive. At the same time the life-forms change from those such as lichens and submerged plants with a minimum of aggregate requirements to forms with an increasingly high balanced need. The period of individual development increases as annuals are succeeded by perennials and the latter yield to dominant shrubs and trees. The final outcome in every sere is the culmination in a population most completely fitted to the mesophytic conditions. Such a climax is permanent because of its entire harmony with a stable habitat. It will persist just as long as the climate remains unchanged, always providing that migration does not bring in a new dominant from another region. . . .

PRINCIPLES OF CLASSIFICATION OF THE SPRUCE COMMUNITIES OF EUROPEAN RUSSIA

V. N. Sukatchew—1928

Reprinted by permission of the publisher from Journal of Ecology **16**: 1–18, 1928.

Representative of community studies in Russia is this early paper by Sukatchew (or Sukachev) who was associated with the Forestry Institute at Leningrad. The major features of much Russian community study are evident in this paper, namely the relating of narrowly defined associations to environmental gradients as components of ecological series.

. . . we are able to trace the following five typical habitats of spruce forest: (1) more or less nutritive clayey loam or sandy loam soils, well drained in places with sufficiently pronounced relief, in the north for the most part adjoining the rivers, (2) similar soils but becoming already moory, with worse drainage, less developed relief, in the north for the most part situated farther from the rivers, (3) soils still more moory, without differentiated relief, level, situated still farther from the rivers. These three types of habitat form, as it were, a connected series. Besides these there are (4) the bottoms of narrow valleys where there is excessive moisture, but the water is for the most part in motion, and (5) places carrying (for the north) exceptionally rich soils, most often connected with neighbouring limestone rocks.

According to these five fundamental habitats of the spruce we can divide the spruce forest into five types which differ in the phytosociological structure of their communities, as well as in the size of the trees. A conspicuous character is the presence and composition of the lower strata of the community.

Therefore the following scheme of classification for spruce associations may be given:

1. Relief adequately developed; site well drained, soils more or less nutritive, loams, clays or sandy loams, not moory—*Piceeta hylocomiosa.*
2. Relief less developed, sites feebly drained, soils the same, but already somewhat moory—*Piceeta polytrichosa.*
3. Relief undeveloped, surface flat, site not drained, soils moory—*Piceeta sphagnosa.*
4. Bottom of depressions with moory soils, but running water—*Piceeta herbosa.*
5. Sites with nutritive well-drained soils, for the most part in the neighbourhood of limestone deposits—*Piceeta fruticosa.*

Each of these types is composed of a series of plant communities. . . .

Considering the different communities formed by the spruce, we see that the *Piceeta hylocomiosa* represent communities, the interrelation of whose elements is particularly perfect. This type is the most persistent, and must be regarded as the most fundamental of the spruce communities, for not only has the dominant tree a great influence on the rest of the vegetation of the community which is very closely adapted to this influence, but the dominant itself is closely adapted to the conditions so brought about: for instance, the carpet of characteristic mosses is specially suited to the regeneration of the spruce from seed. The closeness of these interrelations of different parts of the community is the criterion of high social integration, and probably of long duration.

In this respect the first place among all the communities belonging to this group must be assigned to the *Piceetum oxalidosum* and the *P. myrtillosum*. These two, which are, on the whole, near each other morphologically, appear to be also genetically close. The development of phytosociological integration has proceeded in both during thousands of years. But nevertheless the *P. myrtillosum* is the starting point of a series of communities, which departing from *P. oxalidosum* and passing through *P. polytrichosum*, leads to the extermination of spruce forest, a series connected with the process of conversion of forest into bog, and terminating, so far as Piceeta are maintained, with the *P. sphagnosum*, which is, in its turn, followed by the succession to Pinetum, and the ultimate replacement of forest by bog.

This process, the succession accompanying the increasing bogginess of the soil, is observed in spruce forests where the soil is not enriched by springs or the freshets of small rivers and brooks which so abundantly water our northern forests. The most complex of these wet forests and at the same time those in which the growth of the spruce is best is the *Piceetum fontinale* (Russian *log*). The further development of this association has two possible courses. As the river develops its valley and the bed becomes deeper, the soil becomes better drained, and in the course of time the community may pass over to one of the group of *Piceeta hylocomiosa*. In the second case, where the drainage is bad and peaty deposits continue to accumulate, the feeding of the upper layers of soil by springs and floods decreases every year. This causes an impoverishment of the herb stratum, an increased development of the mosses and a worse growth of the spruce, which result in the replacing of *Piceetum fontinale* by *P. sphagnoso-herbosum* (*sogra*), whose natural course of development again leads in the course of time to sphagnum bog with stunted crooked pine. Thus in this second case we have a series of successions analogous with that mentioned above (*P. oxalidosum* to *P. sphagnosum*). The two series in the end lead to the same thing —the extermination of the spruce forests and their replacement by moss bogs. In both cases the process, according to the concomitant external conditions, may proceed sometimes more rapidly, sometimes more slowly, lingering or stopping at certain stages. . . .

From the preceding characterisation of spruce forest it is evident that the fundamental type, in which the most important features of spruce forest are expressed most completely, is the group of *Piceeta hylocomiosa*. The other groups include either communities formed under conditions of excessive moisture, not characteristic of the usual life conditions of the spruce, or under the influence of conditions nearer to those of broad-leaved forest, and consequently also not characteristic of the spruce. We see, as it were, three fundamental ecological series of communities, originating from the group *P. hylocomiosa*. One of them is connected with the beginning of excessive water supply together with stagnation of the water, i.e. a worse supply of oxygen to the roots and deterioration in the supply of mineral food—this is the series *P. hylocomiosa—P. polytrichosa—P. sphagnosa*. The second series, too, is connected with excessive moisture, but the water is in motion and the roots, consequently, are sufficiently supplied with oxygen, while the mineral food supply is not always improved—this is the series *P. hylocomiosa—P. herbosa*. The third series is connected with an improvement of the mineral food supply without a change in the water régime of the habitat or (and this is the commoner case) with a certain increase of dryness and consequently without deterioration and even with improvement of the supply of the roots with oxygen—this is the series *P. hylocomiosa* —*P. fruticosa*.

In each of these groups there is one principal community in which the characters of the group are represented most typically. Next to this come the communities connected with conditions usually already changing in the direction of an approach to the conditions of another group. This leads to an approach of the structure of the community of the given group to the structure of another group. Here within the limits of each group series of two categories are suggested:

(1) *ecological-edaphic series* connected with a change of the nature of the soil within the limits of a definite region.

(2) *ecological-geographic*, or more exactly *ecological-climatic* series.

Each series will represent vicarious associations. . . .

On closer examination of these series we see that they correspond not only with the ecological but also the genetical connections of the communities. The process of succession takes its course along these very series. So the series, let us call it the series A, connected with alteration of the nutritive mineral content of the soil and the absence of excessive moisture is in its essence a succession from oak forest communities to typical Piceeta, being the result of the impoverishment of the soil due to the influence of the forest communities themselves and characterised by the clearing from the Piceeta of the alien elements of broad-leaved forest. This series leads to the formation of the most characteristic association of Piceeta—*P. oxalidosum*.

The series B, leading in the direction of increased moisture and its stagnation, is the succession of Piceeta to bog. If the impulse to its appearance is usually given by external factors, its whole further course is connected with a change of environment produced by the plant communities themselves. Thus their own action on the environment is the chief cause of the succession of communities in this series.

The median series C, on the contrary, has its origin in communities dependent on excessive soil moisture and running water; it is a succession whose fundamental cause is the change in the external factors of existence, the influence of the plant communities on the environment taking no considerable part in the process. In this series, developing parallel to the development of the valley of the rivulet or brook and the deepening of its bed, and hence to the draining of the bottom of the valley, we have a succession to the community *P. fontinale* from communities of the group *P. hylocomiosa* and ultimately from *P. oxalidosum*.

If the succession from *P. fontinale* is determined, not by a gradual drying of the soil, but by impeded flow of water and gradual accumulation of peat deposits, we shall have the series D, i.e. the succession from *P. fontinale* to *P. sphagnosa* and then to pure bog. . . .

If we take into consideration that the series of Piceeta under discussion represent also successive changes of the structure (morphology) of the communities and the interaction of the members of which they are composed, we shall be fully justified in calling them also phytosociological series. . . .

Thus we see that the establishment of ecological series of spruce communities gives us a clear idea of the phytosociological and genetical interrelations between these communities.

Further, the same series allow us to foresee, within certain limits, the character of new communities, not yet known or described, but which may be detected in the future. Thus communities connecting *P. oxalidosum* and *P. fontinale* are not yet known, but no doubt they must exist since there are thinkable transitional natural conditions between those peculiar to these communities in their typical forms. Since we are already acquainted with the extreme members of this series we may in some degree imagine the composition and structure of intermediate links yet to be discovered. The same applies also to the other series, where we are far from knowing all the members.

Hence, it seems to me, it can be seen that the method of ecological series may have a much more extensive significance than that of elucidating the connection of the vegetation series with environment. In its further development it promises to be of assistance in the construction of such a system of communities, as will offer not only a harmonious picture of the phytosociological and genetical interrelations between them, but will allow us to foretell the existence and character of communities not yet described.

REMARQUES SUR L'ÉTUDE DES GROUPEMENTS DE PLANTES

Josias Braun-Blanquet and Ernst Furrer—1913

Reprinted by permission of the authors and publisher from Bulletin Société Languedocienne de Géographie **36**: 20–41, 1913. Translated by Lawrence Wilson, 1964.

The Braun-Blanquet system of plant community analysis views plant associations as having objective reality like a species and as being describable in comparable ways. The major features of the Braun-Blanquet system which are developed in this essay gave rise to the so-called Zurich-Montpellier "school" of phytosociology which continues under his leadership. This tradition of emphasis on floristic composition and "character-species" has had the widest following in Europe and a strong, although frequently modified, influence elsewhere. An opposing view is given by Cain (see p. 157), a reassessment of the Braun-Blanquet system is given by J. J. Moore (1962. *Journal of Ecology* **50**: *761–769), and a thorough review of phytosociology is given by R. W. Becking* (1957. *Botanical Review* **23**: *411–488*).

The study of plant groups (*synecology*) embraces four principal points of view: 1. *Descriptive synecology* studies the floristic composition of plant groups; 2. *Physiological synecology*, ecology in the limited sense of the word, explains the relations of cause and effect existing between the groups and the external factors (climatic, edaphic and biotic); 3. *Geographical synecology* is concerned with the distribution of the groups and with their regional and altitudinal differences; 4. *Genetic synecology*, finally, studies the differences existing between present-day groups of plants and their past. It is concerned, therefore, with group evolution.

The only solid basis for any study of this nature is a perfect knowledge of the floristic composition of the synecological unit. This unit is designated as *association* in both French and English, *Assoziation* or *Bestand* in German, and *associazione* Italian. Defined, association "*is a plant group having a determined floristic composition, presenting a uniform physiognomy, growing under uniform stational conditions*" (Flahault & Schroeter), *and possessing one or several characteristic species.*

We have felt obliged to introduce into this definition the notion of *characteristic* species (*Charakterpflanzen*, Gradmann's *Leitpflanzen*). *These are species which are localized without exception, or very nearly so, within a given association;* they may be regarded as the surest floristic expression of the ecology of the group.

The concept of characteristics is not new, but it has been subordinated until now to the notion of dominant species. Now, the dominants are often ubiquitous, growing in very different places; consequently, they tell us very little about the ecological character.

The reverse is true when it is a question of characteristic species. When someone mentions the *Aristida pungens*, *Cardamine alpina*, the *Epipogon aphyllum*, *Vaccinium Oxycoccus*, and *Carex pauciflora*, we know at once that we are dealing with an association of shifting sand, snow coombs, spruce, and sphagnum-bogs. Why? Because he has named characteristics of these associations. Needless to say, the characteristics may be dominants at the same time. . . .

Each site presenting uniform life conditions and bearing one or several characteristic species, realizes, in our opinion, a definite association. The association may be an organized community from which each member benefits, but it need not necessarily be such. It is utterly impossible for us to ascertain just how far the competition among the species extends, just as it is impossible to determine the value of the utilitarian tie which binds the individuals together. Steep rock formations, often considered to be an environment of open vegetation, are sometimes carpeted with lichens, algae, or mosses forming with a few phanerogams living in the tufts of moss or in the clefts of the rocks a close-knit community obedient to the general laws of association. . . .

A balance between plant competition on the one hand and the external factors of the moment on the other marks this more or less lasting stage which characterizes a constituted association. The duration of the state of balance and of the optimum development of the association varies greatly. This duration is almost indefinite for associations due to climate (associations of arctic countries and lofty summits in particular); it is ephemeral in the case of certain transitory associations (the association of *Myricaria* and willows on alluvial lands along rivers), and especially so in the case of cultural or semicultural associations (wheat-, flax-, hemp-, etc. fields, forest clearings). The presence of the characteristics, which generally appear only after the complete establishment of the association and which are the first to disappear as soon as the conditions of life undergo a change, allow us to consider the association as definitely established. . . .

It goes without saying that one or several species characteristic of an association in a given region may not be characteristic elsewhere, if the climate differs ever so little. A characteristic species of the second order may become of first order on approaching the limits of its area. *Betula nana*, strictly localised in our high marshes of the Jura and the pre-Alps where it finds its northern limits, grows abundantly almost everywhere in the mountains of Norway and Lapland. . . .

The comparative geographical study of associations must reveal these facts and, at the same time, make known to us the absolutely characteristic species, never going beyond the limits of the area of association.

It is evident that one cannot distinguish all possible associations solely by means of characteristic species. That is possible only in the case of 1) *temporary groupings*, associations on the way to becoming fixed and possessing no characteristic traits; 2) *mixed associations*, the product of a reciprocal penetration by several associations. . . . The associations are infinite, and the phytogeographer may rest satisfied with describing the most apparent of these mixed associations, those which cover a more or less large area. Let us not lose sight of the fact that the primary object in the study of groups is not an inventory of each and every clump of earth, but the search for *a unit comparable to the species, capable of serving as a basis for research in comparative geographical botany*, and for synecological investigations. . . .

As Mr. Flahault noted as early as 1900, the study of associations requires one to take into account not only characteristic species, but also the complete inventory of its flora.

The floristic inventory of the association includes *characteristic* species of the first and second order (*Charakterpflanzen*), *constants* (*Brockmann-Jerosch's Konstanten*) appearing in at least half the surveys of a given association, *accessory* species figuring again in a fourth of the surveys of more or less accidental species. To designate the density of each species in the association, use is made either of the terms *solitariae*, *sparsae*, *coposae*, *gregariae* and *sociales*, introduced by *Drude*, or of the figures 1 to 10. The figure 10 designates the absolute dominance of a species in a closed growth. . . .

As regards a *method* to follow in distinguishing the associations, in individualising and delimiting them, *two procedures* are at the disposal of the beginner who is still unfamiliar with characteristic species. . . .

The first means, *floristic* in character, consists of provisionally delimiting the given stands by the use of one or more dominant species. Nothing is easier than the task of distinguishing and delimiting these stands. . . .

The second method of arriving at a knowledge of associations is essentially *topographic*. The phytogeographer selects well-defined topographical units evidencing a vegetation having the same ecological character: rock formation on the shady side of a mountain, the floodplains of a river, ponds of stagnant water, the low-water shore of a lake (Gadeceau), stone-falls, etc. He takes an inventory and determines what are the characteristic species for each of these topographic sites. . . .

As regards assigning names to associations, we recommend the practice of Messrs. Flahault and Schroeter who favor using a name drawn from the vernacular, or adding the suffix *-etum* to the generic or specific name of the dominant species. Let us only avoid exaggerating the value of the dominants whose name the association bears. Basically, they represent but one element of the association; wherever they appear *en masse*, one must make certain that the other elements are to be found as well, for only on this condition can one speak of association. The fact that very often the dominant species is at the same time characteristic in no way matters. . . .

Every association is made up of individuals (*Einzelbeständen*, *Einzelassoziationen*) just as the species is composed of individuals which to us seem identical. The two terms are, therefore, philosophical abstractions which must be made to figure in a kind of diagnosis by basing each on the common characters binding individuals of the same type together. There are clearly distinct associations (those of beeches, of *Salicornia*, of *Aristida pungens*); others behave like polymorphous species and their delimitation is difficult. Since one speaks of transitory species, one could speak of mixed associations and indefinite associations. These last cover, even in middle Europe, and there because of man's influence, a considerable area. . . .

The study of the plant groups of limited area must, of necessity, rest upon the fundamental units. "Associations are the solid base of botanical geography" (*Flahault*).

But the study of classification procedures which enable one to draw up a tentative inventory and to outline an initial synthesis of results achieved is to be urged.

One of the most frequently recommended means consists of grouping the associations in keeping with their physiognomic and ecological affinities. The notions of "*formation*" and "*vegetation-type*" in the sense defined by the participants in the Brussels Congress correspond to this tendency.

> After all, it seems that we may consider a formation as a contemporary expression of certain life-conditions which is *independent* of floristic composition (p. 6), and a formation is composed of associations which *differ in their floristic composition*, but which correspond to like stational conditions and assume analogous forms of vegetation.

To Mr. Schroeter's way of thinking and Mr. Warming's, this notion of formation, based solely upon physiognomy and ecology, about corresponds to a kind of systematics.

This last manner of looking at the matter is not ours. For us the method which most nearly conforms with the principles governing this study seems to consist in grouping the associations according to *their floristic affinities* and to reason with respect to the associational groups thus established as one would with respect to the associations themselves. The term superior to the association would then be the associational group, *not given by the same life-form*, but by a *similar floristic composition, by the presence of common characteristics.*

As for the term "formation," also frequently used by German authors to express what we here designate under the name of *associational group*, it seems desirable to us to use it in its original sense. . . .

Formation would then be the physiognomic and ecological expression of the association, as the biological form is the physiognomic and ecological expression of the species. . . .

DIE GRUNDGESETZMÄSSIGKEITEN IM AUFBAU DER VEGETATIONSDECKE

L. G. Ramensky—1926

Reprinted by permission of the publisher from Botanisches Centralblatt N. F. 7: 453–455, 1926,) an abstract by Selma Ruoff of the original Russian article which appeared in Westnik Opitnogo Dela Woronej, 1924. Translated by Edward J. Kormondy, 1964.

The concepts of Clements (p. 140), Braun-Blanquet (p. 147), Sukatchew (p. 144), and others, are developed on the premise of a fundamental unit of natural communities. These association units are considered to be discrete, describable and amenable to categorization and classification into a hierarchical structure. In sharp contrast and dissent are the views of Ramensky and Gleason (p. 153). In this abstract of Ramensky's exposition, the two major principles, that of vegetational continuity (i.e., nondiscrete association units) and species individuality, are succinctly expressed. It is noteworthy that the Russian Ramensky, the American Gleason and the Frenchman Lenoble developed these principles simultaneously yet independently of each other.

. . . The author follows the concept of the coenose introduced by Gams and gives the following definition: "A coenose is an ecologically limited, locally homogeneous plant grouping (the concrete individual coenose) or the totality of plant groups of ecological and floristic delimited similarity (the abstract coenose); the historical and topological resemblance of such groups can be different." He repudiates the phytosociological and plant population viewpoints because of their anthropomorphisms and characterizes the behavior of the coenobiota as decidedly "antisocial.". . .

In considering the moderating law of the coenose one must take into account the production of propagation units (seeds, spores) and their importance for the maintenance of the coenose; in herbaceous coenoses (meadows, steppes and moors) repair appears to follow vegetative processes and the importation of propagation units to play no great part. But this very vegetative propagation often produces a zone of mixing at the limits of two coenoses. In the instance of stenocoenoses, in which the area is segmented into many small lobes or is entirely divided, the influence of these anomalous limits manifests itself mostly over their entire surface; they must not, therefore, be compared directly with macrocoenoses, which homogeneously cover continuously great surfaces (meadows, steppes).

The historical factor is of relevance for a coenose only in the background when an equilibrium is reached between the other factors and the structure of the community, be it a continuous absolute balance (the ideal extreme case) or a dynamic balance which shifts itself slowly in parallel with alterations in external conditions. A diffuse distribution of species is a characteristic of attained equilibrium and at the same time an indication of a high degree of competition among the plants.

The plant cover cannot be understood as a mass phenomenon through the analysis of small parts (neither from uniform coenoses); the ecological moderating law in vegetation composition can be determined only through the summarizing of statistical surveys of greater areas and then the obtaining of averages. The surface appearance of a coenose, that is the minimal area in which the correct moderation law makes itself felt numerically, can be very different. In the smallest coenose the significant factor in development of the surface appears to be frequency, whereas abundance is more important in larger coenoses. . . .

On the basis of his numerous plant surveys coupled with different methods, the author comes to the conclusion that the plant cover modifies itself continuously in space. The sharp boundary between coenoses is an individual instance in need of special explanation (influence of culture, discontinuous alteration of other factors, etc.) The rule of continuity in the three dimensional composition of plant cover will be supplemented and clarified by the rule of ecological individuality of plant species; each species reacts to the other unique factors and occurs as an independent member in the coenose; there are no two groups which end with identical abundance in a coenose. The possible combinations for the association are very great and each one is a group of individual coenoses in which the greatest abundance and the greater annual change is attained.

The kaleidoscopic alteration in the spatial composition of meadows, steppes and low moors (woods and sphagnum bogs appear homogenous) speaks decidedly against a classification of inflexible units. "Groups are not stable, only the rules of plant combinations" and these support research. As a goal of investigation, the author denotes an arrangement of coenoses in ecological sequence with the corresponding abundance curves of their species and according to the coordinates of their factors. The ideal would be the combining of all isolated coenose studies into a uniform coordinated scheme.

THE INDIVIDUALISTIC CONCEPT OF THE PLANT ASSOCIATION

H. A. Gleason—1926

Reprinted by permission of the publisher from Bulletin of the Torrey Botanical Club **53**: 7–26, 1926.

It is Gleason's interpretation that each community is unique, having arisen randomly by environmental selection of those reproductive parts of plants which happen to enter the area in question. In questioning the objective reality of plant associations, Gleason exerted considerable influence, particularly among American workers. His view is inherent in the continuum concept of Curtis (1951. *Ecology* **32**: *476–496) and Whittaker (1951. Northwest Science* **25**: *17–31) and with some emendation in the natural area concept of Cain (see p. 157). In recognition of his outstanding influence in ecology, the Ecological Society of America honored him as Eminent Ecologist in 1959.*

As a basis for the presentation of the individualistic concept of the plant association, the reader may assume for illustration any plant of his acquaintance, growing in any sort of environment or location. During its life it produces one or more crops of seeds, either unaided or with the assistance of another plant in pollination. These seeds are endowed with some means of migration by which they ultimately come to rest on the ground at a distance from the parent plant. Some seeds are poorly fitted for migration and normally travel but a short distance; others are better adapted and may cover a long distance before coming to rest. All species of plants occasionally profit by accidental means of dispersal, by means of which they traverse distances far in excess of their average journey. Sometimes these longer trips may be of such a nature that the seed is rendered incapable of germination, as in dispersal by currents of salt water, but in many cases they will remain viable. A majority of the seeds reach their final stopping-point not far from the parent, comparatively speaking, and only progressively smaller numbers of them are distributed over a wider circle. The actual number of seeds produced is generally large, or a small number may be compensated by repeated crops in successive years. The actual methods of dispersal are too well known to demand attention at this place.

For the growth of these seeds a certain environment is necessary. They will germinate between folds of paper, if given the proper conditions of light, moisture, oxygen, and heat. They will germinate in the soil if they find a favorable environment, irrespective of its geographical location or the nature of the surrounding vegetation. Herein we find the *crux* of the question. The plant individual shows no physiological response to geographical location or to surrounding vegetation *per se*, but is limited to a particular complex of environmental conditions, which may be correlated with location, or controlled, modified, or supplied by vegetation. If a viable seed migrates to a suitable environment, it germinates. If the environment remains favorable, the young plants will come to maturity, bear seeds in their turn, and serve as further centers of distribution for the species. Seeds which fall in unfavorable environments do not germinate, eventually lose their viability and their history closes.

As a result of this constant seed-migration, every plant association is regularly sowed with seeds of numerous extra-limital species, as well as with seeds of its own normal plant population. The latter will be in the majority, since most seeds fall close to the parent plant. The seeds of extra-limital species will be most numerous near the margin of the association, where they have the advantage of proximity to their parent plants. Smaller numbers of fewer species will be scattered throughout the association, the actual number depending on the distance to be covered, and the species represented depending on their means of migration, including the various accidents of dispersal. This thesis needs no argument in its support. The practical universality of seed dispersal is known to every botanist as a matter of common experience.

An exact physiological analysis of the various species in a single association would certainly show that their optimal environments are not precisely identical, but cover a considerable range. At the same time, the available environment tends to fluctuate from year to year with the annual variations of climate and with the accumulated reactionary effects of the plant population. The average environment may be near the optimum for some species, near the physiological limit of others, and for a third group may occasionally lie completely outside the necessary requirements. In the latter case there will result a group of evanescent species, variable in number and kind, depending on the accidents of dispersal, which may occasionally be found in the association and then be missing for a period of years. . . .

Nor are plants in general, apart from these few restricted species, limited to a very narrow range of environmental demands. Probably those species which are parasitic or which require the presence of a certain soil-organism for their successful germination and growth are the most highly restricted, but for the same reason they are generally among the rarest and most localized in their range. Most plants can and do endure a considerable range in their environment.

With the continuance of this dispersal of seeds over a period of years, every plant association tends to contain every species of the vicinity which can grow in the available environment. Once a species is established, even by a single seed-bearing plant, its further spread through the association is hastened, since it no longer needs to depend on a long or accidental migration, and this spread is continued until the species is eventually distributed throughout the area of the association. In general, it may be considered that, other things being equal, those species of wide extent through an association are those of early introduction which have had ample time to complete their spread, while those of localized or sporadic distribution are the recent arrivals which have not yet become completely established.

This individualistic standpoint therefore furnishes us with an explanation of several of the difficulties which confront us in our attempts to diagnose or classify associations. Heterogeneity in the structure of an association may be explained by the accidents of seed dispersal and by the lack of time for complete establishment. Minor differences between neighboring associations of the same general type may be due to irregularities in immigration and minor variations in environment. Geographical variation in the floristics of an association depends not alone on the geographical variation of the environment, but also on differences in the surrounding floras, which furnish the immigrants into the association. Two widely distant but essentially similar environments have different plant associations because of the completely different plant population from which immigrants may be drawn.

But it must be noted that an appreciation of these conditions still leaves us unable to recognize any one example of an association-type as the normal or typical. Every association of the same general type has come into existence and had its structure determined by the same sort of causes; each is independent of the other, except as it has derived immigrants from the other; each is fully entitled to be recognized as an association and there is no more reason for regarding one as typical than another. Neither are we given any method for the classification of associations into any broader groups. . . .

Let us consider next the relation of migration and environmental selection to succession. We realize that all habitats are marked by continuous environmental fluctuation, accompanied or followed by a resulting vegetational fluctuation, but, in the common usage of the term, this is hardly to be regarded as an example of succession. But if the environmental change proceeds steadily and progressively in one direction, the vegetation ultimately shows a permanent change. Old species find it increasingly difficult or impossible to reproduce, as the environment approaches and finally passes their physiological demands. Some of the migrants find establishment progressively easier, as the environment passes the limit and approaches the optimum of their requirements. These are represented by more and more individuals, until they finally become the most conspicuous element of the association, and we say that a second stage of a successional series has been reached.

It has sometimes been assumed that the various stages in a successional series follow each other in a regular and fixed sequence, but that is frequently not the case. The next vegetation will depend entirely on the nature of the immigration which takes place in the particular period when environmental change reaches the critical stage. Who can predict the future for any one of the little ponds considered above? In one, as the bottom silts up, the chance migration of willow seeds will produce a willow thicket, in a second a thicket of *Cephalanthus* may develop, while a third, which happens to get no shrubby immigrants, may be converted into a miniature meadow of *Calamagrostis canadensis*. . . .

It is a fact, of course, that adjacent vegetation, because of its mere proximity, has the best chance in migration, and it is equally true that in many cases the tendency is for a environment, during its process of change, to approximate the conditions of adjacent areas. Such an environmental change becomes effective at the margin of an association, and we have as a result the apparent advance of one association upon another, so that their present distribution in space portrays their succession in time. The conspicuousness of this phenomenon has probably been the cause of the undue emphasis laid on the idea of successional series. But even here the individualistic nature of succession is often apparent. Commonly the vegetation of the advancing edge differs from that of the older established portion of the association in the numerical proportion of individuals of the component species due to the sorting of immigrants by an environment which has not yet reached the optimum, and, when the rate of succession is very rapid, the pioneer species are frequently limited to those of the greatest mobility. It also happens that the change in environment may become effective throughout the whole area of the association simultaneously, or may begin somewhere near the center. In such cases the pioneers of the succeeding association are dependent on their high mobility or on accidental dispersal, as well as environmental selection.

It is well known that the duration of the different stages in succession varies greatly. Some are superseded in a very short time, others persist for long or even indefinite periods. This again introduces difficulties into any scheme for defining and classifying associations. . . .

The sole conclusion we can draw from all the foregoing considerations is that the vegetation of an area is merely the resultant of two factors, the fluctuating and fortuitous immigration of plants and an equally fluctuating and variable environment. As a result, there is no inherent reason why any two areas of the earth's surface should bear precisely the same vegetation, nor any reason for adhering to our old ideas of the definiteness and distinctness of plant associations. As a matter of fact, no two areas of the earth's surface do bear precisely the same vegetation, except as a matter of chance, and that chance may be broken in another year by a continuance of the same variable migration and fluctuating environment which produced it. Again, experience has shown that it is impossible for ecologists to agree on the scope of the plant association or on the method of classifying plant communities. Furthermore, it seems that the vegetation of a region is not capable of complete segregation into definite communities, but that there is a considerable development of vegetational mixtures. . . .

In conclusion, it may be said that every species of plant is a law unto itself, the distribution of which in space depends upon its individual peculiarities of migration and environmental requirements. Its disseminules migrate everywhere, and grow wherever they find favorable conditions. The species disappears from areas where the environment is no longer endurable. It grows in company with any other species of similar environmental requirements, irrespective of their normal associational affiliations. The behavior of the plant offers in itself no reason at all for the segregation of definite communities. Plant associations, the most conspicuous illustration of the space relation of plants, depend solely on the coincidence of environmental selection and migration over an area of recognizable extent and usually for a time of considerable duration. A rigid definition of the scope or extent of the association is impossible, and a logical classification of associations into larger groups, or into successional series, has not yet been achieved. . . .

CHARACTERISTICS OF NATURAL AREAS AND FACTORS IN THEIR DEVELOPMENT

Stanley A. Cain—1947

Reprinted by permission of the author and publisher from Ecological Monographs **17**: 185–200, 1947.

With certain emendations, Cain's viewpoint follows that of Gleason (see p. 153). The value of this excerpt, however, is in its succinct consideration of the limitations of the phytosociological viewpoint (see Braun-Blanquet, p. 147) concerning the objective reality of plant associations. Cain also suggests an alternate conceptual basis for plant community studies.

The drawing of a parallel between associations and species is not tenable. The members of a species are related by descent and reproduce their kind; the members of an association have no such genetic connection. They arrive at their more or less similar state by the successional route from a variety of beginnings, and reproduce their kind only by the most devious and protracted labors. The individuals of the most variable species have nothing like the motley array of antecedents that bring forth the associations. In the work of the phytosociologists there is a grouping of associations into alliances and orders in a manner similar to the grouping of species into genera, families, etc., but if the basic unit lacks objective reality, the hierarchy must be even less sound.

The phytosociologists who have the strongest faith in the integrity of the association believe that the floristic assemblage is the primary feature of the association, and that the association can be studied in terms of its constant species or its characteristic species just as the species can be studied morphologically without preoccupation with its biology or ecology. For the Scandinavian phytosociologists the association is characterized by the constant species, a certain number of species for any association which reoccur in every quadrat and every stand examined with a regularity of 80 to 90 per cent, and usually with a considerable dominance or coverage. These are highly social or gregarious species. For the members of what we may call the Braun-Blanquet school of plant sociology, which includes most of the phytosociologists from Holland to Italy and from France to Poland and the Balkans, the association is recognized by its characteristic species which have a high degree of fidelity to the floristic assemblage which is called the association. These may also be called indicator species.

These investigators only secondarily concern themselves with questions of life form and the physiognomy of the plant communities, and with the relations of the communities to the habitat. Their approach is in the first place a floristic one. Let us examine further whether the association is definable in these terms.

There are certain facts in nature which the plant geographer can study. The species are facts, in most instances at least; and the areas of the species are facts which can be considered with reasonable preciseness. Environments are facts. There are recognizable habitats. They can be rather well described for small enough areas; but we are confronted with merging phenomena and larger areas are progressively more poorly delimitable. The life form of a species is a fact, and the physiognomy of an aggregation of species is describable within acceptable limits. But does the association in the abstract, characterized by its floristic assemblage and the special features of certain of its members have a comparable objective reality? I do not bring into question the reality of the stand, which is the concrete example of an association (the synécie of Gaussen, the association individual of Braun-Blanquet, the fragment of association of DuRietz), but the reality of the abstraction—the association as a composite of the several association individuals.

In nature there is a habitat. It is occupied by plants of a number of species. The number of species composing the community of the habitat and just which ones they are depend upon several factors: the available flora, the ecological characteristics of the species that are available, the chances of and the time which has been available for dissemination into the area of the habitat, the competition among the members, and their life forms. The individual plant community has objective reality—sharply delimited at its borders if the habitat changes strongly in a short space, poorly delimited if the habitat changes gradually over a greater space. But so far as the flora of the community is concerned, it is the result of the superposition of areas of the species. Each species of the stand will have its individual and often quite different total area, and each has a more or less different ecological amplitude and modality. They live together in the particular community because they chance to have overlapping areas and are biologically successful in the particular habitat.

When comparing different stands that are similar, unless one blindfolds himself by preconceptions of the reality of the association in the abstract, it is soon realized that the farther removed one stand is from another the more different are their floristic assemblages, as Gleason emphasized in his paper on the individualistic association. Here arise the questions which have always plagued the phytogeographers: how different can two association individuals be and still belong to the same association? What is to be required in the way of constant or characteristic species?

The investigations of the phytosociologists produce results with the appearance of a high degree of accuracy, with statistical data on coverage, frequency, density, constancy, and fidelity, in impressive tabular comparisons of stands of an association. And yet it seems to me, having tried these methods myself, and without impugning the honesty of the investigators, that there is more artifice here than science in the selection of stands for representation of the association. . . .

My general conclusion is that plant geographers have a largely unfinished task in the adequate study and description of existing vegetation, and that much of their work must be in terms of natural areas. In this connection I am wholly in agreement with Edward H. Graham who says that the term "natural area" is a very useful and realistic one although incapable of exact definition. One virtue of the term is its very indefiniteness. Like the general term "community," it does not commit one to the necessity of certain difficult decisions; but it is an even broader term than community, suggesting a recognition of the simultaneous action of all operative factors and the joint existence of such diverse phenomena as organisms and different physical states of the atmosphere, soil, etc. *A natural area*, then, *is a geographic unit of any order of size with sufficient common characteristics of various sorts to be of some practical usefulness in biogeography*. Wildlife managers, grazing and forest administrators, and other working ecologists approach such a usage in their common practice.

It does not follow from this argument that students should discontinue their efforts toward analytic studies of the environment, the fauna and flora, and the communities, nor that efforts toward synthesis and classification are to be abandoned. It is suggested, however, that it be kept in mind that single-factor operation does not occur in biological nature, that the environment apparently can not be completely analyzed, and that diverse analytic data can not at present be synthesized back again into anything like the natural whole of the ecosystem. Elsewhere I have called this the "Humpty-Dumpty problem," and "All the King's horses and all the King's men can't put Humpty-Dumpty back together again." When all these limitations of phytogeographical study are kept in mind, one finds that many useful approximations can be made, coincidences observed between biological phenomena and physical ones, and classifications erected. The temptation of standardization and the erection of supposedly universal systems is more easily avoided and natural objects are not cut or stretched to fit the bed of Procrustes. . . .

A CONSIDERATION OF CLIMAX THEORY: THE CLIMAX AS A POPULATION AND PATTERN

R. H. Whittaker—1953

Reprinted by permission of the author and publisher from Ecological Monographs **23**: 41–78, 1953.

In this well documented paper, Whittaker analyzes the two opposing concepts concerning the nature of the climax community and proposes an alternate. Whittaker views the climax as a population pattern corresponding to the pattern of environmental variables. In certain respects this concept is an amalgam of the monoclimax of Clements (p. 140) and polyclimax concepts; in other respects it brings the study of the community into the framework of the ecosystem approach described in the next section. For a thorough analysis and evaluation of the classification of natural communities Dr. Whittaker's paper (Botanical Reviews **28:** *1–239, 1962) is highly recommended.*

. . . In place of the monoclimax, three major propositions on the nature and structure of climaxes and their relativity may be formulated:

1. The climax is a steady-state of community productivity, structure, and population, with the dynamic balance of its populations determined in relation to its site.

2. The balance among populations shifts with change in environment, so that climax vegetation is a pattern of populations corresponding to the pattern of environmental gradients, and more or less diverse according to diversity of environments and kinds of populations in the pattern.

3. Since whatever affects populations may affect climax composition, this is determined by, or in relation to, all "factors" of the mature ecosystem—properties of each of the species in-

volved, climate, soil and other aspects of site, biotic interrelations, floristic and faunistic availability, chances of dispersal and interaction, etc. There is no absolute climax for any area, and climax composition has meaning only relative to position along environmental gradients and to other factors.

The following secondary or corollary propositions are suggested as of possible significance for synecological research:

A. Propositions of climax determination. Climax composition is determined, as indicated in (3) above, by all factors which are intrinsic to, or act upon, the population on a sustained or repeated basis and do not act with such severity as to destroy the climax population and set new succession in motion. Factors determining climax population will thus include:

1. Characteristics of the populations involved. The balance among populations will necessarily be determined by the kinds of populations entering the community and by the peculiarities of each. The place of a given species in the balance will depend on its ability to maintain a population against environmental resistance, determined by its genetics. Since genetics of species may change along gradients, changing genetics of the species should be part of the background of changing balance among species along gradients. Since a species differs genetically from one place to another, these genetic differences may influence the different places or degrees of importance of a species in climax balances.

2. Climate. All climaxes are adapted to climate (and hence are climatic climaxes); but the climate which acts on and determines a climax population is necessarily the local climate of its site, not the general climate of an area.

3. Site. The climax balance is determined by environment of a specific site, and the climax population has meaning only for a kind of site. For the early assumption that climax was independent of site may be substituted the hypothesis that any significant difference in site implies a difference in climax population. As all climax stands occur on sites having some kind of topographic relation to other sites, all climaxes are topographic, as well as climatic, climaxes.

4. Soil. Soil parent-material, as arbitrarily separated from other aspects of site, is a climax determinant; for the traditional assumption that vegetation on any soil parent-material converges to the regional climax may be substituted the hypothesis that any significant edaphic difference, physical or chemical, may imply difference in climax population. All climaxes are edaphic, as well as topographic and climatic, climaxes. . . .

5. Biotic factors. Natural communities are organic systems of plants and animals in environment; in much of what has been said about the vegetation pattern might be substituted the more awkward phrase natural-community pattern. In the functioning system the balances among plant populations exist in relation to, and are partially determined by, animals acting directly on the plants through consumption and trampling, indirectly through soil, etc. All climaxes are biotic climaxes, balanced in relation to their animal populations. . . .

6. Fire. Periodic burning is an environmental factor to which some climaxes are necessarily adapted. In the absence of fire the climax populations might well develop to something different; but such an ideal climax is not on the ground subject to measurement. The burning may cause some population fluctuation, and it may then be difficult to draw a distinction between fire (and windfall, etc.) as environmental factors to which some climaxes are adapted and as disturbances intro-

ducing still greater instability and initiating successions in others. A continuous series from climaxes fully adapted to fire and scarcely affected by a single burn, through climaxes in which minor changes are produced by each burning and those in which the vegetational structure is altered, but not destroyed, to climaxes which are entirely destroyed by a single fire may be expected. Without attempting to draw a clear line where none exists, it may be thought that, in fire-adapted climaxes, fire either does not destroy the dominant populations or does not cause replacement of the dominant growth-form as in other climaxes.

7. Wind. Although wind is a part of the environment of all climax stands, some stands may show marked effect of wind on composition or physiognomy, especially, toward higher latitudes and altitudes and other stands may have windfall permitting reproduction as a normal part of their relation to environment. The combination of sea-wind and salt-spray is particularly effective in producing locally distinctive climaxes along coasts.

8. Other factors. Various other factors may determine locally what self-maintaining or climax populations can exist in a site including, for terrestrial communities, snow-effects, fog as it affects the coastal redwoods, the fog vegetation of the Peruvian desert, and the mossy or cloud forests of many tropic mountains, salt water and tide levels affecting such coastal vegetation as mangrove swamps, although these, not simply seral communities which disappear to be replaced by a climax, may be incompletely stabilized, migratory vegetation in the sense of Crampton, communities of shifting equilibrium in the sense of Alechin.

9. Floristics and faunistics. Climax composition will necessarily be determined by the plant and animal species available in the area. Climax populations in similar environments will vary from place to place for floristic and faunistic reasons, and a recognized climax population type or association will usually have a limited range.

10. Chance. Climax composition must, finally, be considerably affected by chances of dispersal and occupation and of population interactions.

B. Propositions on climax relativity. It has been indicated that the climax population has meaning only relative to the environmental conditions of its site, and the inappropriateness of dichotomous logic has been indicated in several connections. The following aspects of climax relativism are suggested:

1. Climax and succession. There are no distinctions between climax and succession or, more concretely, between climax and seral stands, except those of relative instability and relative significance of directional change. This relativity was expressed by Cowles, "As a matter of fact we have a variable approaching a variable rather than a constant," and has been indicated by various authors.

2. Climax and seral species. There is no reason why some species should not be both seral and climax. Climax species may dominate succession as in desert successions; a species may enter a stand in succession and persist at a different population level into the climax: a species may enter climax stands on one kind of site in an area but only seral stands on another, and may enter climax stands in one area but only seral stands in another. While some species seem clearly seral or climax under specific conditions, for many it is a question of relative position along the time-scale of succession under particular circumstances.

3. Climax and seral types. Types, associations, or stratal communities defined by species may, correspondingly, be seral in one circumstance and

climax in another or may be self-maintaining and successional at different times. Untenable is a familiar kind of logic: Type A (e.g. pines) is being replaced by type B (oak-hickory) on site number 1 (a north slope); therefore, type A growing on site number 2 (a southwest slope) will also ultimately be replaced by type B. Chain-linking of successional observations without regard for site (Type A was seen replacing type B, B replacing C, C replacing D, etc.; therefore, B, C, etc. are all seral to A) is also untenable.

C. Propositions on climax recognition. A number of criteria have been used either explicitly or implicitly in the traditional recognition of monoclimaxes. It may be profitable to examine some of these which seem no longer tenable in this section and to discuss some which seem applicable in the next section.

1. Unity of growth-form. "The first criterion is that all the climax dominants must belong to the same major life form, since this indicates a similar response to climate and hence, a long association with each other." The world-wide occurrence of communities of mixed dominance and of several physiognomic types within a given climatic area may be sufficient commentary.

2. Area of climax. The monoclimax has been thought to be climax of a definite geographic region, so that the climax could be recognized by essential similarity over a large area and occurrence of one or more of the dominants throughout the area. Areal extent is irrelevant to achievement of the climax steady-state, however; and there is almost no lower limit on the area of a climax type. Such restricted types as the summit balds of mountains, Appalachian shale barrens, and southeastern granite flat-rocks, pines on altered andesite in Nevada, stands as limited as the small marsh in a morainic depression and patch of "alpine rain-forest" at the head of a glacial valley described by Ives are, if self-maintaining, climax vegetation. Removal of size restrictions on climax types has, with the variety of populations present, the consequence that distinguishable climax types of the United States are essentially innumerable. While this must certainly be the case, stand types can very well be grouped subjectively into associations-abstract for some purposes.

3. Convergence on different sites. Convergence of different successions to similarity of vegetation on different sites is a criterion based on the first monoclimax assumption. The convergence is only partial, however, leading to climax vegetation which may be expected to differ on different types of sites. Granting the significance of such partial convergence on differing sites as occurs, it is not a basis of recognizing the self-maintaining condition.

4. Upland position. While the vegetation type prevailing on the uplands of an area may be more extensive than other types in the area, it is no more climax than they. Points 2, 3, and 4, may have meaning in relation to the prevailing climax rather than in recognition of the climax steady-state.

5. Physiography. Convergence was achieved through both biological and physiographic processes in the interpretation of Cowles, but physiographic processes act through too long a period to be directly related to the climax as a biological phenomenon. The consequence of erosion of an area down to a peneplain would be not to produce a uniform environment uniformly occupied by one of the vegetation types already in the area, but to produce a less diverse surface of different climate occupied by other kinds of climax stands. In spite of the impossibility of clearly separating biotic and physiographic, autogenic and allogenic succession, it is the former, biological

process, and not the hypothetical result of the latter, physical process, which is the concern of synecology. Since some stands, at least, may reach the climax state in almost any area whether physiographically young, mature, or old, occupation of topographically mature sites may bear little relation to climax recognition.

6. Soil maturity. While relations among climate, vegetation, and soil are recognized, these apply more to vegetation as growth-form than to vegetation as populations. As aspects of the ecosystem, vegetation and soil are, together, related to environment and one another, with neither simply determining the other. Soil, vegetation, and environment may consequently be expected to vary together, *pari passu*, through time and space; which is to say that the ecosystemic pattern varies in time and space and hence the coupled aspects of the ecosystem selected for study vary in parallel, though in no simple manner. The alternative definitions of soil maturity, in terms of profile development or of equilibrium with environment, are partially independent, and profile maturity of soil is not in itself a criterion of the climax state. Conditions of some sites in any area and of most sites in some areas may be such as to prevent soils from developing to profile maturity as, in an extreme case, the "infantile" soils of the arctic. Soils in other areas may, in the course of development to the self-maintaining state, become degraded and podsolized so that a less productive vegetation and apparently less mature soil characterize the climax.

7. Mesophytism. The most mesophytic type of an area is no more "the climax" than other, less mesophytic, self-maintaining stands. The course of succession will usually, though not necessarily, lead from apparently less mesophytic to apparently more mesophytic types; but it does not follow that a given xerophytic or hydrophytic stand is becoming more nearly mesophytic. A more mesophytic species is not to be chosen over a less mesophytic one as climax except as it is shown, for a given type of site, that the former replaces the latter. A balance between more and less mesophytic species may exist on sites too dry to support a purely mesophytic stand without implying succession.

8. Tolerance. Succession will often involve more tolerant species replacing less tolerant ones, but in an area the more tolerant species may be climax on one site and the less tolerant ones on another. There is no reason why such intolerant species as the pines should not form climaxes, either in open stands in which they may reproduce continuously or in denser stands in which they may reproduce only periodically. There is no reason why more and less tolerant species should not form mixed climax stands, provided the stand is open enough to permit the latter to reproduce, or is sufficiently opened at times by fires, windfalls, etc., to permit the less tolerant species to reproduce. . . .

9. Higher growth-form. Apart from the difficulty of using criteria of higher and lower growth-forms, vegetational stature, at least, will usually increase through the succession into the climax. There is no reason, however, why heath, bog, or grassland should not in some areas replace forest as climax even though such replacement violates our usual assumptions of trends through succession and of forests as climaxes wherever forests occur. There is no reason why such simple and open communities as those of cliffs, hammadas, alpine rocks and scree, and arctic fjaeldmark should not form self-maintaining stands or why the simple algae of a mountain lake should not form a "primitive" climax.

10. Relation to successional trends. As indicated for stature and soil, so for

productivity, diversity, etc. These features of communities will usually increase through the succession to the climax, but there is no reason why, in a given case, the usual direction should not be reversed. In general, climax status should be determined not by abstract or generalized conceptions of what should be ultimate, but by what populations actually replace other populations and then maintain themselves. . . .

THE CONCEPT OF THE ECOSYSTEM

One of the ends to which science directs itself is the development of an encompassing theory. In ecology, the principle of the ecosystem provides such a unifying framework within which specialized study at the individual, population and community level can be meaningfully conducted.

The concept of the ecosystem as an ecological unit comprising living and nonliving components interacting to produce a stable system is not new. Those who have read more or less consecutively in this anthology have recognized that many ecologists discussed the interrelations of a particular biotic assemblage with its environment and the interrelations of biotic units within the assemblage. However, the theoretical development of the concept and the implementing of studies oriented to its clarification are largely products of the period since 1940, *the major impetus occurring in the 1950's.*

ECOSYSTEM AS THE BASIC UNIT IN ECOLOGY

Francis C. Evans—1956

Reprinted by permission of the author and publisher from Science **123**: 1127–1128, 1956.

Although the term ecosystem *was first proposed by Tansley in* 1935, *the context in which it is used today is much broader in scope. Systematic treatment and development of the concept in its current sense is largely associated with Eugene Odum beginning with his 1953 text Fundamentals of ecology. However, the following succinct statement by Professor Evans, of the University of Michigan, provides an excellent introduction to this section.*

The term *ecosystem* was proposed by Tansley as a name for the interaction system comprising living things together with their nonliving habitat. Tansley regarded the ecosystem as including "not only the organism-complex, but also the whole complex of physical factors forming what we call the environment." He thus applied the term specifically to that level of biological organization represented by such units as the community and the biome. I here suggest that it is logically appropriate and desirable to extend the application of the concept and the term to include organization levels other than that of the community.

In its fundamental aspects, an ecosystem involves the circulation, transformation, and accumulation of energy and matter through the medium of living things and their activities. Photosynthesis, decomposition, herbivory, predation, parasitism, and other symbiotic activities are among the principal biological processes responsible for the transport and storage of materials and energy, and the interactions of the organisms engaged in these activities provide the pathways of distribution. The food-chain is an example of such a pathway. In the nonliving part of the ecosystem, circulation of energy and matter is completed by such physical processes as evaporation and precipitation, erosion and deposition. The ecologist, then, is primarily concerned with the quantities of matter and energy that pass through a given ecosystem and with the rates at which they do so. Of almost equal importance, however, are the kinds of organisms that are present in any particular ecosystem and the roles that they occupy in its structure and organization. Thus, both quantitative and qualitative aspects need to be considered in the description and comparison of ecosystems.

Ecosystems are further characterized by a multiplicity of regulatory mechanisms, which, in limiting the numbers of organisms present and in influencing their physiology and behavior, control the quantities and rates of movement of both matter and energy. Processes of growth and reproduction, agencies of mortality (physical as well as biological), patterns of immigration and emigration, and habits of adaptive significance are among the more important groups of regulatory mechanisms. In the absence of such mechanisms, no ecosystem could continue to persist and maintain its identity.

The assemblage of plants and animals visualized by Tansley as an integral part of the ecosystem usually consists of numerous species, each represented by a population of individual organisms. However, each population can be regarded as an entity in its own right, interacting with its environment (which may include other organisms as well as physical features of the habitat) to form a system of lower rank that likewise involves the distribution of matter and energy. In turn, each individual animal or plant, together with its particular microenvironment, constitutes a system of still lower rank. Or we may wish to take a world view of life and look upon the biosphere with its total environment as a gigantic ecosystem. Regardless of the level on which life is examined, the ecosystem concept can appropriately be applied. The ecosystem thus stands as a basic unit of ecology, a unit that is as important to this field of natural science as the species is to taxonomy and systematics. In any given case, the particular level on which the ecosystem is being studied can be specified with a qualifying adjective—for example, community ecosystem, population ecosystem, and so forth.

All ranks of ecosystems are open systems, not closed ones. Energy and matter continually escape from them in the course of the processes of life, and they must be replaced if the system is to continue to function. The pathways of loss and replacement of matter and energy frequently connect one ecosystem with another, and therefore it is often difficult to determine the limits of a given ecosystem. This has led some ecologists to reject the ecosystem concept as unrealistic and of little use in description or analysis. One is reminded, however, of the fact that it is also difficult, if not impossible, to delimit a species from its ancestral or derivative species or from both; yet this does not destroy the value of the concept. The ecosystem concept may indeed be more useful when it is employed in relation to the community than to the population or individual, for its limits may be more easily determined on that level. Nevertheless, its application to all levels seems fully justified.

The concept of the ecosystem has been described under many names, among them those of *microcosm*, *naturkomplex*, *holocoen* and *biosystem*. Tansley's term seems most successfully to convey its meaning and has in fact been accepted by a large number of present-day ecologists. I hope that it will eventually be adopted universally and that its application will be expanded beyond its original use to include other levels of biological organization. Recognition of the ecosystem as the basic unit in ecology would be helpful in focussing attention upon the truly fundamental aspects of this rapidly developing science.

THE LAKE AS A MICROCOSM

Stephen A. Forbes—1887

Reprinted by permission of the publisher from Illinois Natural History Survey Bulletin No. 15, pp. 537–550, 1925, a reprinting of an article which first appeared in the Bulletin of the Peoria Scientific Association, pp. 77–87, 1887.

In the tradition of Mobius' biocoenosis (see p. 121), Forbes showed considerable insight into the dynamic interrelationships between the living and nonliving components of stable systems. In some few respects, his microcosm *is but semantically different from today's* ecosystem. *In addition to careful observations, and perceptive insights, Forbes was a gifted writer; part of the classic quality of this essay is its literary charm. The breadth of viewpoint belies Forbes' narrow speciality as an applied entomologist with the Illinois Natural History Survey.*

A lake . . . forms a little world within itself—a microcosm within which all the elemental forces are at work and the play of life goes on in full, but on so small a scale as to bring it easily within the mental grasp.

Nowhere can one see more clearly illustrated what may be called the *sensibility* of such an organic complex, expressed by the fact that whatever affects any species belonging to it, must have its influence of some sort upon the whole assemblage. He will thus be made to see the impossibility of studying completely any form out of relation to the other forms; the necessity for taking a comprehensive survey of the whole as a condition to a satisfactory understanding of any part. If one wishes to become acquainted with the black bass, for example, he will learn but little if he limits himself to that species. He must evidently study also the species upon which it depends for its existence, and the various conditions upon which *these* depend. He must likewise study the species with which it comes in competition, and the entire system of conditions affecting their prosperity; and by the time he has studied all these sufficiently he will find that he has run through the whole complicated mechanism of the aquatic life of the locality, both animal and vegetable, of which his species forms but a single element. . . .

The amount and variety of animal life contained in them as well as in the streams related to them is extremely variable, depending chiefly on the frequency, extent, and duration of the spring and summer overflows. This is, in fact, the characteristic and peculiar feature of life in these waters. There is perhaps no better illustration of the methods by which the flexible system of organic life adapts itself, without injury, to widely and rapidly fluctuating conditions. Whenever the waters of the river remain for a long time far beyond their banks, the breeding grounds of fishes and other animals are immensely extended, and their food supplies increased to a corresponding degree. The slow or stagnant backwaters of such an overflow afford the best situations possible for the development of myriads of Entomostraca, which furnish, in turn, abundant food for young fishes of all descriptions. There thus results an outpouring of life—an extraordinary multiplication of nearly every species, most prompt and rapid, generally speaking, in such as have the highest reproductive rate, that is to say, in those which produce the largest average number of eggs and young for each adult.

The first to feel this tremendous impulse are the protophytes and Protozoa, upon which most of the Entomostraca and certain minute insect larvæ depend for food. This sudden development of their food resources causes, of course, a corresponding increase in the numbers of the latter classes, and, through them, of all sorts of fishes. The first fishes to feel the force of this tidal wave of life are the rapidly-breeding, non-predaceous kinds; and the last, the game fishes, which derive from the others their principal food supplies. Evidently each of these classes must act as a check upon the one preceding it. The development of animalcules is arrested and soon sent back below its highest point by the consequent development of Entomostraca; the latter, again, are met, checked, and reduced in number by the innumerable shoals of fishes with which the water speedily swarms. In this way a general adjustment of numbers to the new conditions would finally be reached spontaneously; but long before any such settled balance can be established, often of course before the full effect of this upward influence has been exhibited, a new cause of disturbance intervenes in the *disappearance of the overflow*. As the waters retire, the lakes are again defined; the teeming life which they contain is restricted within daily narrower bounds, and a fearful slaughter follows; the lower and more defenceless animals are penned up more and more closely with their predaceous enemies, and these thrive for a time to an extraordinary degree. To trace the further consequences of this oscillation would take me too far. Enough has been said to illustrate the general idea that the life of waters subject to periodical expansions of considerable duration, is peculiarly unstable and fluctuating; that each species swings, pendulum-like but irregularly, between a highest and a lowest point, and that this fluctuation affects the different classes successively, in the order of their dependence upon each other for food. . . .

It would be quite impossible within reasonable limits, to go into details respecting the organic relations of the animals of these waters, and I will content myself with two or three illustrations. As one example of the varied and far-reaching relations into which the animals of a lake are brought in the general struggle for life, I take the common black bass. In the dietary of this fish I find, at different ages of the individual, fishes of great variety, representing all the important orders of that class; insects in considerable number, especially the various water-bugs and larvæ of day-flies; fresh-water shrimps; and a great multitude of Entomostraca of many species and genera. The fish is therefore directly dependent upon all these classes for its existence. Next, looking to the food of the species which the bass has eaten, and upon which it is therefore indirectly dependent, I find that one kind of the fishes taken feeds upon mud, algæ, and Entomostraca, and another upon nearly every animal substance in the water, including mollusks and decomposing organic matter. The insects taken by the bass, themselves take other insects and small Crustacea. The crawfishes are nearly omnivorous, and of the other crustaceans some eat Entomostraca and some algæ and Protozoa. At only the second step, therefore, we find our bass brought into dependence upon nearly every class of animals in the water.

And now, if we search for its competitors we shall find these also extremely numerous. In the first place, I have found that all our young fishes except the Catostomidæ feed at first almost wholly on Entomostraca, so that the little bass finds himself at the very beginning of his life engaged in a scramble for food with all the other little fishes in the lake. In fact, not only young fishes but a multitude of other animals as well, especially insects and the larger Crustacea, feed upon these Entomostraca, so that the competitors of the bass are not confined to members of its own class. Even mollusks, while they do not directly compete with it do so indirectly, for they appropriate myriads of the microscopic forms upon which the Entomostraca largely depend for food. But the enemies of the bass do not all attack it by appropriating its food supplies, for many devour the little fish itself. A great variety of predaceous fishes, turtles, water-snakes, wading and diving birds, and even bugs of gigantic dimensions destroy it on the slightest opportunity. It is in fact hardly too much to say that fishes which reach maturity are relatively as rare as centenarians among human kind.

As an illustration of the remote and unsuspected rivalries which reveal themselves on a careful study of such a situation, we may take the relations of fishes to the bladderwort[1]—a flowering plant which fills many acres of the water in the shallow lakes of northern Illinois. Upon the leaves of this species are found little bladders—several hundred to each plant—which when closely examined are seen to be tiny traps for the capture of Entomostraca and other minute animals. The plant usually has no roots, but lives entirely upon the animal food obtained through these little bladders. Ten of these sacs which I took at random from a mature plant contained no less than ninety-three animals (more than nine to a bladder), belonging to twenty-eight different species. Seventy-six of these were Entomostraca, and eight others were minute insect larvæ. When we estimate the myriads of small insects and Crustacea which these plants must appropriate during a year to their own support, and consider the fact that these are of the kinds most useful as food for young fishes of nearly all descriptions, we must conclude that the bladderworts compete with fishes for food, and tend to keep down their number by diminishing the food resources of the young. The plants even have a certain advantage in this competition, since they are not strictly dependent on Entomostraca, as the fishes are, but sometimes take root, developing then but very few leaves and bladders. This probably happens under conditions unfavorable to their support by the other method. These simple instances will suffice to illustrate the intimate way in which the living forms of a lake are united.

[1]Utricularia.

Perhaps no phenomenon of life in such a situation is more remarkable than the steady balance of organic nature, which holds each species within the limits of a uniform average number, year after year, although each one is always doing its best to break across boundaries on every side. The reproductive rate is usually enormous and the struggle for existence is correspondingly severe. . . .

It is a self-evident proposition that a species can not maintain itself continuously, year after year, unless its birth-rate at least equals its death-rate. If it is preyed upon by another species, it must produce regularly an excess of individuals for destruction, or else it must certainly dwindle and disappear. On the other hand, the dependent species evidently must not appropriate, on an average, any more than the surplus and excess of individuals upon which it preys, for if it does so it will continuously diminish its own food supply, and thus indirectly but surely exterminate itself. The interests of both parties will therefore be best served by an adjustment of their respective rates of multiplication such that the species devoured shall furnish an excess of numbers to supply the wants of the devourer, and that the latter shall confine its appropriations to the excess thus furnished. We thus see that there is really a close *community of interest* between these two seemingly deadly foes.

And next we note that this common interest is promoted by the process of natural selection; for it is the great office of this process to eliminate the unfit. If two species standing to each other in the relation of hunter and prey are or become badly adjusted in respect to their rates of increase, so that the one preyed upon is kept very far below the normal number which might find food, even if they do not presently obliterate each other the pair are placed at a disadvantage in the battle for life, and must suffer accordingly. Just as certainly as the thrifty business man who lives within his income will finally dispossess his shiftless competitor who can never pay his debts, the well-adjusted aquatic animal will in time crowd out its poorly-adjusted competitors for food and for the various goods of life. Consequently we may believe that in the long run and as a general rule those species which have survived, are those which have reached a fairly close adjustment in this particular.

Two ideas are thus seen to be sufficient to explain the order evolved from this seeming chaos; the first that of a general community of interests among all the classes of organic beings here assembled, and the second that of the beneficent power of natural selection which compels such adjustments of the rates of destruction and of multiplication of the various species as shall best promote this common interest.

THE ACCUMULATION OF ENERGY BY PLANTS

Edgar Nelson Transeau 1926

Reprinted by permission of the publisher from the Ohio Journal of Science **26**: 1–10, 1926.

If he is to study energy flow in an ecosystem, the ecologist needs information about the energy relations of the only group of organisms that can transform radiant energy into a form useable by other organisms. Transeau's study of the energy budget of a cornfield was considerably in advance of its time and provided the basis for what has subsequently become a highly active area of research—primary production.

. . . Let us now examine the energy budget of a hypothetical acre of corn in the heart of the corn belt in north central Illinois where corn attains yields as great as anywhere, and not far from Madison, Wisconsin, one of the stations at which solar radiation has been studied. The growing season is from June 1 to September 8, one hundred days. The best yields have been with 10,000 plants to the acre. One hundred bushels, with a dry weight of

2160 kg. per acre, is the yield assumed although it is not a maximum crop for the corn belt. How well an acre of corn covers the area is shown by the fact that during the latter half of the season nearly two acres of leaves are exposed to the light.

At maturity the average corn plant contains about 20 per cent of dry matter and about 80 per cent of water. Of the dry matter, carbon makes up about 44.58 per cent. This is the most important figure for our calculations derived from the chemical analyses of the corn plants. We must also know the total amounts of mineral elements present which is 5.37 per cent from which we can derive the fact that 94.63 per cent of the plant's dry weight is organic matter. The dry weight of an average corn plant growing under these circumstances is 600 g., of which 216 g. makes up the grain 200 g. the stalk, 140 g. the leaves, and 44 g. the roots. The total weight of the 10,000 plants is 6000 kg. Subtracting from this the 322 kg. of mineral elements in the ash we have left 5678 kg. of organic matter, of which 2675 kg. is carbon.

To estimate the amount of photosynthesis we must determine the amount of carbon, because carbon enters the plant only by photosynthetic reduction of CO_2. The total carbon is 2675 kilograms and the glucose equivalent of this carbon is 6687 kilograms. This is the amount of primary sugar equivalent to the carbon accumulated in the mature plant.

TABLE 3. *Glucose equivalent of respiration*

Estimated rate of CO_2 release = 1% of the dry wt per day	
Average dry weight for season (½ total wt.)	= 3000 kg.
Average rate of CO_2 release (.01 × 3200) per day	= 30 kg.
Total CO_2 release during season	= 3000 kg.
Carbon equivalent: $C:CO_2$ = 12:44	= 818 kg.
Glucose equivalent $C_6H_{12}O_6:C_6$ = 180:72	= 2045 kg.

At maturity however, only a part of the carbon remains, for some has been lost as CO_2 in respiration (Table 3). The average rate of CO_2 loss is not far from one per cent of the dry weight per day. This would cause a daily loss of 30 kilograms of CO_2, and during the entire season a loss of 3000 kilograms. The glucose equivalent to this amount of carbon dioxide is 2045 kilograms.

Adding the amount of this lost glucose to the glucose equivalent of the carbon in the plant, gives the total glucose manufactured as 8732 kilograms. It requires energy equivalent to 3760 calories to produce one kilogram of glucose. Hence it required not far from 33 million calories to produce the entire photosynthetic product. (Table 4).

TABLE 4. *Energy consumed in photosynthesis*

Glucose equivalent of accumulated carbon	6687 kg.
Glucose equivalent of carbon oxidized	2045 kg.
Total glucose manufactured	8732 kg.
Energy required to produce 1 kg. glucose	3760 Cal.
Total energy consumed in photosynthesis	33 million Cal.

We are now in a position to estimate the efficiency of the corn plant as a photosynthetic agent: (Table 5).

TABLE 5. *Efficiency of photosynthesis*

Total energy available on acre during the growing season	2043 million Cal.
Total energy used in photosynthesis	33 million Cal.
Per cent of available energy used by the corn plant in photosynthesis, (efficiency of corn plant)	1.6%
Of the total light spectrum measured, however, only about 20% is used in photosynthesis, hence the efficiency of the photosynthetic process is	8%

The total energy available according to the Smithsonian figures is 2043 million Calories. The energy utilized is 33 million, or 1.6 per cent. In photosynthesis however, only certain rays are effective, and these furnish about 20 per cent of the energy measured by the pyrheliometer. Consequently the efficiency of photosynthesis in 100-bushel corn is 8 per cent.

Another source of energy loss to the plant is transpiration. From the water requirement studies of corn it is probable that in Illinois not far from 276 kilograms of water are evaporated during the growing season for every kilogram of its dry weight. The total weight of water lost in this way therefore is one and a half million kilograms. This is equal to 408,000 gallons or sufficient water to cover the acre to a depth of fifteen inches.

The energy necessary to evaporate one kilogram of water at the average temperature of the growing season is 593 calorics. Consequently 910 million Calories are expended in this way. This is equivalent to 44.5 per cent of the available energy.

TABLE 7. *Energy released in respiration*

Glucose consumed in respiration	2045 kg.
One kilogram of glucose releases	3760 Cal.
Total energy released in Respiration	7.7 million Cal.
Of the energy made potential in photosynthesis, Respiration releases	23.4%

Assuming that photosynthesis goes on 12 hours each day and respiration 24 hours each day, the average daily rate of photosynthesis is about 8 times the rate of respiration.

Respiration again releases a part of the energy rendered potential in photosynthesis. As we have seen 2045 kilograms of glucose are thus oxidized, and in consequence 7.7 million Calories are released within the plant. This energy raises the temperature of the plant and escapes to the environment, or it is used in synthesis of fats, proteins and other reduced organic substances.

The energy released in respiration amounts to 23.4 per cent—almost one-fourth of the energy absorbed in photosynthesis. This is far more than is needed to account for the endothermic reactions associated with food transformations within the plant.

Assuming that photosynthesis goes on 12 hours and respiration 24 hours each day, the average rate of photosynthesis must be about 8 times the rate of respiration.

We may now summarize the energy budget [Table 8]:

TABLE 8. *Summary of budget*

Total energy available	2043 million Cal.
Used in photosynthesis	33 million Cal.
Used in transpiration	910 million Cal.
Total energy consumed	943 million Cal.
Energy not directly used by the plants	1100 million Cal.
Energy released by respiration	8 million Cal.
Of the available energy, 100-bushel-corn uses about	46%
The environment takes up about	54%

As a result we are in a position to make a number of generalizations regarding the metabolism and growth of plants, both as to materials and energy. (1) An acre of 100-bushel corn uses during the growing season about 408,000 gallons of water or 15 acre-inches. (2) The evaporation of this water consumes about 45 per cent of the available light energy. (3) In photosynthesis the corn plant utilizes about 1.6 per cent of the energy available; its efficiency is about 8 per cent. (4) An acre of 100-bushel corn manufactures on the average 200 pounds of sugar a day. (5) Of the energy rendered potential in photosynthesis, 23.4 per cent is again released in respiration. (6) Of the sugar manufactured nearly one-fourth is oxidized in respiration. (7) Respiration releases several times as much energy as is needed to account for the reductions in the synthesis of fats, proteins and other compounds. (8) At maturity the grain contains about one-fourth of the total energy utilized in photosynthesis, or about .5 per cent of the energy available. (9) The average rate of photosynthesis is about eight times the rate of respiration. (10) Since the young corn seedling weighs .3 grams and the mature plant weighs 600 grams, on the basis of the compound interest law of growth the average daily increment in dry weight is 7.9 per cent....

THE ANNUAL ENERGY BUDGET OF AN INLAND LAKE

Chancey Juday—1940

Reprinted by permission of the publisher from Ecology **21**: 438–450, 1940.

Transeau's energy budget calculations (see p. 171) were limited to one growing season of a single crop. Juday's study not only covers an entire year but considers the totality of energy relations of a system. The complexity of studying community metabolism is obvious in this paper which represented a major forward step in ecosystem analysis. Its influence on Lindeman's research and formulation of his trophic-dynamics concept is also apparent (see p. 179). Juday, with E. H. Birge, pioneered limnological studies in the United States and established the University of Wisconsin as the center of such studies.

The variation in the quantity of solar radiation delivered to the surface of an inland lake during the course of the year is the principal factor in determining the physical, chemical and biological cycle of changes that take place within the water. This is true especially of lakes which are situated in temperate latitudes where there are considerable differences between summer and winter temperatures of the air and of the water. . . .

The annual energy budget of a lake may be regarded as comprising the energy received from sun and sky each year and the expenditures or uses which the lake makes of this annual income of radiation. In general the annual income and outgo substantially balance each other. This is true more particularly of the physical energy budget. Considerable biological material produced in one energy year lives over into the next, but this overlapping crop of organisms is much the same in quantity from year to year so that it plays approximately the same annual role. For this reason it does not require any special consideration. There is a certain amount of organic material contributed to the bottom deposits in the deeper water and to peat formation in the shallow water which lasts for long periods of time, but the annual energy value of these materials is so small in most cases that they may be neglected. . . .

. . . the monthly means of solar and sky radiation delivered to the surface of Lake Mendota during the 28 year period ranged from a minimum of 3,568 calories in December to a maximum of 16,392 calories in July. The annual means for the 28 years varied from a minimum of 108,597 calories in 1935 to a maximum of 129,659 calories in 1937. . . . the annual mean for the 28 years is 118,872 calories. . . .

The respective amounts of energy included in the four items of the physical energy budget which have been considered so far are indicated in table III.

TABLE III. *Quantity of solar and sky radiation used by Lake Mendota in various physical and biological processes*

The results are indicated in gram calories per square centimeter of surface.

Item	Calories
Melting of ice in spring	3,500
Annual heat budget of water	24,200
Annual heat budget of bottom	2,000
Energy lost by evaporation	29,300
Annual surface loss	28,500
Loss by conduction, convection and radiation	30,324
Biological energy budget (maximum)	1,048

The sum of these four items is 71,000 calories, which is approximately 60 per cent of the mean quantity of energy delivered to the surface of Lake Mendota annually by sun and sky. . . .

BIOLOGICAL ENERGY BUDGET

A certain amount of the solar radiation that passes into the water of Lake Mendota is utilized by the aquatic plants in the process of photosynthesis. The products of this assimilation, namely, proteins, fats and carbohydrates, thus constitute the primary accumulation or storage of the energy derived from the sub-surface illumination. Since this organic material manufactured by the plants serves, either directly or indirectly, as a source of food for all of the non-chlorophyllaceous organisms that inhabit the lake, these latter forms, therefore, constitute a secondary stage in the storage of the energy accumulated by the aquatic plants. The original amount of energy represented by these secondary organisms varies with the different forms, depending upon the number of links in their respective food chains; in general they represent a comparatively small proportion of the primary organic material manufactured by the plants.

Chemical analyses of the various aquatic organisms have now progressed far enough to enable one to compute their energy values from the standards that have been established by food chemists. The standard values are 5,650 calories per gram of protein, 9,450 calories per gram of fat and 4,100 calories per gram of carbohydrate, on a dry weight basis. These values do not represent the total quantity of energy utilized by the aquatic organisms, however, because a part of the synthesized material is oxidized in the metabolic processes of the living organisms. These metabolic oxidations result in the production of heat which is transmitted to the water, but the quantity of heat derived from this source is extremely small in comparison with that which comes from direct insolation.

The amount of organic matter consumed in the metabolism of plants is much smaller than that in animals because several grams of plant material may be consumed in the production of one gram of animal tissue even in animals that feed directly on plants; the predaceous animals represent a still larger quantity of the original photosynthesized material.

Plankton... In view of all of these complexities, it may be estimated that the average turnover in the organic matter of the mean standing crop of plankton takes place about every two weeks throughout the year. It would be more frequent than this in spring and summer, and less frequent in winter. A turnover of 26 times per year would give an annual yield of 6,240 kilograms

TABLE IV. *Annual production of plankton, bottom flora, bottom fauna and fish, as well as crude protein, ether extract (fat), and carbohydrate constituents of the organic matter*

The results are stated in kilograms per hectare on a dry, ash-free basis. The plankton yield is based on a turnover every two weeks during the year. The average quantity of dissolved organic matter is included also.

	Dry organic matter	Crude protein	Ether extract	Carbohydrate
Total plankton	6240	2704	431	3105
Phytoplankton .	5850	2501	383	2966
Zooplankton	390	203	48	139
Bottom flora . .	512	64	6	442
Bottom fauna .	45	33	4	8
Fish	5	3.4	1	0.6
Dissolved organic matter	1523	334	68	1121
Total organic matter	8325	3138.4	510	4676.6

of dry organic matter per hectare of surface as indicated in table IV. This material would consist of 2,704 kilograms of protein, 431 kilograms of fat and 3,105 kilograms of carbohydrate. Approximately 94 per cent of the organic matter comes from the phytoplankton and 6 per cent from the zooplankton.

Bottom flora. . . . the annual crop of large aquatics amounted to 2,000 kilograms per hectare, dry weight. If evenly distributed over the entire lake, this crop would give a yield of 628 kilograms per hectare. A little more than 18 per cent of this material consisted of ash, so that the organic matter was equivalent to 512 kilograms per hectare. . . .

. . . the energy values. . . are given in table IV. The 512 kilograms of dry organic matter per hectare consisted of 64 kilograms of protein, 6 kilograms of ether extract or fat and 442 kilograms of carbohydrate.

The bottom deposits, especially in the deeper water, contain a rather large population of bacteria. . . . While these organisms are present in considerable numbers, they are so small in size that they add very little to the crop of organic matter in the lake; so they have been disregarded. Likewise fungi are fairly abundant in the bottom deposits, but no quantitative study of them has yet been made; it seems probable that their contribution to the organic content of the lake is negligible from an energy standpoint.

Bottom fauna. . . The macroscopic bottom fauna yielded 45 kilograms of dry organic matter per hectare; of this amount 33 kilograms consisted of protein, 4 kilograms of ether extract or fat and 8 kilograms of carbohydrate. While some of these organisms live more than one year, others pass through two or three generations in a year; the two groups of organisms are generally considered as balancing each other, so that the above quantities may be taken as the annual crop of this material as shown in table IV.

Considerable numbers of protozoa and other microscopic animals have been found in the bottom deposits, but no quantitative study of them has been made. It seems probable, however, that these minute forms would not add an appreciable amount of organic matter to the total weight of the bottom fauna.

Fish. No accurate census of the fish caught by anglers in Lake Mendota each year has ever been made so that the assessment of this part of the biological crop can be estimated only roughly. . . . adding the carp crop to that of the game and pan fish gives an annual fish yield of 22 kilograms per hectare, live weight. On a dry, ashfree basis, the total yield amounts to a little more than 5 kilograms per hectare as indicated in table IV. By far the greater part of this material consists of protein and fat.

Energy value of annual crop. Table IV shows that the total quantity of stored and accumulated energy in the form of dry organic matter in the annual crop of plants and animals amounts to 6,802 kilograms per hectare; of this quantity protein constitutes a little more than 2,804 kilograms, ether extract or fat 442 kilograms and carbohydrates 3,556 kilograms. On the basis of the energy equivalents of these three classes of organic matter, as indicated in a previous paragraph, the total energy value of the annual crop amounts to 346 gram calories per square centimeter of lake surface (table V).

TABLE V. *Energy values of the organic matter in the organisms, together with the estimated amounts of energy represented in their metabolism, and in the dissolved organic matter*

The values are stated in gram calories per square centimeter of lake surface. The results for phytoplankton and zooplankton are based on a turnover every two weeks during the year.

Phytoplankton	299
Metabolism	100
Zooplankton	22
Metabolism	110
Bottom flora	22
Metabolism	7
Bottom fauna and fish	3
Metabolism	15
Dissolved organic matter	71
Total	649

In addition to the organic material in the plants and animals, the water contains a certain amount of organic matter which cannot be recovered with a high speed centrifuge. It is either in true solution or is in such a finely divided state that it cannot be obtained with a centrifuge; for lack of a better term it has been called "dissolved organic matter" as compared with the "particulate organic matter" which can be recovered from the water with a centrifuge. The water of Lake Mendota contains 10 to 14 milligrams per liter, dry weight, of this dissolved organic matter; the mean of some 60 determinations is 12 milligrams per liter. When computed to an area basis, the average weight of this material is 1,523 kilograms per hectare, dry weight, of which 334 kilograms are protein, 68 kilograms fat and 1,121 kilograms carbohydrate. The energy value of this dissolved organic matter is about 71 gram calories per square centimeter.

Utilization of solar energy. The chlorophyll-bearing aquatic plants are responsible for the utilization of the subsurface radiation; that is, the sun furnishes the power and the chlorophyll and associated pigments of the plants serve as the machines for the manufacture of the fundamental organic matter of the lake. Table IV shows that the phytoplankton and the large aquatic plants constitute the major item in the annual yield of biological material. Together they contribute 6,362 kilograms of dry organic matter per hectare as compared with 440 kilograms of zooplankton, bottom fauna and fish; that is, the plant contribution is 93 per cent and the animal part is 7 per cent of the total organic matter.

Table V gives the energy value of the various constituents of the annual biological crop. The two groups of plants, namely phytoplankton and large aquatics, have an energy value of 321 gram calories as compared with 25 gram calories per square centimeter in the animals. The 321 gram calories represented in the organic matter of the plants is only 0.27 of one per cent of the mean annual radiation delivered to the surface of the lake, namely 118,872 calories. Two corrections need to be made in this result, however. (1) As already indicated some 28,500 calories of solar energy are lost at the surface of the water and thus do not reach the aquatic vegetation. Deducting this amount leaves 90,372 calories which pass into the water and thus become available for the plants. On this basis the percentage of utilization is increased to a little more than 0.35 of one per cent of the available radiation. (2) A certain amount of the organic matter synthesized by the plants is used in their metabolism and this does not appear in the percentage of utilization given above. Experiments show that some of the algae utilize in their metabolic processes about one-third of the organic matter that they synthesize. No data are available for the large aquatics, but assuming that they also utilize a similar proportion in their metabolism, the two groups of plants would represent a utilization of 428 calories which is equivalent to 0.47 of one per cent of the annual quantity of solar energy that actually enters the water.

This percentage is based on an average turnover in the phytoplankton every two weeks throughout the year, but there is some evidence that the turnover takes place more frequently, especially from April to October. With an average turnover once a week in the organic matter of the phytoplankton during the year, the energy value of this crop would be 798 calories, including metabolism; adding to this amount the 29 calories in the annual crop of bottom flora gives a total of 827 calories which is utilized by the plants. This is 0.91 of one per cent of the 90,372 calories of energy that penetrate the water and become available to the plants; in round numbers this may be regarded as a utilization of one per cent.

This small percentage of utilization of solar energy by aquatic plants shows that Lake Mendota is not a very efficient manufacturer of biological products in so far as utilizing the annual supply of solar and sky radiation is concerned; on the other hand it belongs to the group of highly productive lakes.

While the aquatic plant crop appears

to be inefficient in its utilization of solar energy, it compares very favorably with some of the more important land crops in this respect. Transeau states that only 1.6 per cent of the total available energy is used by the corn plant in photosynthesis during a growing period of 100 days, or from June 1 to September 8. . . . These computations for cultivated crops, however, take into account only the quantity of solar radiation available during comparatively brief growing periods and thus do not cover the entire year as indicated for the aquatic plants.

Energy value of animals. The organic content of the animal population of the lake represents a conversion and further storage of the material manufactured by the plants, but no direct utilization of solar energy is involved in the transformation. It may be regarded as an expensive method of prolonging the existence of a certain portion of the original plant material. As previously indicated, it may take five grams of plant food to produce one gram of animal tissue, so that the plant equivalent of the animal crop may be reckoned as five times as large as the organic content of the animals; in the predatory animals, however it would be much larger.

Table V shows that the energy value of the bottom and fish population is 25 gram calories per square centimeter; on the fivefold basis, this would represent the conversion of at least 125 gram calories of original plant organic matter. This utilization is approximately 40 per cent of the potential energy stored in the annual plant crop of 321 gram calories which is based on a turnover in the phytoplankton every two weeks during the year. A turnover in the phytoplankton every week would give a plant crop of 620 calories and an animal utilization of a little more than 20 per cent.

Dissolved organic matter. The energy value of the dissolved organic matter is indicated as 71 gram calories per square centimeter in table V. This material is constantly being supplied to the water by the various organisms and the standing crop of it remains fairly uniform in quantity during the different seasons of the year as well as in different years. While there is a regular turnover in this organic matter, it needs to be taken into account only once in computing the organic crop of the lake because it has its source in the plants and animals for which an annual yield has already been computed. . . .

THE TROPHIC-DYNAMIC ASPECT OF ECOLOGY

Raymond L. Lindeman—1942

Reprinted by permission of the publisher from Ecology 23: 399–418, 1942.

This paper incorporates the most significant formulation in the development of modern ecology. It provided not only a conceptual framework within which to work but also stimulated a great profusion of effort because of the basic questions it posed. Hutchinson stated the case well in a postscript to the paper, "... here for the first time, we have the interrelated dynamics of a biocoenosis presented in a form that is amenable to a productive abstract analysis." Lindeman's potentially productive career which began at the University of Wisconsin and ended at Yale was foreshortened at age 27 *while the following paper was in press.*

The trophic-dynamic viewpoint, as adopted in this paper, emphasizes the relationship of trophic or "energy-availing" relationships within the community-unit to the process of succession. From this viewpoint, which is closely allied to Vernadsky's "biogeochemical" approach and to the "oekologische Sicht" of Friederichs, a lake is considered as a primary ecological unit in its own right, since all the lesser "communities" are dependent upon other components of the lacustrine food cycle for their very existence. Upon further consideration of the trophic cycle, the discrimination between living organisms as parts of the "biotic community" and dead organisms and inorganic nutritives as parts of the "environment" seems arbitrary and unnatural. The difficulty of drawing clear-cut lines between the living *community* and the nonliving *environment* is illustrated by the difficulty of determining the status of a slowly dying pondweed covered with periphytes, some of which are also continually dying.... much of the nonliving nascent ooze is rapidly reincorporated through "dissolved nutrients" back into the living "biotic community." This constant organic-inorganic cycle of nutritive substance is so completely integrated that to consider even such a unit as a lake primarily as a biotic community appears to force a "biological" emphasis upon a more basic functional organization.

This concept... is inherent in the term *ecosystem*, proposed by Tansley for the fundamental ecological unit.... The *ecosystem* may be formally defined as the system composed of physical-chemical-biological processes active within a space-time unit of any magnitude, i.e., the biotic community *plus* its abiotic environment....

TROPHIC DYNAMICS

Qualitative food-cycle relationships. Although certain aspects of food relations have been known for centuries, many processes within ecosystems are still very incompletely understood. The basic process in trophic dynamics is the transfer of energy from one part of the ecosystem to another. All function, and indeed all life, within an ecosystem depends upon the utilization of an external source of energy, solar radiation. A portion of this incident energy is transformed by the process of photosynthesis into the structure of living organisms. In the language of community economics introduced by Thienemann, autotrophic plants are *producer* organisms, employing the energy obtained by photosynthesis to synthesize complex organic substances from simple inorganic substances. Although plants again release a portion of this potential energy in catabolic processes, a great surplus of organic substance is accumulated. Animals and heterotrophic plants, as *consumer* organisms, feed upon this surplus of potential energy, oxidizing a considerable portion of the consumed substance to release kinetic energy for metabolism, but transforming the remainder into the complex chemical substances of their own bodies. Following death, every organism is a potential source of energy for saprophagous organisms (feeding directly on dead tissues), which again may act as energy sources for successive categories of consumers. Heterotrophic bacteria and fungi, representing the most important saprophagous consumption of energy, may be conveniently differentiated from animal consumers as specialized *decomposers* of organic substance. Waksman has suggested that certain of these bacteria be further differentiated as *transformers* of organic and inorganic compounds. The combined action of animal consumers and bacterial decomposers tends to dissipate the potential energy of organic substances, again transforming them to the inorganic state. From this inorganic state the autotrophic plants may utilize the dissolved nutrients once more in resynthesizing complex organic substance, thus completing the food cycle. . . .

Productivity. DEFINITIONS. The quantitative aspects of trophic ecology have been commonly expressed in terms of the productivity of the food groups concerned. Productivity has been rather broadly defined as the general rate of production, a term which may be applied to any or every food group in a given ecosystem. . . .

In the following pages we shall consider the quantitative relationships of the following productivities: λ_0 (rate of incident solar radiation), λ_1 (rate of photosynthetic production), λ_2 (rate of primary or herbivorous consumption), λ_3 (rate of secondary consumption or primary predation), and λ_4 (rate of tertiary consumption). The total amount of organic structure formed per year for any level Λ_n, which is commonly expressed as the annual "yield," actually represents a value uncorrected for dissipation of energy by (1) respiration, (2) predation, and (3) postmortem decomposition. Let us now consider the quantitative aspects of these losses.

RESPIRATORY CORRECTIONS. The amount of energy lost from food levels by catabolic processes (respiration) varies considerably for the different stages in the life histories of individuals, for different levels in the food cycle and for different seasonal temperatures. In terms of annual production, however, individual deviates cancel out and respiratory differences between food groups may be observed. . . .

Considering that predators are usually more active than their herbivorous prey, which are in turn more active than the plants upon which they feed, it is not surprising to find that respiration with respect to growth in producers (33 per cent), in primary consumers (62 per cent) and in secondary consumers ($>$100 per cent) increases progressively. These differences probably reflect a trophic principle of wide application: the percentage loss of energy due to respiration is progressively greater for higher levels in the food cycle.

PREDATION CORRECTIONS. In considering the predation losses from each level, it is most convenient to begin with the highest level, Λ_n. In a mechanically perfect food cycle composed of organically discrete levels, this loss by predation obviously would be zero. Since no natural food cycle is so mechanically constituted, some "cannibalism" within such an arbitrary level can be expected, so that the actual value for predation loss from Λ_n probably will be somewhat above zero. The predation loss from level Λ_{n-1} will represent the total amount of assimilable energy passed on into the higher level (i.e., the true productivity, λ_n), plus a quantity representing the average content of substance killed but not assimilated by the predator. . . . The predation loss from level Λ_{n-2} will likewise represent the total amount of assimilable energy passed on to the next level (i.e., λ_{n-1}), plus a similar factor for unassimilated material, as illustrated by the data of tables II and III. The various categories of parasites are somewhat comparable to those of predators, but the details of their energy relationships have not yet been clarified.

DECOMPOSITION CORRECTIONS. In conformity with the principle of Le Chatelier, the energy of no food level can be completely extracted by the organisms which feed upon it. In addition to the energy represented by organisms which survive to be included in the "annual yield," much energy is contained in "killed" tissues which the predators are unable to digest and assimilate. . . . Although the data are insufficient to warrant a generalization, these values suggest increasing digestibility of the higher food levels, particularly for the benthic components of aquatic cycles.

The loss of energy due to premature death from non-predatory causes usually must be neglected, since such losses are exceedingly difficult to evaluate and under normal conditions probably represent relatively small components of the annual production. . . .

Following non-predated death, every organism is a potential source of energy for myriads of bacterial and fungal saprophages, whose metabolic products provide simple inorganic and organic solutes reavailable to photosynthetic producers. These saprophages may also serve as energy sources for successive levels of consumers, often considerably supplementing the normal diet of herbivores. . . .

APPLICATION. The value of these theoretical energy relationships can be illustrated by analyzing data of the three ecosystems for which relatively comprehensive productivity values have been published (table I). . . . The calorific values in table I, representing annual production of organic matter, are uncorrected for energy losses.

TABLE I. *Productivities of food-groups in three aquatic ecosystems, as g-cal/cm²/year, uncorrected for losses due to respiration, predation and decomposition. Data from Brujewicz ('39), Juday ('40) and Lindeman ('41b)*

	Caspian Sea	Lake Mendota	Cedar Bog Lake
Phytoplankters: Λ_1	59.5	299	25.8
Phytobenthos: Λ_1	0.3	22	44.6
Zooplankters: Λ_2	20.0	22	6.1
Benthic browsers: Λ_2	}	1.8*	0.8
Benthic predators: Λ_3	} 20.6	} 0.9*	0.2
Plankton predators: Λ_3 . . .	}	}	0.8
"Forage" fishes: $\Lambda_3(+\Lambda_2?)$.	0.6	?	0.3
Carp: $\Lambda_3(+\Lambda_2?)$.	0.0	0.2	0.0
"Game" fishes: $\Lambda_4(+\Lambda_3?)$.	0.6	0.1	0.0
Seals: Λ_5	0.01	0.0	0.0

*Roughly assuming that $\frac{2}{3}$ of the bottom fauna is herbivorous.

Correcting for the energy losses due to respiration, predation and decomposition, as discussed in the preceding sections, casts a very different light on the relative productivities of food levels. The calculation of corrections for the Cedar Bog Lake values for producers, primary consumers and secondary consumers are given in table II. The application of similar corrections to the energy values for the food levels of the Lake Mendota food cycle given by Juday, as shown in table III, indicates that Lake Mendota is much more productive of producers and primary consumers than is Cedar Bog Lake, while the production of secondary consumers is of the same order of magnitude in the two lakes.

TABLE II. *Productivity values for the Cedar Bog Lake food cycle, in g-cal/cm²/year, as corrrected by using the coefficients derived in the preceding sections*

Trophic level	Uncorrected productivity	Respiration	Predation	Decomposition	Corrected productivity
Producers: Λ_1	70.4 ± 10.14	23.4	14.8	2.8	111.3
Primary consumers: Λ_2	7.0 ± 1.07	4.4	3.1	0.3	14.8
Secondary consumers: Λ_3	1.3 ± 0.43*	1.8	0.0	0.0	3.1

*This value includes the productivity of the small cyprinoid fishes found in the lake.

TABLE III. *Productivity values for the Lake Mendota food cycle, in g-cal/cm²/year, as corrected by using coefficients derived in the preceding sections, and as given by Juday ('40)*

Trophic Level	Uncorrected productivity	Respiration	Predation	Decomposition	Corrected productivity	Juday's corrected productivity
Producers: Λ_1	321*	107	42	10	480	428
Primary consumers: Λ_2	24	15	2.3	0.3	41.6	144
Secondary consumers: Λ_3	1†	1	0.3	0.0	2.3	6
Tertiary consumers: Λ_4	0.12	0.2	0.0	0.0	0.3	0.7

*Hutchinson gives evidence that this value is probably too high and may actually be as low as 250.

†Apparently such organisms as small "forage" fishes are not included in any part of Juday's balance sheet. The inclusion of these forms might be expected to increase considerably the productivity of secondary consumption.

Biological efficiency. The quantitative relationships of any food-cycle level may be expressed in terms of its efficiency with respect to lower levels. Quoting Hutchinson's definition, "the efficiency of the productivity of any level (Λ_n) relative to the productivity of any previous level (Λ_m) is defined as (λ_n/λ_m) 100. If the rate of solar energy entering the ecosystem is denoted as λ_0, the efficiencies of all levels may be referred back to this quantity λ_0." In general, however, the most interesting efficiencies are those referred to the previous level's productivity (λ_{n-1}), or those expressed as (λ_n/λ_{n-1}) 100. These latter may be termed the *progressive efficiencies* of the various food-cycle levels, indicating for each level the degree of utilization of its potential food supply or energy source. All efficiencies discussed in the following pages are progressive efficiencies, expressed in terms of relative productivities ((λ_n/λ_{n-1}) 100). It is important to remember that efficiency and productivity are not synonymous. Productivity is a rate (i.e., in the units here used, cal/cm²/year), while efficiency, being a ratio, is a dimensionless number. The points of reference for any efficiency value shoud always be clearly stated.

The progressive efficiencies ((λ_n/λ_{n-1}) 100) for the trophic levels of Cedar Bog Lake and Lake Mendota, as obtained from the productivities derived in tables II and III, are presented in table IV. In view of the uncertainties concerning some of the Lake Mendota productivities, no definite conclusions can be drawn from their relative efficiencies. The Cedar Bog Lake ratios, however, indicate that the progressive efficiencies increase from about 0.10 per cent for production, to 13.3 per cent for primary consumption, and to 22.3 per cent for secondary consumption. . . . These progressively increasing efficiencies may well represent a fundamental trophic principle, namely, that the consumers at progressively higher levels in the food cycle are progressively more efficient in the use of their food supply.

TABLE IV. *Productivities and progressive efficiencies in the Cedar Bog Lake and Lake Mendota food cycles, as g-cal/cm²/year*

	Cedar Bog Lake		Lake Mendota	
	Productivity	Efficiency	Productivity	Efficiency
Radiation......	≤118,872		118,872	
Producers: Λ_1..	111.3	0.10%	480*	0.40%
Primary consumers: Λ_2	14.8	13.3%	41.6	8.7%
Secondary consumers: Λ_3	3.1	22.3%	2.3†	5.5%
Tertiary consumers: Λ_4	–	–	0.3	13.0%

*Probably too high; see footnote of table III.

†Probably too low; see footnote of table III.

At first sight, this generalization of increasing efficiency in higher consumer groups would appear to contradict the previous generalization that the loss of energy due to respiration is progressively greater for higher levels in the food cycle. These can be reconciled by remembering that increased activity of predators considerably increases the chances of encountering suitable prey. The ultimate effect of such antagonistic principles would present a picture of a predator completely wearing itself out in the process of completely exterminating its prey, a very improbable situation. However, Elton pointed out that food-cycles rarely have more than five trophic levels. Among the several factors involved, increasing respiration of successive levels of predators contrasted with their successively increasing efficiency of predation appears to be important in restricting the number of trophic levels in a food cycle. . . .

TROPHIC-DYNAMICS IN SUCCESSION

Dynamic processes within an ecosystem, over a period of time, tend to produce certain obvious changes in its species-composition, soil characteristics and productivity. Change, according to Cooper, is the essential criterion of succession. From the trophic-dynamic viewpoint, succession is the process of development in an ecosystem, brought about primarily by the effects of the organisms on the environment and upon each other, towards a relatively stable condition of equilibrium.

It is well known that in the initial phases of hydrarch succession (oligotrophy→eutrophy) productivity increases rapidly; it is equally apparent that the colonization of a bare terrestrial area represents a similar acceleration in productivity. In the later phases of succession, productivity increases much more slowly. . . .

SUCCESSIONAL PRODUCTIVITY CURVES

In recapitulating the probable photosynthetic productivity relationships in hydrarch succession, we shall venture. . . a hypothetical hydrosere, developing from a moderately deep lake in a fertile cold temperate region under relatively constant climatic conditions. The initial period of oligotrophy is believed to be relatively short. . . . with productivity rapidly increasing until eutrophic stage-equilibrium is attained. The duration of high eutrophic productivity depends upon the mean depth of the basin and upon the rate of sedimentation, and productivity fluctuates about a high eutrophic mean until the lake becomes too shallow for maximum growth of phytoplankton or regeneration of nutrients from the ooze. As the lake becomes shallower and more senescent, productivity is increasingly influenced by climatic fluctuations and gradually declines to a minimum as the lake is completely filled with sediments. . . .

Efficiency relationships in succession. The successional changes of photosynthetic efficiency in natural areas (with respect to solar radiation, i.e., (λ_1/λ_0) 100) have not been intensively studied. In lake succession, photosynthetic efficiency would be expected to follow the same course deduced for productivity, rising to a more or less constant value during eutrophic stage-equilibrium, and declining during senescence, as suggested by a photosynthetic efficiency of at least 0.27 per cent for eutrophic Lake Mendota and of 0.10 per cent for senescent Cedar Bog Lake. For the terrestrial hydrosere, efficiency would likewise follow a curve similar to that postulated for productivity. . . .

DYNAMICS OF PRODUCTION IN A MARINE AREA

George L. Clarke—1946

Reprinted by permission of the author and publisher from Ecological Monographs **16**: 321–335, 1946.

Problems and confusion in the description and measurement of the energy relations within ecosystems, and concomitantly in the attempt to compare the energetics of ecosystems, were considerably clarified by Clarke. In this clear-cut discussion of concepts of production, he indicates the limitations of traditionally used measurements and suggests a basis for meaningful comparison which is now widely followed. (*See p. 27 for another paper by Clarke.*)

CONCEPTS OF PRODUCTION

All the ideas and measurements of productivity which have an ecological application, may be grouped under the following three fundamental concepts:

Standing crop—the amount of organisms *existing* in the area at the time of observation.

Material removed—the amount of organisms *removed* from the area per unit time by man, or in other ways.

Production rate—the amount of organisms *formed* within the area per unit time.

All three of these major concepts of productivity are important, and are essential for a complete understanding of the operation of the area as an ecological complex. In addition, the quantities involved are to a certain extent mutually dependent. To avoid ambiguity in discussing the ecological relationships of the area, it is suggested that the terms "productivity" and "production" be not used in referring to the standing crop or to the material removed unless a phrase is added to make the meaning clear. Measurements made under any of the three categories may be stated in terms of number of individuals, weight or "biomass," energy content, or any other characteristic (such as chlorophyll content) which may be adequate for the given situation. Evaluation on the basis of energy content has the advantage that the efficiency of the utilization of the incident solar radiation may be calculated directly.

Standing crop. Measurements of the standing crop, and hence of the concentration, of the various species inhabiting the area are essential in judging the harmful or beneficial effect of crowding within the species, and the effectiveness with which dependent species can feed upon forage species. When applied to the exploitation of a natural population by man, the magnitude of the standing crop similarly influences the size of the catch per unit effort. However, a knowledge of the standing crop does not give any information as to the time which has been required to produce the crop, or its replaceability.

To illustrate these points, the changes of population size with time for three hypothetical situations are represented diagrammatically in Figure 2. In the first situation the growth rate of the population is much more rapid than in the second, but conditions are such that the same size of standing crop is attained provided that the season is sufficiently long for the maximum value to be reached. In this case, the final size of the standing crop gives no information as

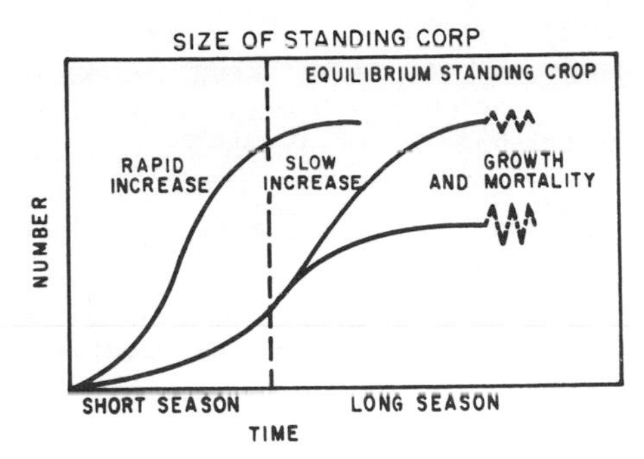

FIG. 2. *Changes of population size with time in three hypothetical situations (for full explanation see text).*

to the rate of net increase. If, however, the standing crop is measured before the asymptotic level is approached, the situation with the more rapid increase will have the larger standing crop. The size of the standing crop at any time is the result of the summation of the excess of production over destruction from the beginning of the growth of the population to the moment of observation.

In the third hypothetical situation, the same length of time is required for the population to reach a maximum size as in the second situation, but the maximum level reached is lower. In both situations, the population may fluctuate above and below the average limiting value (broken lines at right of curves), and since equilibrium is being maintained, at least temporarily, the average rate of production must be exactly balanced by the average rate of destruction. . . .

Material removed. The material removed from an area may fall into several categories. In the first place, the amount of organisms harvested by man during a certain period may be measured and designated as the *yield.* In addition, other organisms may be permanently removed from the area by wind or currents, or by emigration accomplished by the organisms' own locomotion. Organisms which grow in the area but which are consumed, or die in other ways, and decompose so as to enter the ecological cycle again within the same area are not considered to be a yield in the sense recommended here. However, dead organic matter which has become permanently inaccessible, as for example, if buried under bottom deposits, is an irrevocable loss to the system, and hence forms another subdivision of the material removed.

These different subdivisions have in common the fact that in each instance the particular material which is removed from the area does not return again to that area. . . . Because of the inevitable loss of materials (and energy) at each level in the food chain, the yield will ordinarily be much smaller than the supply. Measurement of the ratio of yield to supply, and hence the efficiency of the formation of the yield, is therefore of great importance to . . . ascertain whether the actual yield represents a needlessly low utilization or an overexploitation of the area.

Production rate. The concept of the production rate as the amount of organisms formed per unit time (per unit area or volume) is complicated by the fact that in most natural areas organic matter is being formed or transformed at several trophic levels simultaneously, i.e., by the plants and animals of the food chain which depend upon one another. In order for measurements of production rate to be useful it is necessary to keep separate the values for the various trophic levels and in each case to distinguish between gross and net rates of formation.

These trophic relations among the components of the production pyramid may be . . . [considered] first, for a situation in which the constructive and destructive processes are equal so that there is no gain or loss in the amounts of organisms present at the end of the period over that at the beginning. . . .

In tracing the energy and material

through the production pyramid we may start with the incident light which falls upon the area. A portion of this light (small, in the aquatic environment) reaches the plant cells and is absorbed by them. A small portion of the absorbed energy appears as the carbohydrate which has been formed by photosynthesis (P_1). The amount of material produced by this anabolic process (or of the energy represented) is termed the *gross plant production.* It has also been called the *primary production* because the animal substances which result from consuming the plants, and each other, are transformations of the original plant material, and thus represent alternative forms of the same material (and energy).... A large part of the gross production is lost as the result of catabolic processes. This loss may be measured by the amount of respiration. The remaining fraction of the gross production accounts for the new plant growth (P_2) and this is termed the *net plant production,* or simply, the *plant production,* for unit area and time.

Since in the case considered there is no permanent increase or decrease in plant material, all of this new plant growth is destroyed and the energy transformed before the end of the period. Part of the plant material produced is consumed by herbivores and the remainder dies in some other manner and decomposes. In many situations a large proportion of the plant material consumed is not assimilated by the herbivores, but is passed through the gut undigested. This fraction (U) may be added to that which has decomposed following destruction in other ways.

A similar analysis may be made of the material which enters into each of the successive trophic levels represented by the animals and colorless plants....

At the end of the period for this hypothetical case of complete equilibrium the standing crop is of exactly the same magnitude as at the beginning and there has obviously been no yield. Production has been going on, however, at definite rates at the various levels, and in this case destruction of the materials has exactly balanced their formation during the period....

Let us consider now a second case, in which smaller amounts of organisms are destroyed than are formed during the period. Under these circumstances the growth (P_2) of any one of the categories of organisms would be accounted for at the end of the period in three ways: one portion consumed, one portion decomposed, and one portion remaining in existence and representing an increment which may be termed the *net increase* (P_3). The standing crop at the end of the period is consequently larger than at the beginning of the period by the amount of the net increase. In a situation in which the amount of destruction during the period was greater than the amount of production, the net increase (P_3) would be negative, and the standing crop would be reduced.

If this surplus material is permanently removed from the system by man, it will constitute a yield. Obviously these organisms could not continue to be removed from the system in succeeding periods unless an equal amount of material, as nutrients or in some other form, were added each period. If the organisms representing the net increase are not removed from the system, and if circumstances are such that they can continue in existence in the area, there will be a permanent increase in the size of the standing crop. Again, this can take place only to the extent to which an equivalent supply of nutrients or other materials are added to the area. The standing crops of lakes are frequently seen to increase in this way with the result that the lakes become more eutrophic and the process is known as *eutrophication.*

In the discussion of production rate thus far nothing has been said about the length of the period considered. The time required for each type of organism to complete its growth, to die and decompose, and to start the cycle over again is known as its period of *turnover*. The length of the turnover period usually differs widely for the organisms at the different trophic levels of the production pyramid, and may differ for the same level in different situations and at different seasons of the year. The green plants of a terrestrial area may have essentially only one turnover per year, whereas the phytoplankton of an aquatic area may turnover within short periods varying widely from a few days to several weeks. In the latter case the same material may be used over again several times during the year, and it would thus have little meaning to add up the increments of growth for the whole year in an attempt to reach a "total" annual value. If the growth of the plants is measured as energy, it is permissible to summate the amount of energy which has been transformed during the year since the energy can be used by the plants only once. A comparison may thus be made between the annual incident radiation and the energy content of the plants produced.

In the case of the organisms at successively higher trophic levels, both the materials and the energy are used over again one or more times. A summation of amounts of production at all trophic levels for a long period, such as a year, therefore similarly has little meaning. . .

. . . Production is therefore best measured as a set of rates applying to the gross production, net production, and net increase for each category of organisms or each trophic level. . . .

TROPHIC STRUCTURE AND PRODUCTIVITY OF SILVER SPRINGS, FLORIDA

Howard T. Odum—1957

Reprinted by permission of the author and publisher from Ecological Monographs **27**: 55–112, 1957.

The significance of this paper lies in its extensive application of Lindeman's trophic-dynamics concept. It has been a model for subsequent studies on different ecosystems. It also introduced an energy flow model which has had successful instructional value in incorporating the various energy relations of an ecosystem into a readily comprehensible pattern. Following a productive career as Director of the Institute of Marine Science, of the University of Texas, Odum recently assumed the directorship of the terrestrial ecology program of the Puerto Rico Nuclear Center.

The study of Silver Springs reported here has been made with the purpose of determining the basic structure and workings of flowing water ecosystems by the careful study of one stream under some unusually favorable conditions provided. In recent years such holistic consideration of the energy flux and biomass have provided a fruitful approach to the understanding of many types of ecological communities. . . . Diagrammatically, the object of the energy approach may be said to be the complete quantitative determination of the states and flow in Figure 7 as well as the control mechanisms by which such a picture is sustained. The story in this paper concerns the details and workings previewed in Figure 7. . . .

Energy flow diagram. In Figure 7 the flow of energy through the community in Silver Springs was shown according to trophic levels. The use of the diagram is applicable in general form to any system. It shows distinctly the workings of the first two laws of thermodynamics. According to the first law the total influx of energy equals the total flux out. According to the second law, especially as interpreted with the optimum efficiency maximum power hypothesis. . ., wherever an energy transformation occurs most of the energy is dispersed into heat that is unavailable for further use by the organisms in the community.

Since the overall metabolism has now been estimated. . . it is now possible to make some rough estimates of the component flow rates. Where estimates are complete, the diagram may be used as a check since the parts must agree with the whole. Where estimates are incomplete the diagram may be used to fill in the part from the total. The figure must be regarded as extremely tentative because of the many possible errors and incomplete data.

As discussed in the animal growth rate section, there are several procedures required to work out the flow rates of production at the various trophic levels. To obtain the respiration of a trophic level one determines the standing crops, estimates the respiratory metabolism per gram, and multiplies to obtain the total respiratory metabolism in each trophic level. The net production of the trophic level follows from the determination of the growth rates (output)

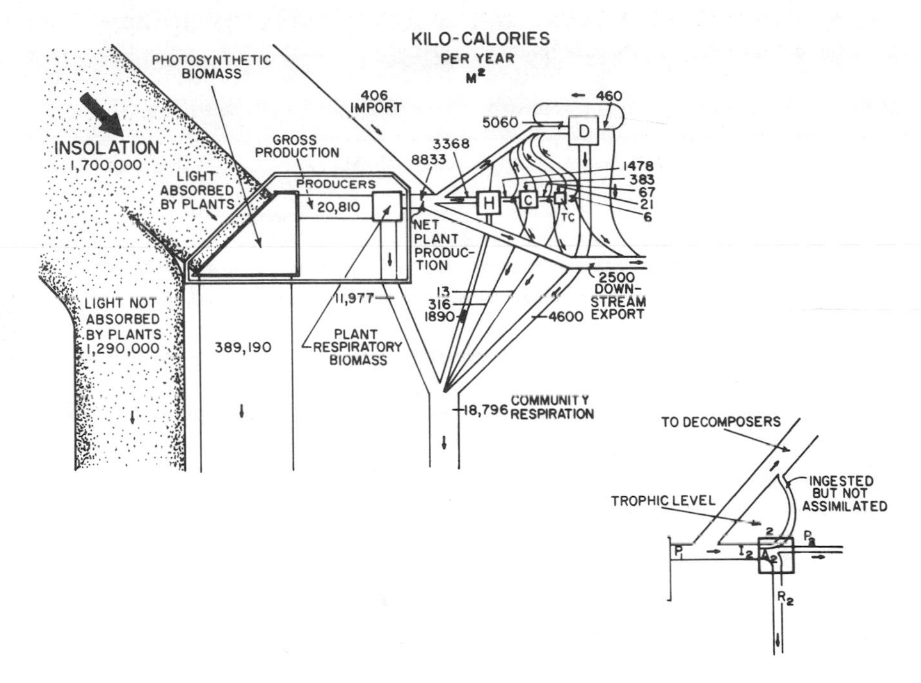

FIG. 7. *Energy flow diagram with estimates of energy flows in kilo-calories per square meter per year in the Silver Springs community. The small diagram contains symbols used in text discussion (P, production; I, energy intake; A, consumer assimilation; R, respiration).*

directly using varied means depending on the organisms. As described in sections on animal growth rate above, this has been done in some cases and reported as turnover. The best estimates from this table are used in the energy flow diagram in Figure 7. The input of energy into a trophic level is mainly the sum of the respiration and net production if one neglects egested unassimilated matter. The flow picture in Figure 7 shows the relationship of growth, utilization, assimilation, and heat loss for each trophic level. From these concepts one may also derive the several types of efficiencies (ratios × 100) useful in describing ecological systems. These are defined as follows using symbols from the flow diagram:

P = production rate (rate of net organic synthesis in the form of the species of the trophic level or in storage products)

A = rate of assimilation

I = rate of ingestion (consumption) or energy intake

R = rate of respiration

E_u = utilization efficiency

$$= \frac{I_2}{P_1} = \frac{I_3}{P_2} = \frac{I_4}{P_3} = \frac{I_5}{P_4}$$

E_a = assimilation efficiency

$$= \frac{A_2}{I_2} = \frac{A_3}{I_3} = \frac{A_4}{I_4} = \frac{A_5}{I_5}$$

E_t = tissue growth efficiency

$$= \frac{P_2}{A_2} = \frac{P_3}{A_3} = \frac{P_4}{A_4} = \frac{P_5}{A_5}$$

E_e = ecological growth efficiency

$$= \frac{P_2}{I_2} = (E_t)\ (E_a)$$

E_l = Lindeman efficiency (ratio of intakes of trophic levels)

$$= \frac{I_2}{I_1} = (E_e)\ (E_u)$$

E_p = trophic level production ratios

$$= \frac{P_2}{P_1} = (E_u)\ (E_e) = (E_u)\ (E_t)\ (E_a)$$

The data in Figure 7 permit the calculation of the ecological growth efficiencies (E_e) and the trophic level production ratios (E_p, synonomous with Lindeman's usage of trophic level efficiencies only in the first trophic level). The ecological growth efficiencies E_e and the trophic level production ratios are given as follows:

	E_e	E_p	E_l
Plant Net Production	$\frac{8,833}{20,810} = 42\%$	$\frac{8,833}{20,810} = 42\%$	$\frac{20,810}{410,000} = 5\%$
Herbivores	$\frac{1,478}{3,368} = 44\%$	$\frac{1,478}{8,833*} = 17\%*$	$\frac{3,368*}{20,810} = 16\%*$
Carnivores	$\frac{67}{383} = 17\%$	$\frac{67}{1,478*} = 5\%*$	$\frac{383}{3,368*} = 11\%*$
Top Carnivores	$\frac{6}{21} = 29\%$	$\frac{6}{67} = 9\%$	$\frac{21}{383} = 6\%$

Great confusion often results from misunderstanding as to which efficiency is meant. The energy flow diagram is a help in this clarification. In another communication some current uses of the term production as synonomous with assimilation are questioned.

The general principle from Lindeman and Dineen that trophic level efficiency (E_l or E_p) increased along the food chain was not entirely confirmed for Silver Springs although the estimates of rates at the higher trophic levels are probably not accurate enough to test the relationship definitely.

Turnover, climax and steady state. With a gross primary production during a year of 6390 gms/m^2 and with a standing crop biomass of all components of 819 gms/m^2 it is clear from the ratio that the community turnover is 8 times/year. As discussed elsewhere, the smaller the component organism, the more rapid the turnover. Thus the overall community turnover has meaning only in that it expresses the relationship of the size of the community and the total productivity.

Where all of the components of a community turn over several times a year there would be ample opportunity for changes to occur if there were no self regulative mechanisms. In Silver Springs there is apparently a fairly high degree of stability. Shelford & Eddy presented evidence that the climax concept was applicable to streams. The Silver Springs community is strong evidence that where the hydrographic climate is constant the community may develop a steady state. The possible relationship to the balanced aquarium idea is discussed elsewhere.

It is suggested that the stability of a system be measured by the number of times it turns over without change. Thus communities of small organism which persist for a year with a daily turnover may be considered as stable in this sense as a community of large organisms which lasts 300 years while turning over once per year.

The summer pulse of primary production due to the greater influx of light mainly leads to an increase in reproduction in the consumers rather than to pulses, blooms, and changes in populations. The increases in rates at any one trophic level are accompanied apparently by increases in utilization at other trophic levels so that the standing crops do not change markedly. . . .

*These figures have been corrected from the original publication at the request of the author [Ed.].

NITRATE IN THE SEA

H. W. Harvey—1926

Reprinted by permission of the publisher from Journal of the Marine Biological Association of the United Kingdom **14**: 71–88, 1926. Published by Cambridge University Press.

H. W. Harvey, a pioneer in marine biological chemistry, describes here not only the inverse relationship between the size of diatom populations and nitrogen availability but also the regulation of environment by organisms. In the nitrogen cycle, utilizable nitrogen is returned to the system by organisms acting on the bound nitrogen in the excreta and remains of other organisms; the major function of the environment in the process is in physically distributing the requisite materials.

THE NITROGEN CYCLE

Denitrifying bacteria have been found in water near the shore and in mud of the Baltic, but as pointed out by Gran they are not likely to play a part in the economy of the open oceans, since the water almost invariably contains a sufficiency of oxygen for these bacteria, without their having recourse to attack the small quantities of nitrates present.

Azotobacter, fixing dissolved nitrogen has been found in the slime of Baltic algæ and in bottom deposits from near the land. There is no evidence as yet that they are general in occurrence or that they add more than a minute fraction to the combined nitrogen in the sea.

As far as we know the inorganic salts necessary for plant life are always present in sea-water in ample amount except phosphates and nitrates. Iron is a possible exception. The nitrates are converted by the algæ into proteins, etc. Some of these algæ die, and from the decay of their corpses ammonium salts are produced. Others nourish marine animals which in turn are fed upon by other animals. These excrete the products of their metabolism and in due course die; ammonium salts are produced from their corpses and excreta by bacterial action.

Thus we have in the sea a closed cycle.

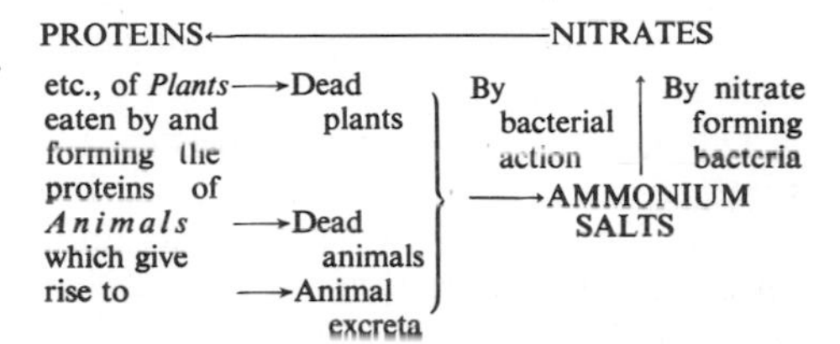

Phosphate is regenerated in a similar manner, and the evidence so far obtained shows that in both cases the cycle is practically a closed one, the increment due to land washings not being very great compared with the amount continually being regenerated from dead marine organisms.

A deficiency of nutrient salts limits both the rate of multiplication of vegetable plankton, and in all probability the rate of carbon assimilation as well. All the energy expended in the vital processes of plants and animals in the sea is derived from the energy of light absorbed during the course of carbon assimilation by phytoplankton—the fixed algæ being but a small proportion of the plant life.

Hence a quantitative knowledge of those factors, which control and limit the multiplication of vegetable plankton and which affect its efficiency as an energy absorber, is the first step in any fundamental inquiry concerning the fertility of the sea.

The consideration of this cycle indicates that the fertility of any area of the open oceans, not subject to considerable inflows of water from other areas, depends upon three main factors. (*a*) The length of time protein formed by phytoplankton remains part of the plant or nourished animal's body. (*b*) The time which elapses during the decay and formation of ammonium salts and phosphate from corpses and excreta. To this must be added the time taken for nitrate forming bacteria to convert the ammonium into nitrates. (*c*) The time which elapses before the reformed nitrate and phosphate again reaches the upper layers where there is sufficient light for photosynthesis.

Dealing with these three factors in turn, the first is controlled by the natural length of life of the plants and animals, and by the proportion of the plants which are eaten. This decides the proportion of total living matter to the rate of loss by natural death. The proportion of total living matter to its rate of loss by respiration and excretion is controlled by *temperature*. In a warm sea the loss will be in excess of that taking place under colder conditions, since the rate of metabolism roughly doubles for a rise of 10°C., and more food will be required by animals to provide for their irreducible metabolism necessary to maintain life.

Of the second factor (*b*) there is little information. Presumably the breakdown products of proteins and phosphoproteins produced in the course of metabolism are excreted mostly as urea and phosphates, and the decay of corpses is largely brought about by bacterial agency. From the analyses of water collected in the Atlantic during the expedition of the *Planet* it appears that there is rarely less than 25 milligrams per cubic metre of ammonium nitrogen in the waters of the open ocean. The distribution of nitrate forming bacteria, possibly identical with the *nitrobacter* of the land in the open ocean is quite unknown.

The third factor (*c*), being the length of time that the reformed nitrate lies unusable below the illuminated upper layers, is of great magnitude. . . . [there is] an enormous store of nitrate below the upper 100-metre layer. A rough calculation indicates an amount somewhere in the order of 250 thousand million metric tons of nitrate-nitrogen in the deeper layers of the great oceans, lying dormant until such time as currents bring the deep water into the upper sunlit layers. There is every reason to suppose that this third factor regulates the speed at which nitrogen and phosphorus pass through the complete cycle in the sea *as a whole*, being the slowest in the series of changes.

In particular shallow areas, however, such as where tidal streams and sufficient surface cooling to set up convection currents reaching to the bottom cause vertical circulation, during the whole or part of the year, the regenerated nitrate is subject to no delay before again becoming available. These areas, usually coastal, are very fertile. The North Sea, English Channel, and the Shallow Shelf between the Grand Banks and Cape Cod are such. Here the conditions are somewhat complicated by a certain amount of inflow of oceanic water, and by the fact that the rate of regeneration of nitrate, and phosphate, from dead organisms overtakes the rate at which plant life utilises it during the autumn and short days of winter. A store of available nitrate and phosphate is thus formed which is rapidly used up as soon as some three hours of sunshine per day occur in the spring in the English Channel. Insufficient illumination becomes the limiting factor during the winter months, delaying for a period the rate at which combined nitrogen and phosphorus passes through the complete cycle.

In the deep open oceans the winter

cooling of the surface layers in temperated and arctic regions will set up convection currents. By lessening the density gradient, the convection currents will be assisted by wave motion in bringing about more effectual mixing with the layers below. Hence in such latitudes, as opposed to the subtropical regions, a small store of nutrient salts may be expected in the spring, and in general a richer plankton particularly in the early summer. In the tropical regions of the Atlantic the heated surface water streams away to form the Gulf Stream, etc., to be replaced by water upwelling from below. Hence in these regions richer plankton may be expected than in the subtropical. These expectations are born out by the results of Hensen's Plankton Expedition.

It is a remarkable fact that plant growth should be able to strip seawater of both nitrates and phosphates, and that in the English Channel the store of these nutrient salts formed during autumn and winter should be used up at about the same time. . . .

HYDROGEN ION CONCENTRATION, SOIL PROPERTIES AND GROWTH OF HIGHER PLANTS

O. Arrhenius—1922

Reprinted by permission of the publisher from Arkiv für Botanik **18**: 1–54, 1922.

There are two major ecological principles developed in this paper: (1) the principle of interaction of factors, namely of substrate, climate and organisms in soil formation and reaction, and (2) the principle of regulation, namely the regulatory role of soil in determining plant associations and the modifying influence of plants on the nature and properties of soil.

We may therefore say, that in every soil there exists a certain concentration of hydrogen ions, and by measuring this, we also measure the actual acidity of the soil.

The question of the origin of this acidity has caused a vivid discussion. It has been shown, that not only humus but also sterilized cotton and other substances quite free from acids are able to "absorb" alkali. There are also pretty many acid mineral soils known, where it is impossible to identify any particular acid, but still they are giving an acid reaction.

This has been explained by so called selective adsorption, but there remained still some very essential points unexplained.

Also with the conceptions of the colloid chemists it has been quite impossible to find any satisfactory solution of the question. But there are many facts speaking for, that we must take a new point of view in the soil-science. . . .

Also several authors have shown that soils are acting as buffers (and it is not the inorganic salts in the soils which are the main factors) so that humus soils are very strong buffers, clays medium and sand weak, but even the buffer action of pure sand is greater than that of e. g. hydrochloric acid or SÖRENSEN's phosphate solutions.

On the other hand clay behaves as gelatine and this behaviour is independent of orgin or original reaction.

It is very probable, that all substances behave in the same manner, i.e., that they are real salt formers. We can thus say that the same laws hold for particles not visible in the ultramicroscope up to stones big as the fist or more.

These ampholytes give a certain hydrogen ion concentration to the solution due to their very low dissociation and this is the chief source of the hydrogen ion concentration of the soil.

After what is said above one may say that the soil is a system of ampholytes, partly dissociated, partly undissociated, water, air and small amounts of salts. . .

The first loose earth crust was probably nearly neutral. This assumption is founded on the fact, that on one hand most volcanic ashes investigated are neutral or nearly neutral, on the other hand that when digging into the soil and penetrating deeper than the uppermost region of great fluctuations one mostly reaches strata, which are practically neutral.

It also seems very probable that the earth came out of its smelting stage in a rather neutral and homogeneous condition.

The factors influencing the development of alkaline and acid soils are chiefly the relation between precipitate and evaporation, the vegetation and the rocks and their debris.

If we assume that the surface of the soil from the beginning had a neutral reaction and that it is acting as an ampholyte it is easily understood how the differences, now so great, have developed. During earlier geological periods the climate was much more moist and rainy and the atmosphere richer in carbonic dioxide. The washing out must then have gone on with a much higher rate than nowadays, and as this is not small it is easy to understand how immense areas have gained in salt content and thus alkalinity whereas others are so well washed out that the soils more or less have come to their isoelectric point.

Through this washing out process and later climate changes new soil conditions have been developed which may be looked at as primary conditions, when we only take a short period into consideration.

The process is going on so that the rainwater loaded with carbon dioxide and acidified by the humus decomposes the alkali- and alkali earth silicates and carries away more readily soluble salts of these elements. In the low lands where the water is spreading over wide areas, e. g. as seepage in the soil or by irrigation, and the evaporation is strong, the solution becomes more and more concentrated and also the carbon dioxide of double carbonates is given off by stillstanding [*sic*], the salts therefore are more or less deposited and the soil made alkaline. . . .

It is only as long as the rocks nearly reach the soil surface that they have a great influence. As soon as covered with debris they loose their direct influence. Also the mineral-soil looses a great deal of its importance as former of the surface soil reaction, when the plants have taken the ground. But indirectly the mineral soil and the rocks are always influencing the soil reaction through the soil water. . . .

Within a very short time, 50 years or less, the ground is covered with a layer of decomposing plant substances, mould or peat, and then this covering layer will play the greatest rôle for the soil acidity as influencing the vegetation, because the plants always first come in contact and grow a greater part of their life in this soil.

Therefore it is impossible to predict

the soil reaction with aid of geological maps, neither using the rocks nor the mineral soils as indicators. One only very generally can state, that one may expect alkaline, neutral or slightly acid soils, where there is much lime in the subsoil, whereas in siliceous regions the soils may be more or less acid. . . .

The most important factor in the formation of the soil reaction, however, are the plants and their humus forming action.

From long ago it has been well known that under certain associations one finds a special soil. The best and most close study of these things is delivered by P. E. MÜLLER in his book on the humus formation in the Danish forests, where he shows that there is a correlation between the two types: Oxalis-Fagus-Wood and Trientalis-Fagus-Wood and the mild and raw humus. But he and many following authors saw in the soil the primary, and the vegetation was looked at as a secondary factor.

Some years ago the author showed, that the soil type, the soil reaction and the vegetation type are dependent of each other, so that the soil reaction is the primary factor but in many and essential ways influenced by the vegetation. . . .

The process may be regarded as follows: The pioneer-plants move in on the mineral soil, and within a short time a rather thick humus layer is formed. In northern countries as southern Sweden there can be formed a layer of up to half a meter or more in 100 years. The rate of humus formation is very different in different places but is at least of the same order of degree in temperate and tropic parts of the world when the climate is humid. The author observed by visiting Verlaten Eiland, one of the islands in the Krakatoa-archipelago destroyed by eruption in 1883, how in the Casuarina vegetation a layer of humus of about 10 cm thickness was formed. In other vegetation types there was found less, down to 5 cm. Also on volcanoes which recently have been in action there were observed rather thick humus deposits, up to 0.5 m., which must have been formed during the last 20—30 years.

As soon as this humus layer is formed the plants are more or less independent of underlying strata and the properties of the humus play the great rôle.

The humus deposits also influence the further developement of the soil profile through their more or less acidifying influence on the percolating water. . . . the saps of different plants have widely different acidity and also plant debris of different plants have a reaction which seems to lie very near to that of the pre-sap from the living plant.

Now it seems . . . as if those plants forming a certain stabilized association, and thus also forming the humus and the reaction, also have their optimal growth at that reaction, but in all unstabilized associations the reaction forming power plays a great rôle in the competition.

But also in stabilized associations there will occur changes. For instance the trees fall or fire devastates the forest and then one gets a natural clearing. It has been shown by OLSEN that on such wind clearings the reaction may change rather much, for instance from 5.2—6.6.

A very great influence is caused by man who sometimes incidentally sometimes consciously changes the soil reaction.

By deforestation, thus preventing a good deal of humus formation, the acidifying action of the soil is decreased. The cattle, when grazing, are also taking away an enormous amount of organic matter which otherwise would have taken a part in the humus formation. . .

More conscious [*sic*] has a change in the reaction been made for agricultural purposes. The first used method was probably the denshiring of woods thus forming alkaline ash and clearing the wood, both actions which change the soil reaction. Later on, when agriculture was more developed the farmers have been using lime, marle and clay to a great extent, trying to improve the soil condition. . . .

THE BIOLOGICAL CONTROL OF CHEMICAL FACTORS IN THE ENVIRONMENT

Alfred C. Redfield—1958

Reprinted by permission of the author and publisher from American Scientist **46**: 205–221, 1958.

Redfield's essay has as its central theme that the nitrate in the sea and the oxygen in the atmosphere are controlled by the biochemical cycle. This is environment regulated by organism. However, the biochemical cycle is ultimately determined by the solubility of phosphate. This is organism regulated by environment. Operationally, both types of regulatory mechanisms function to promote stability. Dr. Redfield has been a staff member of Harvard University and the Woods Hole Oceanographic Institution for over thirty five years.

It is a recognized principle of ecology that the interactions of organisms and environment are reciprocal. The environment not only determines the conditions under which life exists, but the organisms influence the conditions prevailing in their environment. . . .

The purpose of this essay is to discuss the relations between the statistical proportions in which certain elements enter into the biochemical cycle in the sea, and their relative availability in the water. These relations suggest not only that the nitrate present in sea water and the oxygen of the atmosphere have been produced in large part by organic activity, but also that their quantities are determined by the requirements of the biochemical cycle. . . .

THE BIOCHEMICAL CYCLE

The production of organic matter in the sea is due to the photosynthetic activity of microscopic floating plants, the phytoplankton, and is limited to the surface layers where sufficient light is available. The formation of organic matter in the autotrophic zone requires all the elements in protoplasm, of which carbon, nitrogen, and phosphorus are of particular concern. These are drawn from the carbonate, nitrate, and phosphate of the water. Following the death of the plants the organic matter is destroyed, either by the metabolism of animals or the action of microorganisms. Normally, decomposition is completed by oxidation so that carbon, nitrogen, and phosphorus are returned to the sea water as carbonate, nitrate, and phosphate, while requisite quantities of free oxygen are withdrawn from the water.

The autotrophic zone has a depth of 200 meters at most and includes less than five per cent of the volume of the ocean. Below this zone, life depends on organic matter carried down by organisms sinking from above or by the vertical migrations of animals back and forth between the depths. Although the greater part of the nutrient chemicals absorbed in the autotrophic zone complete the cycle in this layer, the portion which sinks as organic matter tends to deplete the surface layers of these chemicals and, with the decomposition of the organic matter in the depths, to enrich this heterotrophic zone with the products of decomposition.

The existence of the vast reservoir of deep water in which organic matter may accumulate and decay out of reach of autotrophic resynthesis is a distinctive feature of the oceanic environment which enables one to separate, in observation and thinking, the constructive and destructive phases of the biochemical cycle. . . .

CORRESPONDENCE BETWEEN REQUIREMENT AND AVAILABILITY OF PHOSPHORUS, NITROGEN, AND OXYGEN

The stoichiometric relations . . . indicate that phosphorus, nitrogen, and oxygen are available in ocean water in very nearly the same proportions as those in which they enter the biochemical cycle. In discussing the remarkable coincidence in the supply and demand for nitrogen and phosphorus it has been pointed out that it might arise from: (1) a coincidence dependent on the accidents of geochemical history; (2) adaptation on the part of the organisms; or (3) organic processes which tend in some way to control the proportions of these elements in the water.

Of the first alternative not much can be said except that the probability that the ratio in the sea be what it is rather than any other is obviously small. That the coincidence applies to the oxygen as well as to the nutrient elements compounds the improbability.

For the second alternative, it may be said that the phytoplankton do have some ability to vary their elementary composition when one element or another is deficient in the medium in which they grow. Such physiology might account for the coincidence in the nitrogen-phosphorus ratios. However, it is not evident how adaptation could determine the oxygen relation since this depends more on the quantity than the quality of the organic matter formed, and the oxygen requirement is felt only after the death of the living plant.

For these reasons the third alternative deserves serious consideration. Mechanisms should be examined by which organic processes may have tended to control the proportions of phosphorus, nitrogen, and oxygen available for life in the sea. . . .

THE PHOSPHORUS-OXYGEN RATIO

. . . It is widely held among geochemists that the primitive atmosphere was devoid of oxygen, or at least contained very much less oxygen than at present. During the course of geological history atmospheric oxygen is thought to have been produced by the photochemical dissociation of water in the upper atmosphere and by the photosynthetic reduction of carbon dioxide, previously present in much greater quantities. . . . Estimates of the quantity of reduced carbon present in the earth's crust as coal and petroleum indicate that photosynthetic processes have been much more than adequate to produce the present oxygen content of the atmosphere. It has not been suggested, to my knowledge, why this process has proceeded just so far as it has; that is, why there is 21 per cent of oxygen in the atmosphere at present, no more or no less. It is, however, on this fact that the quantity of oxygen dissolved in the sea depends.

My supposition is that the actual quantities of oxygen present in the sea may have been regulated by the activities of sulfate-reducing bacteria. This group of bacteria are known to have the ability to use sulfates as a source of oxygen when free oxygen is absent and organic compounds are present to supply a source of energy. The over-all reaction is $SO_4^= \longrightarrow S^= + 2\,O_2$.

The process should be broken down into two steps, each of which takes place in the sea under different environmental conditions, (1) Sulfate Reduction, $SO_4^= + 2\,C \rightarrow 2\,CO_2 + S^=$ which occurs at depth under anaerobic conditions, and (2) Photosynthesis $2\,CO_2 \rightarrow 2\,C + O_2$ which occurs near the surface in the presence of light.

In these equations C represents the reduced carbon present in organic matter. The decomposition of this material by sulfate-reducing bacteria according to the first step also liberates a corresponding quantity of nitrogen and phosphorus, which permit the CO_2 formed to re-enter the biological cycle when the second step comes into play. The CO_2 produced in this way can thus contribute to the production of oxygen in a way in which the excess carbonate normally present in sea water cannot.

The first step, which depends upon the presence of organic matter in excess of the free oxygen required to complete its decomposition, will initiate a mechanism which will tend to increase the oxygen when, and only when, the quantity of available free oxygen is deficient. If the total mechanism has operated on a large enough scale in the course of geochemical history, it may have kept the supply of oxygen available in the sea adjusted to the requirements of the biochemical cycle.

There is very good evidence that sulfate reduction does operate on a large scale in the sea wherever anaerobic conditions exist. . . .

GEOCHEMICAL CONSIDERATIONS

As a final check on these speculations, we can look at the relative availability of the principal materials of the biochemical cycle on the earth's surface, to see if they conform to the postulates...

. . . the numbers of atoms relative to the atoms of phosphorus in the ocean. . . are indicated in Figure 3 which presents in diagrammatic form the biochemical cycle as described.

The diagram shows phosphate, nitrate, and carbonate entering the organic phase of the biochemical cycle near the sea surface, through the process of photosynthesis. Phosphorus, nitrogen, and carbon are selected by the synthetic process in the proportions of 1:15:105. This is the step which coordinates the cycles of the several elements in a unique way and gives meaning to the comparisons. The elements are carried in these proportions to the point of decomposition where they are oxidized to their original state as phosphate, nitrate, and carbonate. The oxygen required is just that set free by photosynthesis. Such a cycle could run indefinitely in an otherwise closed system so long as light is supplied.

To account for the correspondence in the ratios of phosphorus and nitrogen in the organic phase of the cycle and in the inorganic environment, bacterial processes of nitrogen fixation and denitrification are indicated at the upper right and, similarly, the sulfate reduction process is shown at the lower left. This latter is assumed to operate effectively only when the environment becomes anaerobic. Finally, the exchanges with the atmosphere and the sediments of the sea bottom are shown. If these processes are operative it is necessary that supplies are adequate and that their products exist in suitable quantities.

Considering first nitrogen, there exist in sea water for each atom of phosphorus 15 atoms of nitrogen available as NO_3 and a reserve of 510 atoms of nitrogen as dissolved N_2 which may be drawn on by nitrogen-fixing bacteria. In addition, there is a reserve of nitrogen

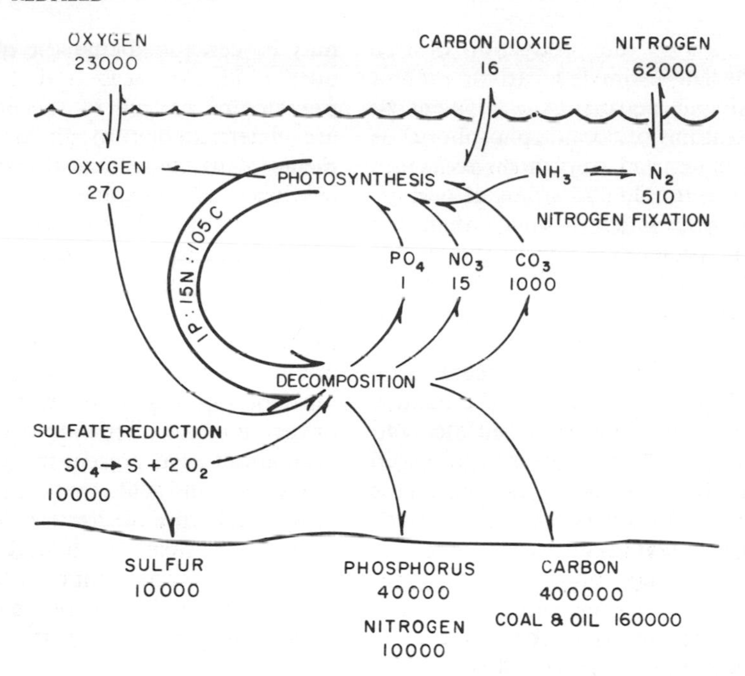

FIG. 3. *The Biochemical Cycle. Numbers represent quantities of respective elements present in the atmosphere, the ocean, and the sedimentary rocks, relative to the number of atoms of phosphorus in the ocean.*

in the atmosphere equivalent to 86,000 atoms of phosphorus, which is available to replace that dissolved in the sea were it to be drawn on. The nitrogen of the sedimentary rocks is about one-sixth that in the atmosphere and twenty times that in the ocean. More than four-fifths of this is fossil nitrogen which may be assumed to be derived from organic matter. Consequently, large quantities of nitrogen have passed through the biochemical cycle in its passage from the atmospheric reserves to be deposited in sediments at the sea bottom. The quantity withdrawn in this way is small, however, in comparison to the reserve in the atmosphere. Clearly, the nitrogen supply is adequate.

Sulfate is one of the most abundant ions in sea water. In this form there is present sulfur equivalent to 10,000 atoms of phosphorus. It would be capable of supplying oxygen equivalent to 40,000 atoms of phosphorus on reduction. Clearly, the sulfate reduction mechanism could continue to operate for a long time. If it has operated as postulated in the past much sulfide may have been removed from the sea. Sedimentary rocks are estimated to contain sulfur equivalent to 10,000 atoms of oceanic phosphorus. If this were all the product of sulfate reduction, this would have produced oxygen equivalent to 40,000 atoms of oceanic phosphorus, which is almost twice that present in the atmosphere. It is not clear how much of the sulfur in sedimentary rocks is present as sulfides, but much of it is. Clearly, much oxygen can have been produced in the past by sulfate reduction and possibly this process has contributed to an important degree in producing the oxygen of the atmosphere.

Carbon is present in the sea, chiefly as carbonate ions, in about ten times the quantity required for the biochemical cycle. Much of the large deposits of carbon in the sedimentary rocks is present as carbonates and cannot have contributed to the production of free oxygen. The estimated carbon present as coal and petroleum, equivalent to 160,000 atoms of oceanic phosphorus, is sufficient to yield oxygen on reduction equivalent to 320,000 atoms of oceanic phosphorus, which is more than ten times the present content of the atmosphere.

The known facts of geochemistry do not appear to contradict the suppositions presented on the mechanism which may have controlled the relative availability of phosphate, nitrate, and oxygen in the sea. Sources of nitrogen and sulfate are available in great excess and the by-products of the reactions can be adequately accounted for. According to these suppositions, phosphorus is the master element which controls the availability of the others. . . .

If the argument presented is sound it may be concluded that the quantity of nitrate in the sea, and the partial pressure of oxygen in the atmosphere are determined through the requirements of the biochemical cycle, by the solubility of phosphate in the ocean. This is a physical property of a unique chemical compound and as such is not subject to change except in so far as alterations in conditions may influence the activity coefficients of the ions involved. It follows then that the nutrient supplies in sea water, and the oxygen content of the atmosphere have been about as at present for a long time in the past and will remain at much the same level into the future. This argument may then be added to those reviewed by Rubey that the composition of sea water and atmosphere has varied surprisingly little at least since early geologic time. . . .

LAKES IN RELATION TO TERRESTRIAL LIFE PATTERNS

Aldo Leopold—1941

Reprinted by permission of the copyright owners, the Regents of the University of Wisconsin, from A symposium on hydrobiology, Madison, The University of Wisconsin Press, pp. 17–22, 1941.

This essay by an outstanding conservationist not only reflects his attitude regarding man's intervention in "our biotic constitution," but also focuses on another aspect of organism-environment regulation. The issue here is the role of organisms in the dynamics of energy exchange between two major environments as one of many interrelations between them.

FOOD CIRCUITS IN SOIL AND WATER

Soil and water are not two organic systems, but one. Both are organs of a single landscape; a derangement in either affects the health of both. We acknowledge this interaction between water and land after erosion or pollution makes them sick, but we lack a "language" for describing their normal interactions. Such a language must deal, for one thing, with their exchanges of nutrient materials.

All land represents a downhill flow of nutrients from the hills to the sea. This flow has a rolling motion. Plants and animals suck nutrients out of the soil and air and pump them upward through the food chains; the gravity of death spills them back into the soil and air. Mineral nutrients, between their successive trips through this circuit, tend to be washed downhill. Lakes retard this downhill wash, and so do soils. Without the impounding action of soils and lakes, plants and animals would have to follow their salts to the coast line.

The rate of retardation depends, for one thing, on the length and the termini of the food chains. A nutrient salt impounded in an oak may take a century to pass through an acorn, a squirrel, a redtail, and parasite before it re-enters the soil for another upward roll. The same particle may take only a year to pass through a corn plant and a fieldmouse to the soil. Again it may pass through a grass, a cow, a pig, and a member of the Townsend Club, emerging not into the soil, but into a sewer and thence into a lake. Civilization shortens food chains, and routes them into lakes and rivers instead of fields and pastures.

The rate of retardation depends also on the fertility of soils. Fertile soils wash slowly. They support long chains if we let them do so. Food circuits are intricately adjusted to maintain normal rates of retardation. A normal soil balances its intake from the decomposition of rocks against its loss from downhill wash. We now know, to our cost, the disturbing effects of too low a rate: erosion. A normal water balances its intake from the soil against its outwash to the sea. Pollution is an excess of intake arising from erosion, or from routing land wastes to water. Underfed soils thus mean overfed waters. Healthy land, by balancing the internal economy of each, balances the one against the other.

The food balance between soils and waters is accomplished not only by circuitous routes of flow, but also by eddies and back-currents. That is to say, some animals pump food back uphill. These local reversals of the downhill flow have not, to my knowledge, been described or measured. They may be important to science, and to land health, or conservation.

MOVEMENTS FROM WATER TO LAND AND FROM LAND TO WATER

Back-currents are likely to be clearly visible in areas inhabited by some animal requiring a larger supply of a particular nutrient than the soil supplics. The red deer on the Scottish highlands is a case in point. Here nutrients are scarce because the soil is derived from sterile rocks. The red deer's yearly production of new antlers calls for more calcium and phosphorus than his highland range can supply. Where and how does he get them?

Fraser Darling records the facts as a calcium-phosphorus food chain. The deer gets a little, but not enough, of these horn-building salts from the native herbs and grasses. His supply increases when fires concentrate in ashes the dilute supplies stored in the heather. Hence gamekeepers practice rotation burning on the moors. To make good his deficiency in horn-building salts, the deer taps the aquatic food chain of the lakes and tarns, where rich supplies are concentrated in aquatic animals. He eats frogs immobilized by frost. As his relative, the reindeer, is reported to do, he may eat duck eggs and dead fish. By acquiring such unusual or "depraved" food habits, the deer requisitions from lakes what his terrestrial range fails to provide.

That the stored salts are what the red

deer is after is shown by certain other extraordinary food habits which help balance his calcium-phosphorus economy. He eats the velvet from his own horns; the bones of dead deer left by hunters; his own cast antlers or those of other deer; the rabbit or vole which has extracted salts from these same materials and then chanced to die. Direct ingestion of lemmings and mice by wild reindeer has been recorded and may also be practiced by the red deer.

The ingestion of aquatic animals by deer is an uphill movement of nutrients; a back-current of the downhill stream. Food which has already "passed" the terrestrial deer but lies temporarily impounded in lakes is pulled back into the terrestrial circuit. On the other hand, the ingestion by deer of velvet, horns, bones, and dead rodents is not a back-current, but rather a short circuit in the usual roll of the food chain. The salts contained in these body parts would normally re-enter the soil and become (in part) available to the deer as plants, but by shorting this normal circuit he recovers them in less time and with less waste.

The quantity of minerals involved in these movements is small, but even small quantities may, on poor soils, be of critical importance. Range managers now realize that the continued "deportation" of phosphorus and calcium in the bones of cattle and sheep may eventually impoverish grazing ranges. Darling hints that deportation in sheep may have helped to impoverish the Scottish moors.

Many animals other than red deer tap aquatic food chains and restore food to terrestrial circuits. Many also move food in the opposite direction. The net retardation, or preponderance of uphill transport, varies from zero upward. The length of uphill transport also varies from short to long distances. Thus river ducks, geese, gulls, terns, rails, bitterns, frogs, snakes, and musk-rats eat in or at the edge of water and die or defecate inland, but they likewise eat inland and die or defecate in water. There is no clear preponderance of uphill transport. The first three range far inland, the others not far. Eagles, crows, swallows, bears, deer, caribou, and moose carry food both to and from water, but they probably move more food uphill than downhill, and to a considerable distance inland. River-spawning salmon which die inland perform a large and long uphill transport. Guano birds, penguins, herons, otters, minks, skunks, bats, and certain water-hatching, land-dying insects perform a preponderance of uphill transport, but only to a short distance inland.

Probably no other food chain concentrates so much food on so small an area as that ending in guano birds. The whole aquatic garden of the south Pacific ships its produce, via the upwelling Humboldt current, to the coastal guanays, which deposit it on their rainless island rookeries as guano. Here then is a bottleneck where the oceanic food circuit achieves a "voltage" of extraordinary intensity. The guano deposits, however, lie so near the shore and in so dry a climate that until they are moved further inland by man they have little effect on terrestrial circuits. Antarctic penguins likewise carry oceanic foods inland, but their deposits are refrigerated and eventually slide back into the sea. As against the long list of higher animals which transport food in a prevalently uphill direction, I can think of only two, man and the beaver, which get most of their food on land and deposit most of it in the water. Marsh-roosting blackbirds also do this, but only in autumn.

Most animals merely circulate food within the terrestrial or aquatic circuit which is their habitat. Thus the diving ducks, except when caught by some land predator, feed from and die into the aquatic circuits. Gallinaceous birds, except when shot by a hunter with modern conveniences, feed from and die into the terrestrial circuits.

LONG-DISTANCE TRANSPLANTATIONS

Migratory birds and fish move food to a distance from its point of origin. Until man began to ship foods and fertilizer, the only long-distance movers were water, air, and migratory animals. Migratory birds must move a considerable volume of food, with more than transitory effects. Thus Hawkins points out that the plant community under passenger pigeon roosts was distinguishable for decades after the pigeons were gone.

Transplantations by migratory animals have no clear orientation uphill or downhill.

SUMMARY AND DISCUSSION

Soil health and water health are not two problems, but one. There is a circulatory system of food substances common to both, as well as a circulatory system within each. The downhill flow is carried by gravity, the uphill flow by animals.

There is a deficit in uphill transport, which is met by the decomposition of rocks. Long food chains, by retarding downhill flow, reduce this deficit. It is further reduced by storage in soils and lakes. The continuity and stability of inland communities probably depend on this retardation and storage.

These movements of food substances seem to constitute, collectively, the nutritional system of the biotic organism. It may be surmised, by analogy with individual plants and animals, that it has qualitative as well as quantitative aspects. The recent history of biology is largely a disclosure of the importance of qualitative nutrition within plants and animals, and within land and water communities. Is it also important as between land and water? Does the wild goose, reconnoitering the farmer's cornfield, bring something more than wild music from the lake, take something more than waste corn from his field?

Such questions are, for the moment, beyond the boundaries of precise knowledge, but not beyond the boundaries of intelligent speculation. We can at least foresee that the prevalent mutilations of soil and water systems, and wholesale simplification of native faunas and floras, may have unpredictable repercussions. Neither agriculturists nor aquiculturists have so far shown any consciousness of this possibility. A prudent technology should alter the natural order as little as possible.

HOMAGE TO SANTA ROSALIA OR WHY ARE THERE SO MANY KINDS OF ANIMALS?

G. Evelyn Hutchinson—1959

Reprinted by permission of the author and publisher from The American Naturalist **93**: 145–159, 1959.

Although he may be best recognized for his contributions to biogeochemistry, Hutchinson's publications in limnology and population ecology have been no less significant. In this essay, notwithstanding its chance homage to a saint of unknown history presumed for purposes of the essay to be the patroness of evolutionary studies, Hutchinson explores the diversity of species as a function of the complexities of trophic organization and niche diversification in achieving stability. Professor Hutchinson's succession of productive students from his "itinerant ivory tower" at Yale and his significant contributions to ecology led to his being recognized as Eminent Ecologist by the Ecological Society of America in 1962.

There are at the present time supposed to be about one million described species of animals. Of these about three-quarters are insects, of which a quite disproportionately large number are members of a single order, the Coleoptera.[1] The marine fauna although it has at its disposal a much greater area than has the terrestrial, lacks this astonishing diversity. If the insects are excluded, it would seem to be more diverse. The proper answer to my initial question [why there are such an enormous number of animal species] would be to develop a theory at least predicting an order of magnitude for the number of species of 10^6 rather than 10^8 or 10^4. This I certainly cannot do. At most it is merely possible to point out some of the factors which would have to be considered if such a theory was ever to be constructed. . . .

[1]There is a story, possibly apocryphal, of the distinguished British biologist, J. B. S. Haldane, who found himself in the company of a group of theologians. On being asked what one could conclude as to the nature of the Creator from a study of his creation, Haldane is said to have answered, "An inordinate fondness for beetles."

FOOD CHAINS

Animal ecologists frequently think in terms of food chains, of the form *individuals of species* S_1 *are eaten by those of* S_2, *of* S_2 *by* S_3, *of* S_3 *by* S_4, etc. In such a food chain S_1 will ordinarily be some holophylic organism or material derived from such organisms. The simplest case is that in which we have a true *predator chain* in Odum's convenient terminology, in which the lowest link is a green plant, the next a herbivorous animal, the next a primary carnivore, the next a secondary carnivore, etc. A specially important type of predator chain may be designated Eltonian, because in recent years C. S. Elton has emphasized its widespread significance, in which the predator at each level is larger and rarer than its prey. This phenomenon was recognized much earlier, notably by A. R. Wallace in his contribution to the 1858 communication to the Linnean Society of London.

In such a system we can make a theoretical guess of the order of magnitude of the diversity that a single food chain can introduce into a community. If we assume that in general 20 per cent of the energy passing through one link can enter the next link in the chain, which is overgenerous (Slobodkin in an unpublished study finds 13 per cent as a reasonable upper limit) and if we suppose that each predator has twice the mass, (or 1.26 the linear dimensions) of its prey, which is a very low estimate of the size difference between links, the fifth animal link will have a population of one ten thousandth (10^{-4}) of the first, and the fiftieth animal link, if there was one, a population of 10^{-49} the size of the first. Five animal links are certainly possible, a few fairly clear cut cases having been in fact recorded. If, however, we wanted 50 links, starting with a protozoan or rotifer feeding on algae with a density of 10^6 cells per ml, we should need a volume of 10^{26} cubic kilometers to accommodate on an average one specimen of the ultimate predator, and this is vastly greater than the volume of the world ocean. Clearly the Eltonian food-chain of itself cannot give any great diversity, and the same is almost certainly true of the other types of food chain, based on detritus feeding or on parasitism. . . .

Effect of size. A second important limitation of the length of a food chain is due to the fact that ordinarily animals change their size during free life. If the terminal member of a chain were a fish that grew from say one cm to 150 cms in the course of an ordinary life, this size change would set a limit by competition to the possible number of otherwise conceivable links in the 1–150 cm range. At least in fishes this type of process (metaphoetesis) may involve the smaller specimens belonging to links below the larger and the chain length is thus lengthened, though under strong limitations, by cannibalism. . . .

Effects of terrestrial plants. The extraordinary diversity of the terrestrial fauna, which is much greater than that of the marine fauna, is clearly due largely to the diversity provided by terrestrial plants. This diversity is actually two-fold. Firstly, since terrestrial plants compete for light, they have tended to evolve into structures growing into a gaseous medium of negligible buoyancy. This has led to the formation of specialized supporting, photosynthetic, and reproductive structures which inevitably differ in chemical and physical properties. . . . A major source of terrestrial diversity was thus introduced by the evolution of almost 200,000 species of flowering plants, and the three quarters of a million insects supposedly known today are in part a product of that diversity. But of itself merely providing five or ten kinds of food of different consistencies and compositions does not get us much further than the five or ten links of an Eltonian pyramid. On the whole the problem still remains, but in the new form: why are there so many kinds of plants? As a zoologist I do not want to attack that question directly, I want to stick with animals, but also to get the answer. Since, however, the plants are part of the general system of communities, any sufficiently abstract properties of such communities are likely to be relevant to plants as well as to herbivores and carnivores. . . .

INTERRELATIONS OF FOOD CHAINS

Biological communities do not consist of independent food chains, but of food webs, of such a kind that an individual at any level (corresponding to a link in a single chain) can use some but not all of the food provided by species in the levels below it. . . .

MacArthur concludes that in the evolution of a natural community two partly antagonistic processes are occurring. More efficient species will replace less efficient species, but more stable communities will outlast less stable communities. In the process of community formation, the entry of a new species may involve one of three possibilities. It may completely displace an old species. This of itself does not necessarily change the stability, though it may do so if the new species inherently has a more stable population than the old. Secondly, it may occupy an unfilled niche, which may, by providing new partially independent links, increase stability. Thirdly, it may partition a niche with a pre-existing species. Elton in a fascinating work largely devoted to the fate of species accidentally or purposefully introduced by man, concludes that in very diverse communities such introductions are difficult. Early in the history of a community we may suppose many niches will be empty and invasion will proceed easily; as the community becomes more diversified, the process will be progressively more difficult. Sometimes an extremely successful invader may oust a species but add little or nothing to stability, at other times the invader by some specialization will be able to compete successfully for the marginal parts of a niche. In all cases it is probable that invasion is most likely when one or more species happen to be fluctuating and are underrepresented at a given moment. As the communities build up, these opportunities will get progressively rarer. In this way a complex community containing some highly specialized species is constructed asymptotically.

Modern ecological theory therefore appears to answer our initial question at least partially by saying that there is a great diversity of organisms because communities of many diversified organisms are better able to persist than are communities of fewer less diversified organisms. Even though the entry of an invader which takes over part of a niche will lead to the reduction in the *average* population of the species originally present, it will also lead to an increase in stability reducing the risk of the original population being at times underrepresented to a dangerous degree In this way loss of some niche space may be compensated by reduction in the amplitude of fluctuations in a way that can be advantageous to both species. The process however appears likely to be asymptotic and we have now to consider what sets the asymptote, or in simpler words why are there not more different kinds of animals?

LIMITATION OF DIVERSITY

It is first obvious that the processes of evolution of communities must be under various sorts of external control, and that in some cases such control limits the possible diversity. Several investigators, notably Odum and MacArthur, have pointed out that the more or less cyclical oscillations observed in arctic and boreal fauna may be due in part to the communities not being sufficiently complex to damp out oscillations. It is certain that the fauna of any such region is qualitatively poorer than that of warm temperate and tropical areas of comparable effective precipitation. . . . It is reasonable to suppose that the total biomass may be involved. If the fundamental productivity of an area is limited by a short growing season to such a degree that the total biomass is less than under more favorable conditions, then the rarer species in a community may be so rare that they do not exist. It is also probable that certain absolute limitations on growth-forms of plants, such as those that make the development of forest impossible above a certain latitude, may in so acting, severely limit the number of niches. . . .

NICHE REQUIREMENTS

The various evolutionary tendencies, notably metaphoetesis, which operate on single food chains must operate equally on the food-web, but we also have a new, if comparable, problem as to how much difference between two species at the same level is needed to prevent them from occupying the same niche. Where metric characters are involved we can gain some insight into this extremely important problem by the study of what Brown and Wilson have called *character displacement* or the divergence shown when two partly allopatric species of comparable niche requirements become sympatric in part of their range.

. . . In the case of the aquatic insects with which I began my address, we have over most of Europe three very closely allied species of Corixa, the largest *punctata*, being about 116 per cent longer than the middle sized species *macrocephala*, and 146 per cent longer than the small species *affinis*. In northwestern Europe there is a fourth species, *C. dentipes*, as large as *C. punctata* and very similar in appearance. A single observation (Brown) suggests that this is what I have elsewhere termed a fugitive species, maintaining itself in the face of competition mainly on account of greater mobility. According to Macan while both *affinis* and *macrocephala* may occur with *punctata* they never are found with each other, so that all three species never occur together. In the eastern part of the range, *macrocephala* drops out, and *punctata* appears to have a discontinuous distribution, being recorded as far east as Simla, but not in southern Persia or Kashmir, where *affinis* occurs. In these eastern localities, where it occurs by itself, *affinis* is larger and darker than in the west, and superficially looks like *macrocephala*.

This case is very interesting because it looks as though character displacement is occurring, but that the size differences between the three species are just not great enough to allow them all to co-occur. Other characters than size are in fact clearly involved in the separation, *macrocephala* preferring deeper water than *affinis* and the latter being more tolerant of brackish conditions. It is also interesting because it calls attention to a marked difference that must occur between hemimetabolous insects with annual life cycles involving relatively long growth periods, and birds or mammals in which the period of growth in length is short and of a very special nature compared with the total life span. In the latter, niche separation may be possible merely through genetic size differences, while in a pair of animals like *C. punctata* and *C. affinis* we need not only a size difference but a seasonal one in reproduction; this is likely to be a rather complicated matter. For the larger of two species always to be larger, it must never breed later than the smaller one. I do not doubt that this is what was happening in the pond on Monte Pellegrino, but have no idea how the difference is achieved. . . .

MOSAIC NATURE OF THE ENVIRONMENT

A final aspect of the limitation of possible diversity, and one that perhaps is of greatest importance, concerns what may be called the mosaic nature of the environment. Except perhaps in open water when only uniform quasi-horizontal surfaces are considered, every area colonized by organisms has some local diversity. The significance of such local diversity depends very largely on the size of the organisms under consideration. In another paper MacArthur and I have . . . pointed out that even if we consider only the herbivorous level or only one of the carnivorous levels, there are likely, above a certain lower limit of size, to be more species of small or medium sized organisms than of large organisms. It is difficult to go much beyond crude qualitative impressions in testing this hypothesis, but we find that for mammal faunas, which contain such diverse organisms that they may well be regarded as models of whole faunas, there is a definite hint of the kind of theoretical distribution that we deduce. In qualitative terms the phenomenon can be exemplified by any of the larger species of ungulates which may require a number of different kinds of terrain within their home ranges, any one of which types of terrain might be the habitat of some small species. Most of the genera or even subfamilies of very large terrestrial animals contain only one or two sympatric species. In this connection I cannot refrain from pointing out the immense scientific importance of obtaining a really full insight into the ecology of the large mammals of Africa while they can still be studied under natural conditions. It is indeed quite possible that the results of studies on these wonderful animals would in long-range though purely practical terms pay for the establishment of greater reservations and National Parks than at present exist. . . .

We may, therefore, conclude that the reason why there are so many species of animals is at least partly because a complex trophic organization of a community is more stable than a simple one, but that limits are set by the tendency of food chains to shorten or become blurred, by unfavorable physical factors, by space, by the fineness of possible subdivision of niches, and by those characters of the environmental mosaic which permit a greater diversity of small than of large allied species. . . .

ON BIRD SPECIES DIVERSITY

Robert H. MacArthur and John W. MacArthur—1961

Reprinted by permission of the authors and publisher from Ecology **42**: 594–598, 1961.

The recognition of the stabilizing role of diversity in ecosystems prompts investigation into the description and regulation of diversity. This paper is an excellent example of such an investigation and its relevance to the discussions by Hutchinson (see page 204), Eugene Odum (see page 211) and Margalef (see page 215) will be readily apparent.

It is common experience that more species of birds breed in a mixed wood than in a field of comparable size. It is also well known that tropical forests seem to support more species than their temperate counterparts. These facts are often explained in terms of the number of "niches" or "ways of life" which the habitat provides. In this paper, a somewhat more precise analysis is attempted.

The actual number of species is better replaced by a number called the "bird species diversity," calculated as follows: Let p_i be the proportion of all of the bird individuals which belong to the ith species. Then the bird species diversity, is $-\sum_i p_i \log_e p_i$. This is a formula used by communication engineers to calculate the information generated, *e.g.*, by a typist who uses the different keys with frequencies p_i. Thus, for instance, a one species community always has zero diversity; 2 species, one with 99 individuals and one with 1 individual, will have diversity of $-.99 \log_e .99 - .01 \log_e .01 = .046 + .010 = .056$ (close to zero), while 2 species each with 50 individuals will have diversity of $.347 + .347 = .694$. This illustrates why diversity is a better measure than actual number of species, for the community with 99 of one and 1 of the other seems closer to the community with one species. Margalef has frequently used a similar measure in his plankton studies. In terms of this, the question becomes: "What is it about the environment which controls the bird species diversity?"

The procedure of the research described here was to census a wide variety of habitats, differing in (1) plant species composition, (2) foliage height profiles, and (3) latitude, and to determine how much each of these factors influenced the bird diversity. . . .

RESULTS

. . . [When] the corresponding foliage height diversity and bird species diversities . . . are plotted as a graph . . . [they show] a close fit to the line: bird species diversity = 2.01 foliage height diversity + .46, calculated by least squares. Various other subdivisions of the profile into horizontal layers were tried, and the layers 0–2′, 2′–25′ and > 25′ were chosen as those layers which made the collection of points on the graph most orderly. . . . The linearity of the cluster of points indicates that the addition of a new layer of a given amount of foliage results in the same increase in bird species diversity, (not however the same increase in number of bird species) no matter which layer (0–2′, 2–25′ or >25′) is added, and no matter which other layers are present to begin with. Thus, we can say that the layers 0–2′, 2′–25′ and >25′ are roughly equally important to the birds. (The reasons for this will be discussed later.) Looked at from this point of view, we can see the trouble with the other subdivisions. For definiteness, consider 0–15′, 15′–30′, > 30′. Adding a 0–15′ layer to a habitat without it causes a much greater increase in bird species diversity than the addition of the layer > 30′. There is nothing biological about the number of layers chosen. Four or 5 layers in a roughly similar subdivision would be more cumbersome to analyse but would presumably be even more accurate. In particular, the layers 0–½′, ½′–6′, 6′–15′ and > 15′ suggested by Elton and Miller allow a rather good prediction of the bird species diversity.

The next question is: How much of the remaining scatter, *i.e.*, how much of the variability in bird species diversity not accounted for by the variation in foliage height diversity, can be accounted for in variations of plant species diversity and latitude? Remarkably enough, the answer is "None". . . . Thus, although plant species diversity alone is a good predictor of bird species diversity it is because plant species diversity is high when foliage height diversity is high, and, when this is taken account of, plant species diversity can contribute nothing further. In other words, habitats of the same profile have the same bird species diversity whether composed of few or many plant species. . . .

DISCUSSION

These results are rather statistical in nature. What is their meaning in terms of individual birds or species? The simplest explanation which seems to account for the observations, describes the "shape" of a bird's niche. Let us return to the picture of many territories distributed over an area and consider the following evolutionary argument. A large number of species can be accommodated in an environment in a variety of ways of which there are 2 extremes. Each species may have different habitat preference and feed throughout this habitat on all kinds of food, or, all species may share the entire habitat, each species feeding on a different variety of food or in a different situation within the habitat. The first extreme violates what might be called the "jack of all trades—master of none" principle that natural selection favors the increased efficiency resulting from a certain amount of specialization. In the other extreme, specialization has proceeded so far that time and energy are wasted in travelling between spots for which the specializations are adapted. It is hard to say just where the balance of these opposing requirements would be reached, but it is clear that greater specialization resulting in increased efficiency would always be favored as long as no time or energy are wasted. And no time or energy will be wasted if niches are "convex" in the sense that between any 2 fairly distant feeding places there will be a fairly natural route also consisting of feeding places. A specialization to a single tree species in a mixed forest would clearly violate this since, in passing from one suitable tree to another, the bird would go through many unsuitable ones. Thus, natural selection would tend to eliminate a situation in which bird species diversity depended upon tree species diversity, unless, as in some fruit eating species, a very remarkable improvement in efficiency is achieved along with the restriction in feeding position. Thus, one principal result of these censuses can be predicted on assuming that niches are convex.

Next, we may ask "why are the layers 0–2′, 2–25′, > 25′ equally important? Is it because birds respond to different heights, or is it because they respond to different configurations of vegetation in different layers?" In the latter case, herbs, bushes and trees presumably correspond to the layers 0–2′, 2–25′ and > 25′ respectively, although small trees count as bushes, etc. There is good evidence for this latter explanation. For, although deciduous forests vary principally with height above the ground and hence have a bird diversity predictable from the height profile, conifers (especially spruce) have a marked "inside" and "outside" for which species are specialized. Hence bird species diversity would be high in a mature spruce forest even if few layers were present. This is precisely what happens in the Maine white spruce wood mentioned earlier, with bird species diversity of 1.712 and foliage height diversity of .287 which is seriously off the graph of deciduous forests.

A different way of looking at the data gives additional insight. Watt has pointed out that plants are distributed in patches. Hutchinson and MacArthur attempted to explain the sizes of coexisting organisms in terms of an environment composed of a mosaic of kinds of patches. Different combinations of patches formed the habitats selected by different species. The present research can be easily interpreted in terms of this picture of the environment. In fact, our results suggest that the patches forming the birds' environmental mosaic are sections of canopy C (over 25′), patches of bushes B from 2–25′, and the herbaceous and other cover H less than 2′ from the ground. And the sequence of patches encountered in moving through the habitat (or in taking ever larger samples) is then represented by a sequence of letters, *e.g.*, C, B, H, H, B, C, . . . with certain random properties but also subject to the condition that the long term frequency of C's, B's, and H's should conform to their respective densities (p_i) in the particular habitat. If the sequence is ergodic, which defines what we call a homogeneous habitat, then it is well known that the uncertainty of the next letters in the sequence is appropriately measured by the formula $-\sum_i p_i \log_e p_i$ which we used. If, instead of considering the uncertainty of future single letters in the sequence, we ask for the uncertainty of future pairs of letters, the formula becomes $-2\sum_i p_i \log_e p_i$ which is $2 \times$ foliage height diversity, which is essentially the predicted value of the bird species diversity. Thus we can say that bird species diversity is determined as if the birds recognized suitable habitats by pairs of foliage types (> 25′, 2–25′, 0–2′). The species area curve could then be predicted from this.

RELATIONSHIPS BETWEEN STRUCTURE AND FUNCTION IN ECOSYSTEMS

Eugene P. Odum—1962

Reprinted by permission of the author and publisher from the Japanese Journal of Ecology **12**: 108–118, 1962.

In defining ecology as the study of the structure and function of ecosystems, Odum brings into much closer alliance these two major traditional approaches in biology. There is intimation of causal relations between the two in line with current thinking on the molecular and subcellular levels of biological organization. By discussing aquatic and terrestrial systems in parallel, Odum strengthens his strongly espoused contention regarding the universality of applying the ecosystem approach. This view is the theme of both editions of his text, Fundamentals of ecology (1953, 1959. Philadelphia, W. B. Saunders, Inc.) which enjoys wide use.

. . . As you know ecology is often defined as: The study of interrelationships between organisms and environment. I feel that this conventional definition is not suitable; it is too vague and too broad. Personally, I prefer to define ecology as: The study of the structure and function of ecosystems. Or we might say in a less technical way: The study of structure and function of nature.

By structure we mean: (1) The composition of the biological community including species, numbers, biomass, life history and distribution in space of populations; (2) the quantity and distribution of the abiotic (non-living) materials such as nutrients, water, etc.; (3) the range, or gradient, of conditions of existence such as temperature, light, etc. Dividing ecological structure into these three divisions is, of course, arbitrary but I believe convenient for actual study of both aquatic and terrestrial situations.

By function we mean: (1) The rate of biological energy flow through the ecosystem, that is, the rates of production and the rates of respiration of the populations and the community; (2) the rate of material or nutrient cycling, that is, the biogeochemical cycles; (3) biological or ecological regulation including both regulation of organisms by environment (as, for example, in photoperiodism) and regulation of environment by organisms (as, for example, in nitrogen fixation by microorganisms). Again, dividing ecological function into these three divisions is arbitrary but convenient for study. . . .

Both aquatic and terrestrial community types have several structural features in common. Both must have the same three necessary biological components: (1) Producers or green plants capable of fixing light energy (i.e., autotrophs); (2) animals or macroconsumers which consume particulate organic matter (i.e., phagotrophs); and (3) microorganism decomposers which dissolve organic matter releasing nutrients (i.e., osmotrophs). Both ecosystems must be supplied with the same vital materials such as nitrogen, phosphorus, trace minerals, etc. Both ecosystems are regulated and limited by the same conditions of existence such as light and temperature. Finally, the arrangement of biological units in vertical space is basically the same in the two contrasting types of ecosystems. Both have two strata, an autotrophic stratum above and a heterotrophic stratum below. The photosynthetic machinery is concentrated in the upper stratum or photic zone where light is available, while the consumer-nutrient regenerating machinery is concentrated largely below the photic zone. It is important to emphasize that while the vertical extent or thickness of communities varies greatly (especially in water), light energy comes into the ecosystem on a horizontal surface basis which is everywhere the same. Thus, different ecosystems should be compared on a square meter basis, not on a cubic or volume basis.

On the other hand, aquatic and terrestrial ecosystems differ in structure in several important ways. Species composition is, of course, completely different; the roles of producers, consumers and decomposers are carried out by taxonomically different organisms which have become adapted through evolution. Trophic structure also differs in that land plants tend to be large in size but few in number while the autotrophs of open water ecosystems (i.e., phytoplankton) are small in size but very numerous. In general, autotrophic biomass is much greater than heterotrophic biomass on land, while the reverse is often true in the sea. Perhaps the most important difference is the following: The matrix, or supporting framework, of the community is largely physical in aquatic ecosystems, but more strongly biological on land. That is to say, the community itself is important as a habitat on land, but not so important in water.

Now, we may ask: How do these similarities and differences in structure affect ecological function?

One important aspect of function is . . . the energy flow through the ecosystems beginning with the incoming solar energy and passing through the successive trophic levels. At each transfer a large part of the energy is dissipated in respiration and passes out of the system as heat. The amount of energy remaining after three steps is so small that it can be ignored in so far as the energetics of the community are concerned. However, tertiary consumers ("top carnivores") can be important as regulators; that is, predation may have an important effect on energy flow at the herbivore level. . . .

The autotrophic-heterotrophic stratification, which we emphasized as a universal feature of community structure, results in two basic food chains. . . . The consumption of living plants by herbivores which live in the autotrophic stratum together with their predators may be considered as the *grazing food chain.* This is the classical food chain of ecology, as, for example, the phytoplankton-zooplankton-fish sequence or the grass-rabbit-fox sequence. However, a large proportion of the net production may not be consumed until dead, thus becoming the start of a rather different energy flow which we may conveniently designate as the *detritus food chain*. This energy flow takes place largely in the heterotrophic stratum. . . . the detritus energy flow takes place chiefly in the sediments of water systems, and in the litter and soil of land systems.

Ecologists have too often overlooked the fact that the detritus food chain is the more important energy pathway in many ecosystems. . . . a larger portion of net production is estimated to be consumed by grazers in the marine bay than in the forest; nine-tenths of the net production of the forest is estimated to be consumed as detritus (dead leaves, wood, etc.). It is not clear whether this difference is a direct or indirect result of the difference in community structure. One tentative generalization might be proposed as follows: communities of small, rapidly growing producers such as phytoplankton or grass can tolerate heavier grazing pressure than communities of large, slow-growing plants such as trees or large seaweeds. . . .

Despite the large difference in relative size of standing crops in the two extreme types of ecosystems, the actual energy flow may be of the same order of magnitude if light and available nutrients are similar. . . . Thus, 80 KCals of phytoplankton may have a net production almost as large as 5000 KCals of trees (or 500 KCals of green leaves). Therefore, productivity is not proportional to the size of the standing crop except in special cases involving annual plants (as in some agriculture). Unfortunately, many ecologists confuse productivity and standing crop. The relation between structure and function in this case depends on the size and rate of metabolism (and rate of turnover) of the organisms.

To summarize, we see that biological structure influences the pattern of energy flow, particularly the fate of net production and the relative importance of grazers and detritus consumers. However, total energy flow is less affected by structure, and is thus less variable than standing crop. A functional homeostasis has been evolved in nature despite the wide range in species structure and in biomass structure. . . .

. . . Now let us turn to structure and function at the population level and consider a second major aspect of function, namely, the cycling of nutrients. . . .

First, we shall take a look at the salt marsh ecosystem and the distribution of the species in the marsh. The mussels live partly buried in the sediments and attached to the stems and rhizomes of the marsh grass, *Spartina alterniflora*. Individuals are grouped into colonies (clumped distribution), but the colonies are widely scattered over the marsh. Numbers average $8/M^2$ for the entire marsh and $32/M^2$ in the most favorable parts of the marsh. Biomass in terms of ash-free dry weight averages 11.5 gms/M^2. When the tide covers the colonies the valves partly open and the animals begin to pump large quantities of water.

Each day the population removes a large part of the phosphorus from the water, especially the particulate fraction. Most of this does not actually pass through the body but is sedimented in the form of pseudofeces which fall on the sediments. Thus, the mussels make large quantities of phosphorus available to microorganisms and to the autotrophs (benthic algae and marsh grass) . . . the energy flow was estimated to be about 0.15 KCals/M^2/day.

The most important finding of the study is . . . the ratio between flux and amount. Note that over one third of the 14 mgms of particulate phosphorus is removed from the water each day by the population, and thereby retained in the marsh. In contrast, less than one per

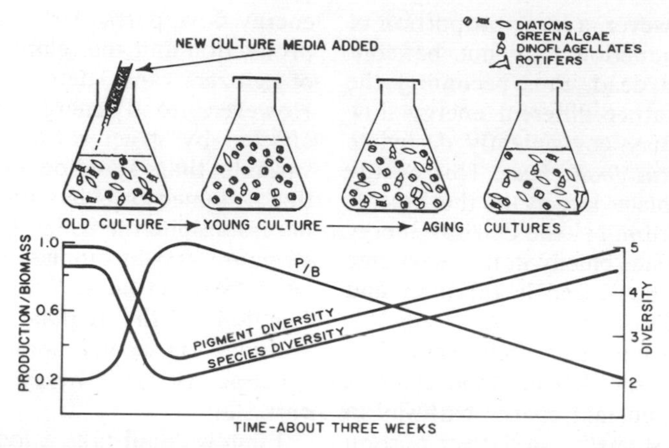

FIG. 3. *The Margelef model of ecological succession showing a simple type of succession which can be demonstrated in laboratory cultures. The flasks show changes in species composition occurring when succession is set in motion by the introduction of new nutrient media into an old "climax" culture. The graph shows resultant changes in two aspects of diversity and in the relation between production and biomass (P/B). See text for details of the experiment.*

cent of the 20 KCals of potential energy (net production estimate) available is actually utilized by the mussel population. In other words, the mussel population has a much more important effect on the community phosphorus cycle than it has on community energy flow . . . .

To summarize, the mussel study brings out two important points: (1) It is necessary to study both energy flow and biogeochemical cycles to determine the role of a particular species in its ecosystem, (2) animals may be important in the ecosystem not only in terms of food energy, but as agents which make basic nutrient more available to autotrophs. . . .

Now let us consider the third important aspect of ecological function, that is, community regulation. Ecological succession is one of the most important processes which result from the community modifying the environment. Fig. 3 illustrates a very simple type of ecological succession which can be demonstrated in a laboratory experiment. Yet the basic pattern shown here is the same as occurs in more complex succession of natural communities. The diagram (Fig. 3) was suggested to me by Dr. Ramon MARGELEF, hence we may call it the MARGELEF model of succession.

At the top of the diagram (Fig. 3) are a series of culture flasks containing plankton communities in different stages of succession. The graph shows changes in two aspects of structure and in one aspect of function. The first flask on the left contains an old and relatively stable community; this flask represents the climax. Diversity of species is high in the climax; species of diatoms, green flagellates, dinoflagellates and rotifers are shown in the diagram to illustrate the variety of plants and animals present. Biochemical diversity is also high as indicated by the ratio of yellow plant pigments (optical density at 430mμ) to chlorophyll-a (optical density at 665mμ). On the other hand the ratio of production to biomass (P/B in Fig. 3) is low in the old or climax culture, and gross production tends to equal community respiration. If we add fresh culture medium to the old culture, as shown in Fig. 3, ecological succession is set in motion. An early stage in succession is shown in the second flask. Species diversity is low, with one or two species of phytoplankton dominant. Chlorophylls predominate so that the yellow/green ratio (O.D.430/O.D.665) is low, indicating low biochemical diversity. On the other hand, production now exceeds respiration so that the ratio of production to biomass becomes higher. In other words, autotrophy greatly exceeds heterotrophy in the pioneer or early succession stage. The two flasks on the right side of the diagram (Fig. 3) show the gradual return to the climax or steady state where autotrophy tends to balance heterotrophy.

The changes which we have just described are apparently typical of all succession regardless of environment ortype of ecosystem. Although much more study is needed, it appears that differences in community structure mainly affect the time required, that is, whether the horizontal scale (X-axis in Fig. 3) is measured in weeks, months or years. . . .

To summarize, I am suggesting that the basic pattern of functional change in ecological succession is the same in all ecosystems, but that the species composition, rate of change and duration of succession is determined by the physical environment and the resultant community structure. . . .

ON CERTAIN UNIFYING PRINCIPLES IN ECOLOGY

Ramon Margalef—1963

Reprinted by permission of the author and publisher from the American Naturalist **97**: 357–374, 1963.

Admonishing ecologists for having been reluctant to orient their efforts in terms of a general theory, Margalef proposes some unifying principles with major emphasis on the maturity of the system as measured by diversity and in terms of energetics. Maturity is a quantitative measure of the pattern in which the components of the ecosystem are arranged and related. In spite of its theoretical orientation, the easy readability of the essay is credit to the author's clear perception and insight. The essay is largely a speculative interpretation encompassing both original and undeveloped ideas. Because of its speculative nature and theoretical ideas it should be read not as an instance of accomplished fact but as a possible indicator of future lines of inquiry.

STRUCTURE OF THE ECOSYSTEM

Ecosystems have a structure, in the sense that they are composed of different parts or elements, and these are arranged in a definite pattern. The interrelations between the constituent elements are the basis of the structure. . .

The main point is that the "real" structure of an ecosystem is a property that remains out of reach, but this complete structure is reflected in many aspects of the ecosystem that can be subjected to observation: in the distribution of individuals into species, in the pattern of the food net, in the distribution of total assimilatory pigments in kinds of pigments, and so on.

Structure, in general, becomes more complex, more rich, as time passes; structure is linked to history. For a quantitative measure of structure it seems convenient to select a name that suggests this historical character, for instance, maturity. In general, we may speak of a more complex ecosystem as a more mature ecosystem. . . . The term maturity suggests a trend, and moreover maintains a contact with the traditional dynamic approach in the study of natural communities, which has always been a source of inspiration.

Maturity, then, is a quality that increases with time in any undisturbed ecosystem. Field ecologists use many criteria to estimate the maturity of an ecosystem, without the need of assessing its precise place in an actual succession. Empirical knowledge of succession leads one to consider as more mature the ecosystems that are more complex; that is, composed of a great number of elements, with long food chains, and with relations between species well defined or more specialized . . . .

THE ECOSYSTEM IN RELATION TO ENERGY AND MASS

The ecosystem has different complementary aspects: If we consider the elements and the relations between the elements, we have the structure, whereas in considering matter and energy, we have to deal with metric properties which are perhaps easier to express. The ecosystem is formed by a certain amount of matter (biomass) and there is a budget of matter and energy.

For the moment, let us consider an ecosystem in a steady state, with a material output equal to the material input. Here we need to consider only two quantities: the matter present, or biomass, in the ecosystem, always to be expressed in the same form (total weight, dry weight); and the potential energy necessary for maintenance in the ecosystem, amounting to total respiration and other losses. Both quantities can be considered in every ecosystem and simply equated to primary production (P) and biomass (B); both concepts are of common usage in ecology. Their relation (P/B) can be stated as flow of energy per unit biomass; it is the turnover rate of Cushing, Humphrey, Banse and Laevastu and the productivity index under natural light conditions of Strickland. . . .

What is important is the empirical relation between structure and energy flow per unit biomass. More mature ecosystems, with a richer structure, have a lower primary production per unit biomass. . . . The ratio P/B is taken as the ratio expressed by *primary production/total biomass*, including all elements of the ecosystem, such as the consumers, etc. In ecosystems of higher maturity there is a more complete use of food, there is a greater proportion of animals, and energy cascades through a more considerable number of steps. This is true in aquatic ecosystems, but in terrestrial ecosystems a somewhat paradoxical situation arises owing to a certain exaggerated dominance of vegetation. On the other hand, the great number of possible kinds of relations in a mature ecosystem allows a higher efficiency in every relation. If these relations are considered as communication channels, less noise comes into them. . . .

The ideas developed so far can be summarized as follows. An ecosystem that has a complex structure, rich in information, needs a lower amount of energy for maintaining such structure. If we consider the interrelations between the elements of an ecosystem as communication channels, we can state that such channels function on the average more effectively, with a lower noise level, if they are multiple and diverse, linking elements not subjected to great changes. Then, loss of energy is lower, and the energy necessary for preventing decay of the whole ecosystem amounts relatively to less. This seems to be one of the basic principles of ecology, probably recognized tacitly by most writers, although rarely put in an explicit way.

SUCCESSION AND FLUCTUATIONS

Any ecosystem not subjected to strong disturbances coming from outside, changes in a progressive and directional way. We say that the ecosystem becomes more mature. The two most noticeable changes accompanying this process are the increase of complexity of structure and the decrease of the energy flow per unit biomass. This theoretical background leads us to accept a sort of natural selection in the possible rearrangements of the ecosystem: Links between the elements of an ecosystem can be substituted by other links that work with a higher efficiency, requiring a change in the elements and often an increase in the number of elements and connections. The new situation now has an excess of potential energy. This can be used in developing the ecosystem further, for instance, by adding biomass after driving more matter into the system. A more complex state, with a reduced waste of energy, allows maintenance of the same biomass with a lower supply of energy—or a higher biomass with the same supply of energy—and replaces automatically any previous state.

The only limit set to this progressive change is interference from the physical environment. Succession can build history only when the environment is stable. In the case of a changing environment, the selected ecosystem will be composed of species with a high reproductive rate and lower special requirements. Such an ecosystem is less diverse and less complex; the energy flow per unit biomass remains relatively high. . . .

. . . The conclusion is that in any estimate of maturity, not only diversity, but also predictability of change with time has to be considered. Ordinarily both characters are correlated. Less mature ecosystems not only have a lower diversity, but in them transition between successive states includes a higher amount of uncertainty. And more diverse ecosystems have, in general, more predictable future states. In other words, in more mature ecosystems the future situation is more dependent on the present than it is on inputs coming from outside. Homeostasis is higher. On the other hand, future states in less mature ecosystems are heavily influenced by external inputs, by changes in the physical environment. . .

In general, the expected differences in the character of fluctuations in less mature and more mature communities would be as follows. In less mature communities, environmental fluctuations are strong and able to stop the trend to increase maturity at a certain level. Maturity does not increase because abiotic fluctuations are too strong, and homeostasis is difficult to attain in a poorly organized, often a pioneer community. In a more stable environment, succession proceeds and maturity increases; now we have to expect rhythms that are more regular, more independent of environment and often endogenous. Anticipatory power has survival value and is the expression of a complex system, able to produce very efficient homeostatic mechanisms. Up to a certain level, these homeostatic mechanisms can protect the system from disruption due to external agents. Maturity is self-preserving. . . .

EXTENSIVE SYSTEMS WITH LOCAL DIFFERENCES IN THE VALUE OF MATURITY

Let us explore what happens along a surface of equal maturity. Remember that at one side we have a subsystem of lower maturity, with a high production per unit biomass, with less strong links between species, subject to wider fluctuations and to an easy dispersal of the elements. At the other side we find a subsystem with a greater biomass for the same energy flow, with well organized relations over elements more strongly localized.

If maturity increases in the less mature system, especially at the proximity of the boundary (which is to be expected from succession) the surface of equal maturity moves towards the less mature subsystem. This is probably accompanied by a flow of energy going the converse way. This means that matter (biomass and non-living matter) goes in both directions, since both coupled subsystems are actually open, but the content of potential energy of such matter is, on the average, higher in the matter going the way of increasing maturity than in the matter going the way of decreasing maturity. The subsystem with a lower maturity maintains a higher ratio between primary production and total present biomass, because it actually loses biomass, in going across the border to the more mature coupled subsystems.

Let us remember that succession is simply the exchange of an excess available energy in the present, for a future increase of biomass. An ecosystem in its present state is less mature and has an excess production that goes to the future and helps reorganize the ecosystem in a more mature form. If there is no available excess production or it is drained out of the system, succession proceeds no further. . . .

UTILITY OF A SYNTHETIC APPROACH

Most of what has been discussed can be summarized in two very simple principles:

(1) The relative amount of energy necessary for maintaining an ecosystem is related to the degree of structure or organization of this ecosystem. Less energy is necessary for a more complex ecosystem, and the natural trend in succession is towards a decreasing flow of energy per unit of biomass and towards increasing organization. Briefly stated the trend is towards increasing maturity.

(2) When two systems of different maturity meet along a boundary that allows an exchange, energy (production) flows towards the more mature subsystem, and the boundary or surface of equal maturity shows a trend to move in an opposite direction to such energy flow.

These general principles clarify many ecological interactions and processes and allow quantitative formulation. They can be used or tested in predicting changes induced by human action. Exploitation is like inflicting a wound upon a heterogeneous organic structure: some tissues or subsystems (more mature) do not regenerate; others (less mature) do and these supply the basis for a further eventual increase of maturity. Maintained exploitation keeps the maturity of the exploited system constantly low. Exploited natural communities come to have a higher primary production per unit biomass, a lower species diversity and, presumably, a lower ratio D_{430}/D_{665}. More energy goes into fluctuations such as those represented by exploited populations or by populations that are integrated into exploited ecosystems. For example, pests have fluctuations with a wider range and shorter periodicity than similar populations that are integrated into more mature, eventually unexploited, ecosystems. Extremely mature ecosystems, such as tropical forests, are unable to go back and are totally disrupted by human exploitation. . . .

. . . Radiation increase can be expected to act destructively to accumulated information (that is, to biomass) but with no effect on potential energy flow; radiation, then, must reduce the maturity of ecosystems, in part by selective destruction of the more mature elements of the ecosystem. Thus, a great increase in radiation may mean a new push given to an already lagging evolution.

Most of the same principles can be applied to human organizations. Taking as criteria the diversification of skills and jobs (diversity), or the relative flow of potential energy, it is possible to map the "maturity" of states and continents in the ecological sense of organization. Energy flow goes from less mature (rural) areas to more mature (urban) areas. The urban centers represent localized elements that have accumulated high amounts of information, fed on the production of neighboring subsystems, and have exerted a directive action. Very old systems can survive with a small flow of energy, and like their ecological counterparts can break down as a consequence of a minor environmental change. It is possible to deal objectively and quantitatively with big and complex structures, if one never forgets the complementary aspects of energy as related to matter, and structure.